ENGINEERING
MATHEMATICS

Kenneth S. Miller

Professor of Mathematics
New York University

ENGINEERING
MATHEMATICS

Dover Publications, Inc. New York

Published in Canada by General Publishing Company, Ltd., 30 Lesmill Road, Don Mills, Toronto,
Ontario.
Published in the United Kingdom by Constable
and Company, Ltd., 10 Orange Street, London WC 2.

This Dover edition, first published in 1963, is
an unabridged and corrected republication of the
second printing of the work first published by
Holt, Rinehart and Winston in 1956.

Standard Book Number: 486-61121-3
Library of Congress Catalog Card Number: 63-21683

Manufactured in the United States of America
Dover Publications, Inc.
180 Varick Street
New York, N.Y. 10014

PREFACE

When the typical engineering student reaches the first year of graduate work, his usual mathematical training includes a little college algebra, analytics, calculus, and a smattering of differential equations. In this text we propose to strengthen this mathematical background by filling in his knowledge on differential equations, in particular giving the general theory of linear differential equations and the practical technique (Frobenius method) of solving differential equations in series. These topics are covered in Chapter Three. To discuss linear differential equations one needs the concept of linear dependence; determinants and matrices are therefore considered earlier (Chapter One), since one can more naturally introduce this concept here. Also, matrix theory is a prerequisite to an adequate discussion of network theory (Chapter Six).

In Chapter Two we cover a variety of special subjects connected with integration. However, no topic is introduced merely for the purpose of exhibiting mathematical gymnastics. For example, the Gamma function is used in solving Bessel's equation, the error function appears in certain problems involving the Fourier integral, Euler's constant appears in Bessel functions of the second kind with purely imaginary argument, Stirling's formula is used in deriving the normal distribution, the sine-integral function arises in examining the transient response of an ideal low pass filter, while elliptic integrals appear in certain probability problems.

Fourier series and integrals (Chapter Four), with some applications not usually found in texts on advanced calculus (for example, correlation functions and the Wiener-Khintchine relations), and the Laplace transform (Chapter Five) are treated. These topics can also be considered as an extension of the theory of differential equations. Finally, Chapter Seven, on engineering probability with emphasis on functions of random variables, is included. Again, this topic is not usually covered in beginning graduate courses, but recent developments in the field of communication engineering have made it indispensable equipment for the well-trained engineer of today.

The level of rigor of this text is, except for the appendices, at the presently accepted standard for engineering schools. While it is suggested that this book be used for the "first year of graduate work," it could be used in undergraduate junior and senior courses. The reason for this apparent paradox is that until recent years many engineering schools did not include mathematics courses beyond the sophomore year, so that invariably a graduate student in engineering had but two years' background in college mathematics. With the recent trend of including more mathematics in the undergraduate curriculum, this book would be suitable for such advanced undergraduate courses.

I should like to thank my good friend, Mr. R. Frank Bitner of Prentice-Hall, for permission to include a number of diagrams from my partial differential equations book; my colleague, Professor Lotfi A. Zadeh of Columbia University, to whom I am indebted for much of the material that appears in Chapter Six; my father, Mr. Wilfred A. Miller, who prepared the originals of all quantitative diagrams from which the final figures were drawn; and, finally, my former honor student, Mr. Leslie E. Blumenson, who meticulously read the entire manuscript, pointed out numerous corrections, and offered many valuable suggestions for the improvement of the text.

K. S. M.

New York City
June, 1956

CONTENTS

ENGINEERING
MATHEMATICS

Chapter One

DETERMINANTS AND MATRICES

1. Introduction

Systems of simultaneous linear algebraic equations occur in the most elementary of mathematical problems. If we are given such a simple problem as finding the intersection of the two straight lines $2x + y = 3$ and $x - 3y = -2$, we are confronted with the task of solving the system of equations

$$2x + y = 3$$
$$x - 3y = -2 \quad .$$

This of course is a trivial problem whose solution is $x = 1$, $y = 1$. More generally we can consider the problem of solving the system of equations

$$a_{11}x_1 + a_{12}x_2 = b_1$$
$$a_{21}x_1 + a_{22}x_2 = b_2$$

for x_1 and x_2, where the a_{ij} and b_i are assumed known. By a straightforward elimination, assuming $a_{11}a_{22} - a_{12}a_{21} \neq 0$, we find that

$$x_1 = \frac{b_1a_{22} - b_2a_{12}}{a_{11}a_{22} - a_{12}a_{21}} \quad ,$$

$$x_2 = \frac{b_2a_{11} - b_1a_{21}}{a_{11}a_{22} - a_{12}a_{21}} \quad .$$

If we define the array of four numbers

$$\begin{vmatrix} A & B \\ C & D \end{vmatrix} \tag{1}$$

as $AD - BC$, then x_1 and x_2 may be written as

$$x_1 = \frac{\begin{vmatrix} b_1 & a_{12} \\ b_2 & a_{22} \end{vmatrix}}{\begin{vmatrix} a_{11} & a_{12} \\ a_{21} & a_{22} \end{vmatrix}},$$

$$x_2 = \frac{\begin{vmatrix} a_{11} & b_1 \\ a_{21} & b_2 \end{vmatrix}}{\begin{vmatrix} a_{11} & a_{12} \\ a_{21} & a_{22} \end{vmatrix}}.$$

Of course the reader recognizes Equation (1) as a *second-order determinant*, and is probably also familiar with at least third-order determinants.

We can easily visualize problems involving four, five, or even n unknowns, $x_1, x_2, \cdots, x_n$; for example, problems in network theory (cf. Chap. 6). To solve such problems by brute-force elimination (as was first done to find x_1 and x_2 above) would be inefficient. A systematic method which enables us to solve linear equations of all orders is the method of *determinants*. Hence our first task will be to define determinants and investigate some of their elementary properties. As the theory develops we will be led into the theory of matrices; and numerous applications of determinants and matrices.

Consider, then, an array of n^2 numbers which we shall denote by D. Such a square array, conventionally written as in Equation (2) below with vertical bars, is called a *determinant* or, more precisely, an $n \times n$ determinant or an nth *order* determinant. Such a determinant clearly has n rows and n columns. The element a_{ij} is the number in the ith row and j^{th} column.

$$D = \begin{vmatrix} a_{11} & a_{12} & \cdots & a_{1n} \\ a_{21} & a_{22} & \cdots & a_{2n} \\ \cdot & \cdot & \cdot & \cdot \\ a_{n1} & a_{n2} & \cdots & a_{nn} \end{vmatrix}. \tag{2}$$

Following standard terminology, the first subscript refers to the row and the second to the column. One also uses the symbol $|a_{ij}|$ to denote the determinant, viz.:

$$D = |a_{ij}| .$$

This notation should not be confused with the absolute value of the element

a_{ij}. The context will make clear which we are considering. Other notations widely used to indicate D will be introduced as the theory unfolds.

So far, our determinant D is an array of n^2 numbers. We have yet to define the *value* of D. The value of D is a number if the a_{ij} are numbers, but, for example, could also be a function of x if the a_{ij} were themselves functions of x. We shall use the symbol D to indicate both the determinant and its *value*.

Consider a product formed by taking one element from each row and each column of D. With no loss of generality we may write such a product as

$$a_{1i_1}a_{2i_2} \cdots a_{ni_n} ,$$

where $i_1, i_2, \cdots, i_n$ represents a rearrangement of the integers $1, 2, \cdots, n$. Clearly there are $n!$ possible permutations. For example, if $n = 3$, the arrangements of the second subscript could be

$$
\begin{array}{ccc}
1 & 2 & 3 \\
1 & 3 & 2 \\
2 & 1 & 3 \\
2 & 3 & 1 \\
3 & 1 & 2 \\
3 & 2 & 1 ,
\end{array}
\tag{3}
$$

and there are $3! = 6$ of them. The interchange of two consecutive numbers in a permutation will be called a *transposition*. For example, 1 3 2 is a transposition of the permutation 1 2 3, since we have interchanged 2 and 3. Now, if $i_1, i_2, \cdots, i_n$ is a certain permutation, let $\sigma = \sigma(i_1, i_2, \cdots, i_n)$ be the number of transpositions necessary to rearrange $i_1, i_2, \cdots, i_n$ into the natural order $1, 2, \cdots, n$. Then we define the value of the determinant D as

$$D = \Sigma(-1)^\sigma a_{1i_1}a_{2i_2} \cdots a_{ni_n} ,$$

where the summation is extended over all permutations of the integers $1, 2, \cdots, n$, and σ is the number of transpositions necessary to rearrange $i_1, i_2, \cdots, i_n$ into the order $1, 2, \cdots, n$.

We see therefore that an $n \times n$ determinant consists of the sum of $n!$ products, each product containing n terms, and the sign of each product is determined by the number of transpositions necessary to rearrange the second subscripts into their normal order. For example, let us evaluate the third-order determinant

$$D = \begin{vmatrix} a_{11} & a_{12} & a_{13} \\ a_{21} & a_{22} & a_{23} \\ a_{31} & a_{32} & a_{33} \end{vmatrix}$$

by this method. The $n! = 3! = 6$ terms will be

$$a_{11}a_{22}a_{33} \quad ,$$

$$a_{11}a_{23}a_{32} \quad ,$$

$$a_{12}a_{21}a_{33} \quad ,$$

$$a_{12}a_{23}a_{31} \quad ,$$

$$a_{13}a_{21}a_{32} \quad ,$$

$$a_{13}a_{22}a_{31} \quad .$$

Note that each of the six products contains one element from each row and column. Now the second subscripts of the above products are the same as those indicated by Equations (3). The first, 1 2 3, is the natural order; hence zero transpositions are required to bring it into the order 1 2 3. Thus $\sigma = 0$, $(-1)^{\sigma} = +1$, and sign of the product $a_{11}a_{22}a_{33}$ is plus. The second set is 1 3 2, and one transposition, namely, interchanging 3 and 2, will bring 1 3 2 into normal order. Hence $\sigma = 1$ for this permutation, $(-1)^{\sigma} = -1$, and the sign of the product $a_{11}a_{23}a_{32}$ is therefore minus. Proceeding in this way, we see that 2 1 3 needs one transposition, 2 3 1 needs two, 3 1 2 needs two, and 3 2 1 needs three to rearrange the permutation; hence

$$D = + a_{11}a_{22}a_{33} - a_{11}a_{23}a_{32} - a_{12}a_{21}a_{33} + a_{12}a_{23}a_{31}$$
$$+ a_{13}a_{21}a_{32} - a_{13}a_{22}a_{31} \quad .$$

To the reader who has evaluated third-order determinants in college algebra, this is a familiar result.

EXERCISES

1. Expand the general second-order and fourth-order determinants by using the definition of determinant.
2. Evaluate the determinants

$$\text{(i)} \quad \begin{vmatrix} 1 & 0 & 3 & 1 \\ -6 & -1 & 0.5 & 7 \\ 0 & 1 & 0.3 & 0 \\ 0 & 5 & 2 & -1 \end{vmatrix}, \quad \text{(ii)} \quad \begin{vmatrix} 2.2 & 3.1 & -4.0 \\ 0 & 5.3 & 0 \\ 6.1 & -8.1 & 2.0 \end{vmatrix}.$$

3. If the f_{ij} are functions of x, prove that the derivative of the determinant

$$\begin{vmatrix} f_{11}(x) & f_{12}(x) & f_{13}(x) \\ f_{21}(x) & f_{22}(x) & f_{23}(x) \\ f_{31}(x) & f_{32}(x) & f_{33}(x) \end{vmatrix}$$

can be written

$$\begin{vmatrix} f'_{11} & f_{12} & f_{13} \\ f'_{21} & f_{22} & f_{23} \\ f'_{31} & f_{32} & f_{33} \end{vmatrix} + \begin{vmatrix} f_{11} & f'_{12} & f_{13} \\ f_{21} & f'_{22} & f_{23} \\ f_{31} & f'_{32} & f_{33} \end{vmatrix} + \begin{vmatrix} f_{11} & f_{12} & f'_{13} \\ f_{21} & f_{22} & f'_{23} \\ f_{31} & f_{32} & f'_{33} \end{vmatrix} ,$$

where the primes indicate differentiation with respect to x.

2. Elementary Properties of Determinants

The above method for evaluating determinants is at best laborious. We shall develop in later sections much simpler and efficient methods for *expanding* a determinant, that is, for finding its numerical value. However, the basic definition is convenient for proving many of the elementary properties of determinants. The following eight theorems are useful in manipulating determinants.

THEOREM 1. Let D be a determinant. If the rows and columns of D are interchanged, then the value of the determinant remains the same.

Proof. Let D be as given by Equation (2), and consider the determinant D' obtained by interchanging rows and columns,

$$D' = \begin{vmatrix} a_{11} & a_{21} & \cdots & a_{n1} \\ a_{12} & a_{22} & \cdots & a_{n2} \\ \cdot & \cdot & \cdots & \cdot \\ a_{1n} & a_{2n} & \cdots & a_{nn} \end{vmatrix} . \tag{4}$$

If we let the element in the ith row and jth column of D' be a'_{ij}, then by definition

$$D' = \Sigma(-1)^{\sigma'} a'_{1i_1} a'_{2i_2} \cdots a'_{ni_n} ,$$

where σ' is the number of transpositions needed to rearrange $i_1, i_2, \cdots, i_n$. Since $a'_{ij} = a_{ji}$, we may also write D' as

$$D' = \Sigma(-1)^{\sigma'} a_{i_1 1} a_{i_2 2} \cdots a_{i_n n} .$$

But the product $a_{i_1 1} a_{i_2 2} \cdots a_{i_n n}$ occurs in D, for if we rearrange the $a_{i_k k}$ we may write it as $a_{1j_1} a_{2j_2} \cdots a_{nj_n}$. Now the number of transpositions needed to put $j_1, j_2, \cdots, j_n$ into natural order is the same as is needed to put $i_1, i_2, \cdots, i_n$ into normal order. Hence the product $a_{i_1 1} a_{i_2 2} \cdots a_{i_n n}$ has the same sign in both D and D', and thus $D = D'$.

We see therefore that any theorem we can prove regarding the rows (columns) of a determinant is also valid for columns (rows). For example, in the next theorem the word "row" could be replaced by "column," and the theorem would still be true.

THEOREM 2. If all the elements of a single row of a determinant are multiplied by a number c, then the value of the determinant is also multiplied by c.

Proof. Let D be given by Equation (2), and let

$$
D_c = \begin{vmatrix}
a_{11} & a_{12} & \cdots & a_{1n} \\
\cdot & \cdot & \cdots \cdot & \cdot \\
ca_{\alpha 1} & ca_{\alpha 2} & \cdots & ca_{\alpha n} \\
\cdot & \cdot & \cdots \cdot & \cdot \\
a_{n1} & a_{n2} & \cdots & a_{nn}
\end{vmatrix}
$$

be the determinant D with its α row multiplied by c. Then, by definition,

$$
D_c = \Sigma(-1)^{\sigma} a_{1i_1} a_{2i_2} \cdots ca_{\alpha i_\alpha} \cdots a_{ni_n}
$$
$$
= c\Sigma(-1)^{\sigma} a_{1i_1} a_{2i_2} \cdots a_{ni_n} = cD .
$$

THEOREM 3. The value of a determinant is zero if any row (column) consists entirely of zeros.

Proof. Suppose the α row consists entirely of zeros. Then, in the expression for D, every product $a_{1i_1} a_{2i_2} \cdots a_{ni_n}$ contains an element from the α row and hence is zero. Therefore the sum of products is zero.

THEOREM 4. The sign of a determinant is changed if two of its rows (columns) are interchanged.

Proof. For simplicity in notation, assume the first two rows are interchanged. Then if D is given by Equation (2),

$$
D' = \begin{vmatrix}
a_{21} & a_{22} & \cdots & a_{2n} \\
a_{11} & a_{12} & \cdots & a_{1n} \\
\cdot & \cdot & \cdots \cdot & \cdot \\
a_{n1} & a_{n2} & \cdots & a_{nn}
\end{vmatrix}
$$

is the determinant with interchanged rows. By definition,

$$
D' = \Sigma(-1)^{\sigma} a_{2i_1} a_{1i_2} a_{3i_3} \cdots a_{ni_n} .
$$

The product $a_{2i_1} a_{1i_2} \cdots a_{ni_n} = a_{1i_2} a_{2i_1} \cdots a_{ni_n}$ will be found in D. Now, if it takes σ' transpositions to rearrange $i_1, i_2, \cdots, i_n$ into normal order, it will take $\sigma' + 1$ transpositions to rearrange $i_2, i_1, \cdots, i_n$ into normal order, since it takes one transposition to rearrange $i_2, i_1, \cdots, i_n$ into the order $i_1, i_2, \cdots, i_n$.

Since $(-1)^{\sigma'} = -(-1)^{\sigma'+1}$, every term in D' is the negative of the term with the same factor in D and hence $D' = -D$.

THEOREM 5. The value of a determinant is zero if two of its rows (columns) are identical.

Proof. Let D be a determinant with two identical rows. If we interchange these two rows, the value D' of the determinant is $-D$ by Theorem 4. But since the two rows are identical, $D' = D$. Hence $D = -D$, or $D = 0$.

THEOREM 6. If in any row (column) of a determinant each term is equal to the corresponding term of any other row (column) multiplied by a number c, then the value of the determinant is zero.

Proof. If D' is the determinant described in the theorem, then by Theorem 2, $D' = cD$, where D has two identical rows. By Theorem 5, $D = 0$; hence $D' = 0$.

THEOREM 7. If two determinants D_1 and D_2 are the same except possibly for elements of a certain row (column), their sum is equal to a determinant D in which the elements of this row (column) are the sums of the corresponding elements of D_1 and D_2 and the elements of the other rows (columns) are the same as in D_1 and D_2.

Proof. For simplicity in notation, assume the corresponding elements in D_1 and D_2 are equal except for the first row. Let the elements in the first row of D_1 be b_{1j} and the elements in the first row of D_2 be c_{1j}. Then

$$D_1 = \Sigma(-1)^{\sigma} b_{1i_1} a_{2i_2} \cdots a_{ni_n} \ ,$$
$$D_2 = \Sigma(-1)^{\sigma} c_{1i_1} a_{2i_2} \cdots a_{ni_n} \ ,$$

and

$$D = D_1 + D_2 = \Sigma(-1)^{\sigma}(b_{1i_1} + c_{1i_1}) a_{2i_2} \cdots a_{ni_n} \ .$$

THEOREM 8. The value of a determinant D is unchanged if each element of any row (column) is multiplied by a number c and the result added to the corresponding element of any other row (column).

Proof. For simplicity in notation, let us assume that the first row has been multiplied by c and added to the second row. Then, if

$$D = \Sigma(-1)^{\sigma} a_{1i_1} a_{2i_2} \cdots a_{ni_n} \ ,$$

the determinant described in the theorem is

$$D' = \Sigma(-1)^{\sigma} a_{1i_1}(a_{2i_2} + ca_{1i_2}) a_{3i_3} \cdots a_{ni_n}$$
$$= \Sigma(-1)^{\sigma} a_{1i_1} a_{2i_2} a_{3i_3} \cdots a_{ni_n} + c\Sigma(-1)^{\sigma} a_{1i_1} a_{1i_2} a_{3i_3} \cdots a_{ni_n} \ .$$

The first sum is D and the second is zero, since the first two rows are identical.

Using 3×3 determinants, verify all the theorems of this section by actual expansion of the determinants involved.

3. Expansion Theorems

As remarked earlier, the expansion of a determinant by actually applying the definition of determinant is laborious. In this section we shall consider various theorems which facilitate and systematize the actual computation of a determinant. We precede our theorems with a few definitions and introduce the reader to more of the terminology of the theory of determinants.

Let $D = |a_{ij}|$ be an nth-order determinant. Then of course D has n rows and n columns. If we strike out any $n - m$ rows and any $n - m$ columns, there results an array, say M, of $m \times m$ elements. The determinant of this array is called a *minor* or, more precisely, an *m*-rowed minor. The elements which appear in both a row and a column that has been struck out form an $(n - m) \times (n - m)$ array N. The determinant of this array is called the *complement* of M. In particular, if we strike out the row and column in which the element a_{ij} appears, we obtain an $(n - 1) \times (n - 1)$ minor D_{ij} called the *complement* of a_{ij}. The *cofactor* A_{ij} of a_{ij} is defined as $(-1)^{i+j} D_{ij}$. Sometimes the cofactor A_{ij} is called the *signed minor* of a_{ij}. If M is an *m*-rowed minor of D in which the $p_1, p_2, \cdots, p_m$ rows and the $q_1, q_2, \cdots, q_m$ columns appear, then the *algebraic complement* of M is defined as

$$\text{algebraic complement of } M = (-1)^{p_1 + \cdots + p_m + q_1 + \cdots + q_m}[\text{complement of } M] \quad .$$

The first major theorem we wish to prove is the *Laplace development* of a determinant. In the interests of clarity, it is convenient to prove first two preliminary lemmas.

LEMMA 1. Let D be an $n \times n$ determinant. Let M be an *m*-rowed minor in D, and let N be its complement. If M is shifted to the upper left-hand corner of D in such a manner that the order of the rows and columns in both M and N remain unchanged, then the sign of D will remain the same if $+ N$ is the algebraic complement of M, or the sign of D will be changed if $- N$ is the algebraic complement of M.

Proof. Let the rows of M be $p_1, p_2, \cdots, p_m$ and the columns be $q_1, q_2, \cdots, q_m$, with $p_j < p_{j+1}$ and $q_k < q_{k+1}$. If we shift the $p_r{}^{\text{th}}$ row, $r = 1, 2, \cdots, m$ to the rth row, we pass over $p_r - r$ rows, thus changing the sign of the determinant $p_r - r$ times (cf. Theorem 4 of the previous section). If we similarly treat the columns, then the value of the determinant is multiplied by

$$(-1)^{p_1 - 1 + p_2 - 2 + \cdots + p_m - m + q_1 - 1 + q_2 - 2 + \cdots + q_m - m}$$
$$= (-1)^{p_1 + p_2 + \cdots + p_m + q_1 + q_2 + \cdots + q_m} \quad .$$

Now, if $+ N$ is the algebraic complement of M, $p_1 + \cdots + p_m + q_1 + \cdots + q_m$ is even, and if $- N$ is the algebraic complement of M, $p_1 + \cdots + p_m + q_1 + \cdots + q_m$ is odd.

LEMMA 2. Let $D = |a_{ij}|$ be an $n \times n$ determinant, and M an m-rowed minor of D. Then the product of M by its algebraic complement is identical with some of the terms occurring in the expansion of D.

Proof. Consider first the case when M stands in the upper left-hand corner of D. A typical term in the expansion of M may be written

$$(- 1)^{\sigma} a_{1i_1} a_{2i_2} \cdots a_{mi_m} \quad ,$$

where σ is the number of transpositions required to rearrange $i_1, i_2, \cdots, i_m$ into normal form. Similarly, any term of N may be written

$$(- 1)^{\sigma'} a_{m+1,\, i_{m+1}} a_{m+2,\, i_{m+2}} \cdots a_{ni_n} \quad .$$

The product of these two terms is

$$(- 1)^{\sigma + \sigma'} a_{1i_1} a_{2i_2} \cdots a_{ni_n} \quad ,$$

which is a term of D. In the general case we invoke Lemma 1.

We can now easily prove our first main result.

LAPLACE DEVELOPMENT. Let $D = |a_{ij}|$ be an $n \times n$ determinant. Choose any m rows in D. With these m rows we may form $\dfrac{n!}{m!(n - m)!}$ different m-rowed minors. The sums of the products of each of these m-rowed minors by their algebraic complements yield the value of D.

Proof. Every term d of D contains one element from each of the m rows mentioned in the statement of the theorem. Since these elements all lie in different columns, they are to be found in one and only one of the m-rowed minors, say M_i. All the other elements of this term in D will lie in the complement N_i of M_i. Hence, by the previous lemma, the term d will be found in only one of the products, namely, $M_i N_i$.

This completes the proof. A special case of this theorem which is probably most frequently used is when $m = 1$. Then the value of the determinant D is given by the expression

$$D = a_{j1} A_{j1} + a_{j2} A_{j2} + \cdots + a_{jn} A_{jn}$$

for any $j = 1, 2, \cdots, n$, where A_{jk} is the cofactor of a_{jk}. This formula expresses an nth-order determinant as the sum of n, $(n - 1)^{\text{st}}$ order determinants. As a corollary, we note that if we multiply a_{jk} by $A_{\beta k}$, with $\beta \neq j$ and sum over k, the result is zero, since the resulting determinant has two identical rows. We may state both these results as a corollary.

COROLLARY. If $D = |a_{ij}|$ is an $n \times n$ determinant and A_{ij} is the cofactor of a_{ij}, then

$$\sum_{k=1}^{n} a_{jk} A_{\beta k} = \delta_{j\beta} D \quad ,$$

where $\delta_{j\beta}$ is the Kronecker delta. That is, $\delta_{j\beta} = 1$ if $j = \beta$, and $\delta_{j\beta} = 0$ if $j \neq \beta$. If columns instead of rows are used the above corollary reads

$$\sum_{k=1}^{n} a_{kj} A_{k\beta} = \delta_{j\beta} D \quad .$$

Another result which enables us freely to manipulate determinants is the *multiplication theorem*. Clearly, since a determinant is a number, the product of two determinants can also be computed as some number. However, the multiplication theorem enables us to express the product of two $n \times n$ determinants as a single $n \times n$ determinant without first computing the original determinants.

MULTIPLICATION THEOREM. Let $D_1 = |a_{ij}|$ and $D_2 = |b_{ij}|$ be two n^{th}-order determinants. Then $D = D_1 D_2$ is an nth-order determinant, $D = |c_{ij}|$, where

$$c_{ij} = \sum_{k=1}^{n} a_{ik} b_{kj} \quad .$$

Proof. Utilizing the Laplace development, we may write

$$
\begin{vmatrix} a_{11} & \cdots & a_{1n} \\ \cdot & \cdots & \cdot \\ a_{n1} & \cdots & a_{nn} \end{vmatrix} \cdot \begin{vmatrix} b_{11} & \cdots & b_{1n} \\ \cdot & \cdots & \cdot \\ b_{n1} & \cdots & b_{nn} \end{vmatrix} = \begin{vmatrix} a_{11} & \cdots & a_{1n} & 0 & \cdots & 0 \\ \cdot & \cdots & \cdot & \cdot & \cdots & \cdot \\ a_{n1} & \cdots & a_{nn} & 0 & \cdots & 0 \\ d_{11} & \cdots & d_{1n} & b_{11} & \cdots & b_{1n} \\ \cdot & \cdots & \cdot & \cdot & \cdots & \cdot \\ d_{n1} & \cdots & d_{nn} & b_{n1} & \cdots & b_{nn} \end{vmatrix},
$$

no matter what the d_{ij} are. (Let the first n rows of the determinant on the right be the m rows of the Laplace development theorem.)

Since the d_{ij} are arbitrary, let

$$d_{ij} = - \delta_{ij} \quad ,$$

where δ_{ij} is the Kronecker delta. Then, if we multiply the first column by $b_{1\alpha}$ and add it to the $(n + \alpha)$ column for $\alpha = 1, 2, \cdots, n$ and further treat the next $n - 1$ columns in the same way, we obtain

$$\begin{vmatrix} a_{11} & \cdots & a_{1n} & a_{11}b_{11} + \cdots + a_{1n}b_{n1} & \cdots & a_{11}b_{1n} + \cdots + a_{1n}b_{nn} \\ \cdot & \cdot & \cdot & \cdot & \cdot & \cdot \\ a_{n1} & \cdots & a_{nn} & a_{n1}b_{11} + \cdots + a_{nn}b_{n1} & \cdots & a_{n1}b_{1n} + \cdots + a_{nn}b_{nn} \\ -1 & \cdots & 0 & 0 & \cdots & 0 \\ \cdot & \cdot & \cdot & \cdot & \cdot & \cdot \\ 0 & \cdots & -1 & 0 & \cdots & 0 \end{vmatrix} \quad ,$$

which immediately reduces to the desired result.

EXERCISES

1. Prove the following identities:

(i)
$$\begin{vmatrix} 0 & a_1 - a_2 & a_1 - a_3 & \cdots & a_1 - a_n \\ a_1 - a_2 & 0 & a_2 - a_3 & \cdots & a_2 - a_n \\ a_1 - a_3 & a_2 - a_3 & 0 & \cdots & a_3 - a_n \\ \cdot & \cdot & \cdot & & \cdot \\ a_1 - a_n & a_2 - a_n & a_3 - a_n & \cdots & 0 \end{vmatrix}$$
$$= (-1)^n 2^{n-2}(a_n - a_1) \prod_{i=1}^{n-1} (a_i - a_{i+1}) \quad , \quad (n \geqq 2) \quad .$$

(ii)
$$\begin{vmatrix} A & 1 & 1 & \cdots & 1 \\ 1 & A & 1 & \cdots & 1 \\ 1 & 1 & A & \cdots & 1 \\ \cdot & \cdot & \cdot & & \cdot \\ 1 & 1 & 1 & \cdots & A \end{vmatrix} = (A + n - 1)(A - 1)^{n-1} \quad .$$

(iii)
$$\begin{vmatrix} A & 1 & 1 & \cdots & 1 \\ -1 & A & 1 & \cdots & 1 \\ -1 & -1 & A & \cdots & 1 \\ \cdot & \cdot & \cdot & & \cdot \\ -1 & -1 & -1 & \cdots & A \end{vmatrix} = \tfrac{1}{2}[(A - 1)^n + (A + 1)^n] \quad .$$

(iv) $\begin{vmatrix} 0 & A & A & \cdots & A \\ B & 0 & A & \cdots & A \\ B & B & 0 & \cdots & A \\ \cdot & \cdot & \cdot & \cdot & \cdot \\ B & B & B & \cdots & 0 \end{vmatrix} = \dfrac{(-1)^{n+1}AB}{A-B}(A^{n-1}-B^{n-1})$.

(v) $\begin{vmatrix} C & A & A & \cdots & A \\ B & C & A & \cdots & A \\ B & B & C & \cdots & A \\ \cdot & \cdot & \cdot & \cdot & \cdot \\ B & B & B & \cdots & C \end{vmatrix} = \dfrac{A(C-B)^n - B(C-A)^n}{A-B}$.

(vi) $\begin{vmatrix} A_1+B & A_2 & A_3 & \cdots & A_n \\ A_1 & A_2+B & A_3 & \cdots & A_n \\ A_1 & A_2 & A_3+B & \cdots & A_n \\ \cdot & \cdot & \cdot & \cdot & \cdot \\ A_1 & A_2 & A_3 & \cdots & A_n+B \end{vmatrix} = B^{n-1}\left[B+\sum_{k=1}^{n}A_k\right]$.

2. Prove that

$$\begin{vmatrix} a_{11} & a_{12} & \cdots & a_{1n} \\ a_{21} & a_{22} & \cdots & a_{2n} \\ \cdot & \cdot & \cdot & \cdot \\ a_{n1} & a_{n2} & \cdots & a_{nn} \end{vmatrix}$$

$$= \frac{1}{a_{11}^{n-2}} \begin{vmatrix} \begin{vmatrix} a_{11} & a_{12} \\ a_{21} & a_{22} \end{vmatrix} & \begin{vmatrix} a_{11} & a_{13} \\ a_{21} & a_{23} \end{vmatrix} & \cdots & \begin{vmatrix} a_{11} & a_{1n} \\ a_{21} & a_{2n} \end{vmatrix} \\ \begin{vmatrix} a_{11} & a_{12} \\ a_{31} & a_{32} \end{vmatrix} & \begin{vmatrix} a_{11} & a_{13} \\ a_{31} & a_{33} \end{vmatrix} & \cdots & \begin{vmatrix} a_{11} & a_{1n} \\ a_{31} & a_{3n} \end{vmatrix} \\ \cdot & \cdot & \cdot & \cdot \\ \begin{vmatrix} a_{11} & a_{12} \\ a_{n1} & a_{n2} \end{vmatrix} & \begin{vmatrix} a_{11} & a_{13} \\ a_{n1} & a_{n3} \end{vmatrix} & \cdots & \begin{vmatrix} a_{11} & a_{1n} \\ a_{n1} & a_{nn} \end{vmatrix} \end{vmatrix}$$.

This result is known as *pivotal condensation* and reduces an nth-order determinant to an $(n-1)^{st}$-order determinant, each of whose terms is a second-order determinant. The element a_{11}, assumed unequal to zero, is called the *pivot*.

4. Cramer's Rule

Our physical introduction to determinants was by way of the solution of systems of linear algebraic equations. Let us return to this problem and give its general solution. Consider, then, a system of n linear equations on the n unknowns $x_1, x_2, \cdots, x_n$:

$$
\begin{aligned}
a_{11}x_1 + a_{12}x_2 + \cdots + a_{1n}x_n &= c_1 \\
a_{21}x_1 + a_{22}x_2 + \cdots + a_{2n}x_n &= c_2 \\
\cdot\ \cdot\ \cdot\ \cdot\ \cdot\ \cdot\ \cdot\ \cdot\ \cdot\ \cdot\ \cdot\ \cdot \\
a_{n1}x_1 + a_{n2}x_2 + \cdots + a_{nn}x_n &= c_n \ .
\end{aligned}
\tag{5}
$$

The coefficients of the x_i form a square array:

$$
\begin{matrix}
a_{11} & a_{12} & \cdots & a_{1n} \\
a_{21} & a_{22} & \cdots & a_{2n} \\
\cdot & \cdot & \cdot\ \cdot\ \cdot & \cdot \\
a_{n1} & a_{n2} & \cdots & a_{nn} \ .
\end{matrix}
$$

We shall call D the determinant of this array, or the *determinant of the coefficients*. The solution of Equations (5) can now be expressed by a theorem known as *Cramer's rule*.

CRAMER'S RULE. Consider the system of equations of Equations (5), and let D, the determinant of the a_{ij}, be unequal to zero. Let A_{ij} be the cofactor of the a_{ij}. Then

$$
x_j = \frac{A_{1j}c_1 + A_{2j}c_2 + \cdots + A_{nj}c_n}{D} \ , \quad j = 1, 2, \cdots, n \ .
$$

Proof. Multiply the kth equation of Equations (5) by $A_{k\alpha}$, $k = 1, 2, \cdots, n$. If we then add all these equations and collect coefficients of the x_i, there results

$$
\sum_{i=1}^{n} (a_{1i}A_{1\alpha} + a_{2i}A_{2\alpha} + \cdots + a_{ni}A_{n\alpha})x_i
$$
$$
= c_1 A_{1\alpha} + c_2 A_{2\alpha} + \cdots + c_n A_{n\alpha} \ .
$$

By the corollary to the Laplace development,

$$
a_{1j}A_{1\beta} + a_{2j}A_{2\beta} + \cdots + a_{nj}A_{n\beta} = \delta_{j\beta} D \ .
$$

Hence

$$Dx_\alpha = c_1 A_{1\alpha} + c_2 A_{2\alpha} + \cdots + c_n A_{n\alpha} \quad ,$$

and

$$x_\alpha = \frac{1}{D} \sum_{k=1}^{n} c_k A_{k\alpha} \quad , \quad \alpha = 1, 2, \cdots, n \quad . \tag{6}$$

Dividing by D is legal, since we have assumed $D \neq 0$.

COROLLARY. If the system of equations of Equations (5) is homogeneous, that is, $c_i = 0$, $i = 1, 2, \cdots, n$, and $D \neq 0$, then $x_1 = x_2 = \cdots = x_n = 0$.

Proof. By Equation (6)

$$x_\alpha = \frac{1}{D} \sum_{k=1}^{n} 0 \cdot A_{k\alpha} = 0 \quad , \quad \alpha = 1, 2, \cdots, n \quad .$$

EXERCISE

In Cramer's rule, show that x_j can be written as the ratio of two determinants, the denominator being $D = |a_{ij}|$ and the numerator being D with the jth column replaced by the $c_1, c_2, \cdots, c_n$.

5. Matrices

In the previous section we solved the problem of n linear equations in n unknowns when the determinant D of the coefficients was unequal to zero. What happens, though, if there are more equations than unknowns, or more unknowns than equations, or suppose $D = 0$? The machinery that has been developed to answer these questions can be found in the theory of matrices. Also, once we have developed the elementary portions of this theory, many other applications of matrices will become apparent.

The definition of a matrix is simple enough. It is simply an array of rs elements,

$$A = \begin{Vmatrix} a_{11} & a_{12} & \cdots & a_{1s} \\ a_{21} & a_{22} & \cdots & a_{2s} \\ \cdots & \cdots & \cdots & \cdots \\ a_{r1} & a_{r2} & \cdots & a_{rs} \end{Vmatrix} = \| a_{ij} \| \quad , \tag{7}$$

which is generally enclosed by pairs of vertical lines as in Equation (7) above. The matrix A is called an $r \times s$ matrix, since it has r rows and s columns. If $r = s$, we have a *square matrix*. Note that a matrix is *not* a number, as was a determinant. However, if we have a square matrix we can consider the *determinant of the matrix*, which *is* a number. If A is a square matrix ($r = s$), then we write $|A|$ or det A to indicate the determinant of the matrix A. We do not define det A if A is not a square matrix.

Since a matrix is a new mathematical quantity, we are at liberty to define equality, sum, and product of matrices any way we please. The following definitions have proved most fruitful.

Definition. (i) If $A = \| a_{ij} \|$ and $B = \| b_{ij} \|$ are two $r \times s$ matrices, then $A = B$ means $a_{ij} = b_{ij}$ for all i and j with $i = 1, 2, \cdots, r$ and $j = 1, 2, \cdots, s$.

(ii) By the sum of A and B, written $A + B$, we mean the matrix $C = \| c_{ij} \|$, where $c_{ij} = a_{ij} + b_{ij}$.

(iii) If A is a matrix and c is a number, then by cA we mean the matrix $\| ca_{ij} \|$.

(iv) If A is an $r \times s$ matrix $\| a_{ij} \|$ and B an $s \times t$ matrix $\| b_{ij} \|$, then their product $C = AB$ is an $r \times t$ matrix $\| c_{ij} \|$, where

$$c_{ij} = \sum_{k=1}^{s} a_{ik} b_{kj} \qquad \begin{aligned} i &= 1, 2, \cdots, r \\ j &= 1, 2, \cdots, t \end{aligned} \quad .$$

Note that equality of matrices, sum of matrices, and multiplication of a matrix by a constant are *not* the same as the corresponding rules for determinants. However, multiplication is the same rule as given for determinants (Laplace development).

Consider for a moment only *square* matrices. Then the *zero matrix* 0 is the matrix all of whose elements are zero.† We sometimes write

$$0 = \| 0_{ij} \|$$

to indicate this. Note that with our definition of addition

$$A + 0 = 0 + A = A \quad ,$$

where A is a square matrix. The *unit matrix* or *identity matrix* I is defined as the matrix which has "one's" down its main diagonal and zero elsewhere. We may write this as

$$I = \| \delta_{ij} \| \quad ,$$

where δ_{ij} is the Kronecker delta. (By the main diagonal of a square matrix we mean the elements a_{kk}, $k = 1, 2, \cdots, n$.) One can verify from the definition of multiplication of matrices that

$$AI = IA = A \quad ,$$

where A is a square matrix.

---

† We also call a rectangular matrix a *zero matrix* if all of its elements are zero (cf. Chap. 6).

We see therefore that square matrices exhibit many of the properties of ordinary numbers if we interpret the 0 matrix as zero and the unit matrix as the number 1. One can also show that

$$A(BC) = (AB)C \quad ,$$

that is, that multiplication is *associative*, and the *distributive* law

$$A(B + C) = AB + AC \quad .$$

However, the analogy fails when we consider commutativity. That is, the equation

$$AB = BA$$

is not necessarily true when A and B are matrices. Example: Let

$$A = \begin{Vmatrix} 1 & 0 \\ 0 & 2 \end{Vmatrix} \quad , \quad B = \begin{Vmatrix} 0 & 3 \\ 1 & 0 \end{Vmatrix} \quad .$$

Then

$$AB = \begin{Vmatrix} 0 & 3 \\ 2 & 0 \end{Vmatrix} \quad , \quad BA = \begin{Vmatrix} 0 & 6 \\ 1 & 0 \end{Vmatrix} \quad ,$$

and $AB \neq BA$. Matrices also have the property that AB may equal zero when neither A nor B is zero; for example,

$$\begin{Vmatrix} 1 & 0 \\ 0 & 0 \end{Vmatrix} \cdot \begin{Vmatrix} 0 & 0 \\ 1 & 2 \end{Vmatrix} = \begin{Vmatrix} 0 & 0 \\ 0 & 0 \end{Vmatrix} \quad ,$$

and neither of the matrices on the left is the zero matrix.

EXERCISES

1. If A, B, and C are square matrices, prove that

   (i) $A(BC) = (AB)C$

   (ii) $A(B + C) = AB + AC$.

2. If A and B are square matrices, prove that

   $$\det AB = (\det A)(\det B) \quad .$$

If a matrix has but a single column, we call it a *column matrix* or a *column vector*. Similarly, if it has but a single row, we call it a *row matrix* or a *row vector*. In matrix terminology, vectors are matrices with a single row or column. One of the advantages of matrix notation is that it allows us to write certain complicated expressions in a very compact form. Suppose, for example, that A is the square matrix $\| a_{ij} \|$ and x is the column vector

$$\left\| \begin{array}{c} x_1 \\ x_2 \\ \vdots \\ x_n \end{array} \right\|$$

with components $x_1, x_2, \cdots, x_n$, while c is the column vector

$$\left\| \begin{array}{c} c_1 \\ c_2 \\ \vdots \\ c_n \end{array} \right\|$$

with components $c_1, c_2, \cdots, c_n$. Then Equations (5) may be written as

$$Ax = c \quad,$$

for, if we write this in expanded matrix notation, we obtain

$$\left\| \begin{array}{cccc} a_{11} & a_{12} & \cdots & a_{1n} \\ a_{21} & a_{22} & \cdots & a_{2n} \\ \cdot & \cdot & \cdots & \cdot \\ a_{n1} & a_{n2} & \cdots & a_{nn} \end{array} \right\| \cdot \left\| \begin{array}{c} x_1 \\ x_2 \\ \vdots \\ x_n \end{array} \right\| = \left\| \begin{array}{c} c_1 \\ c_2 \\ \vdots \\ c_n \end{array} \right\| \,.$$

Actually, carrying out the multiplication on the left, we obtain

$$\left\| \begin{array}{c} a_{11}x_1 + a_{12}x_2 + \cdots + a_{1n}x_n \\ a_{21}x_1 + a_{22}x_2 + \cdots + a_{2n}x_n \\ \cdot \quad \cdot \quad \cdot \quad \cdot \quad \cdot \quad \cdot \\ a_{n1}x_1 + a_{n2}x_2 + \cdots + a_{nn}x_n \end{array} \right\| = \left\| \begin{array}{c} c_1 \\ c_2 \\ \vdots \\ c_n \end{array} \right\| \,.$$

But, by definition of equality of matrices, this implies the n equations of Equations (5).

If A is a square matrix, we have noted that we can consider the *determinant of the matrix* det A. If det $A \neq 0$, we shall say that A is a *nonsingular matrix*, while if det $A = 0$, we call A *singular*. Suppose A is a square matrix; then we can ask the question: Does there exist a matrix B such that $AB = I$, where

I is the identity matrix? If such a matrix exists, we shall call it the *inverse matrix* and write $B = A^{-1}$. Then the equation $AB = I$ becomes

$$A A^{-1} = I \quad . \tag{8}$$

The matrix A^{-1} will exist only if A is nonsingular. For if det $A = 0$, then

$$\det A\, A^{-1} = (\det A)(\det A^{-1}) = \det I \quad .$$

But det $A = 0$, and det $I = 1$. Hence the above equation is impossible. However, if det $A \neq 0$, we shall actually construct A^{-1}. Let

$$A = \| a_{ij} \| \quad , \quad \det A \neq 0 \quad ,$$

and let A_{ij} be the cofactor of a_{ij}. Let

$$B = \| b_{ij} \|$$

be a square matrix with

$$b_{ij} = \frac{A_{ji}}{|A|} \quad .$$

Then we assert that

$$AB = I \quad ,$$

for the element in the ith row and j^{th} column of AB is

$$\sum_{k=1}^{n} a_{ik} b_{kj} = \sum_{k=1}^{n} a_{ik} \frac{A_{jk}}{|A|} = \frac{1}{|A|} (\delta_{ij}|A|) = \delta_{ij} \quad .$$

Thus B is the inverse of A, and we write $B = A^{-1}$.

EXERCISES

1. Prove that the inverse of A^{-1} is A.
2. Prove that if $AA^{-1} = I$ then A^{-1} is unique and $A^{-1}A = I$.
3. Prove that $(AB)^{-1} = B^{-1}A^{-1}$.

The solution of Equations (5), which we have written in matrix notation as

$$Ax = c \quad ,$$

can now be solved in the following way. Multiply both sides of the above equation by A^{-1}. Then

$$A^{-1}(Ax) = A^{-1}c \quad .$$

But $A^{-1}A = I$. Hence

$$x = A^{-1}c \quad , \tag{9}$$

and we have found x. This point of view is very convenient in certain investigations. In fact, Equation (9) is merely Cramer's rule. However, from the practical point of view there is just as much labor in computing A^{-1} as in applying Cramer's rule. Nevertheless, Equation (9) indicates that the solution of linear equations is identical with the problem of inverting a matrix.

6. Linear Dependence

The idea of linear dependence is an important one in all branches of mathematics. We introduce it at the present time because a knowledge of this concept will facilitate our exposition of certain phases of matrix theory. It will also be used in Chapter 3 when we consider—what seems like a very diverse topic compared to matrices—the theory of linear differential equations.

Linear dependence is a generalization of the idea of proportion. For example, if the ratio of two functions of x is independent of x, we shall say the functions are linearly dependent. Let us, however, consider a more general setting. Suppose we have a collection of n objects $f_1, f_2, \cdots, f_n$. They may be functions of x, vectors, matrices, or other mathematical entities. If there exist numbers $a_1, a_2, \cdots, a_n$ not all zero such that

$$a_1 f_1 + a_2 f_2 + \cdots + a_n f_n = 0 \quad , \tag{10}$$

then we shall say that the $f_1, f_2, \cdots, f_n$ are *linearly dependent*. In the contrary case we shall say they are *linearly independent*. Or wording the concept of linear independence in a positive way, we shall say that the n quantities $f_1, f_2, \cdots, f_n$ are *linearly independent* if every relation of the form

$$a_1 f_1 + a_2 f_2 + \cdots + a_n f_n = 0$$

implies that all the a_k are zero.

For example, suppose $f_1 = e^x$ and $f_2 = 3e^x$. Then

$$3 \cdot f_1 + (-1) \cdot f_2 \equiv 0 \quad ;$$

hence f_1 and f_2 are linearly dependent. On the other hand, if $f_1 = \sin x$ and $f_2 = \cos x$, we assert that f_1 and f_2 are linearly independent. For suppose the contrary. Then there would exist an a_1 and an a_2, not both zero such that

$$a_1 \sin x + a_2 \cos x \equiv 0 \quad . \tag{11}$$

In particular, if $x = \pi/2$, the above relation must hold. But if $x = \pi/2$, then Equation (11) becomes

$$a_1 + a_2 \cdot 0 = 0 \quad ,$$

or

$$a_1 = 0 \quad .$$

Similarly, Equation (11) must be true if $x = 0$. But in this case we have

$$a_2 = 0 \quad .$$

Thus, if Equation (11) holds for all x, then a_1 and a_2 must both be zero.

The reader can also see that the column vectors

$$x_1 = \left\| \begin{matrix} 2 \\ -1 \\ 3 \end{matrix} \right\| \quad , \quad x_2 = \left\| \begin{matrix} 3 \\ -1.5 \\ 4.5 \end{matrix} \right\| \quad , \quad x_3 = \left\| \begin{matrix} -4 \\ 2 \\ -6 \end{matrix} \right\|$$

are linearly dependent, since

$$2x_1 + 0 \cdot x_2 + 1 \cdot x_3 \equiv 0 \quad ;$$

that is, the vector $2x_1 + 0 \cdot x_2 + x_3$ is the zero vector

$$\left\| \begin{matrix} 0 \\ 0 \\ 0 \end{matrix} \right\|$$

An immediate extension of the definition of linear independence is as follows: An element f is said to be linearly dependent on the elements $f_1, f_2, \cdots, f_n$ if there exist constants a_k such that

$$f = a_1 f_1 + a_2 f_2 + \cdots + a_n f_n \quad .$$

It follows that if $f_1, f_2, \cdots, f_n$ are linearly dependent, then some f_i is linearly dependent on the remaining f_k's. For if $f_1, f_2, \cdots, f_n$ are linearly dependent, then there exists a relation

$$a_1 f_1 + a_2 f_2 + \cdots + a_n f_n = 0 \quad , \tag{12}$$

and not all of the a_k are zero. Suppose $a_i \neq 0$. Then we may write Equation (12) as

$$f_i = -a_i^{-1} a_1 f_1 - \cdots - a_i^{-1} a_{i-1} f_{i-1} - a_i^{-1} a_{i+1} f_{i+1} - \cdots - a_i^{-1} a_n f_n$$

Other immediate properties of linear dependence will be left as exercises for the reader.

EXERCISES

1. Prove that if f is linearly dependent on $f_1, f_2, \cdots, f_n$ but not on $f_1, f_2, \cdots, f_{n-1}$ then f_n is linearly dependent on $f_1, f_2, \cdots, f_{n-1}, f$.

2. Prove that if h is linearly dependent on $f_1, f_2, \cdots, f_n$ and if every f_i is

linearly dependent on $g_1, g_2, \cdots, g_m$ then h is linearly dependent on $g_1, g_1, \cdots, g_m$.

3. Two sets of vectors (functions, matrices, and so forth) $f_1, f_2, \cdots, f_n$ and $g_1, g_2, \cdots, g_m$ are said to be *equivalent* if every g_i is linearly dependent on the f_j's and every f_j is linearly dependent on the g_i's. Prove that if $f_1, f_2, \cdots, f_n$ is a set of vectors not all zero then there exists a subset of linearly independent vectors equivalent to $f_1, f_2, \cdots, f_n$.

4. If $f_1, f_2, \cdots, f_n$ and $g_1, g_2, \cdots, g_m$ are two sets of linearly independent vectors which are equivalent prove that $n = m$.

7. Rank of a Matrix

If A is an $r \times s$ matrix $\| a_{ij} \|$, then there exist square submatrices of all orders not exceeding min $[r, s]$. Consider the determinants of these submatrices. The order of the determinant of the largest square matrix in A which does not vanish is called the *rank of the matrix*, $r(A)$. Clearly

$$r(A) \leq \min [r, s] \quad .$$

For example, the rank of the matrix

$$\begin{Vmatrix} 1 & 0 \\ 2 & 0 \end{Vmatrix}$$

is one, while the rank of

$$\begin{Vmatrix} 1 & 4 \\ 6 & 3 \end{Vmatrix}$$

is two. The rank of a nonsingular $n \times n$ square matrix is n.

We now apply the concept of linear dependence to prove the following theorem:

THEOREM. Let $A = \| a_{ij} \|$ be an $n \times n$ matrix. Then
(i) If $r(A) = n - 1$, there exist constants $c_1, c_2, \cdots, c_n$ not all zero such that

$$c_1 a_{1j} + c_2 a_{2j} + \cdots + c_n a_{nj} = 0 \quad , \quad j = 1, 2, \cdots, n \quad .$$

(ii) If $r(A) = n$, then any relation of the form

$$c_1 a_{1j} + c_2 a_{2j} + \cdots + c_n a_{nj} = 0 \quad ,$$

which holds for all $j, j = 1, 2, \cdots, n$, implies $c_1 = c_2 = \cdots = c_n = 0$.

Proof. Case (i): Let D be the determinant of A. For definiteness assume that the $(n-1) \times (n-1)$ determinant in the upper left-hand corner of A has rank $n-1$. Then, by the corollary to the Laplace development,

$$\sum_{k=1}^{n} a_{kj} A_{k\beta} = \delta_{j\beta} D \quad.$$

If we let $\beta = n$, and recall that $D = 0$ by hypothesis, then

$$\sum_{k=1}^{n} A_{kn} a_{kj} = 0 \quad.$$

The A_{kn} are the c_k of the theorem. They are not all zero, since in particular $A_{nn} \neq 0$.

Case (ii): Consider the expressions

$$c_1 a_{1j} + c_2 a_{2j} + \cdots + c_n a_{nj} = 0 \quad, \quad j = 1, 2, \cdots, n$$

as a system of linear equations on the n quantities c_i, $i = 1, 2, \cdots, n$. Then, since $D \neq 0$ by hypothesis, we have by the corollary to Cramer's rule that

$$c_j = 0 \quad, \quad j = 1, 2, \cdots, n \quad.$$

EXERCISE

Generalize the above theorem as follows: Let $A = \| a_{ij} \|$ be an $m \times n$ matrix of rank β. Let a nonsingular matrix of order β lie in the upper left hand corner of A. Prove that for every r, $r = 1, 2, \cdots, m - \beta$ there exist constants $k_{1r}, k_{2r}, \cdots, k_{\beta r}, k_{\beta+r,r}$ such that

$$k_{1r} a_{1j} + k_{2r} a_{2j} + \cdots + k_{\beta r} a_{\beta j} + k_{\beta+r,r} a_{\beta+r,j} = 0$$

for $j = 1, 2, \cdots, n$ and $k_{\beta+r,r} \neq 0$ for $r = 1, 2, \cdots, m - \beta$.

In Case (i) of the above theorem we shall say that the rows of the matrix are *linearly dependent*. This is in harmony with the definition given in the previous section. We may also consider the linear forms

$$\lambda_i(x) = a_{i1} x_1 + a_{i2} x_2 + \cdots + a_{in} x_n \quad, \quad i = 1, 2, \cdots, n \quad.$$

Suppose that the matrix A of the coefficients a_{ij} is singular, that is, $r(A) < n$. Then, by the previous theorem, there exist constants $c_1, c_2, \cdots, c_n$ not all zero such that

$$\sum_{i=1}^{n} c_i a_{ij} = 0 \quad, \quad j = 1, 2, \cdots, n \quad.$$

If we multiply the λ_i by c_i and sum over i, we obtain

$$\sum_{i=1}^{n} c_i \lambda_i = x_1 \sum_{i=1}^{n} c_i a_{i1} + x_2 \sum_{i=1}^{n} c_i a_{i2} + \cdots + x_n \sum_{i=1}^{n} c_i a_{in} = 0 \quad.$$

We say in this case that the linear expressions $\lambda_i(x)$, $i = 1, 2, \cdots, n$ are *linearly dependent*. In the contrary case we say they are *linearly independent*.

EXERCISE

Generalize the above result to the case where

$$\lambda_i(x) = a_{i1}x_1 + a_{i2}x_2 + \cdots + a_{in}x_n \ , \quad i = 1, 2, \cdots, m$$

with $m \neq n$.

8. Linear Equations

In deducing Cramer's rule we assumed that the number of equations equaled the number of unknowns, and, further, that the determinant of the coefficients was nonzero. We now have sufficient machinery available to describe the general case. Consider, then, the following system of m linear equations in n unknowns,

$$
\begin{aligned}
a_{11}x_1 + a_{12}x_2 + \cdots + a_{1n}x_n + b_1 &= 0 \\
a_{21}x_1 + a_{22}x_2 + \cdots + a_{2n}x_n + b_2 &= 0 \\
\cdot \quad \cdot \quad \cdot \quad \cdot \quad \cdot \quad \cdot \quad \cdot \quad \cdot \quad \cdot \quad \cdot \quad \cdot \quad \cdot \quad \cdot \quad & \\
a_{m1}x_1 + a_{m2}x_2 + \cdots + a_{mn}x_n + b_m &= 0 \ .
\end{aligned}
\tag{13}
$$

For present applications we prefer to write the b_i's on the left-hand side of the equation. Let the matrix of the a_{ij} coefficients be denoted by A,

$$
A = \|a_{ij}\| =
\left\|
\begin{array}{cccc}
a_{11} & a_{12} & \cdots & a_{1n} \\
a_{21} & a_{22} & \cdots & a_{2n} \\
\cdot & \cdot & \cdot & \cdot \\
a_{m1} & a_{m2} & \cdots & a_{mn}
\end{array}
\right\| ,
$$

and let

$$
B =
\left\|
\begin{array}{ccccc}
a_{11} & a_{12} & \cdots & a_{1n} & b_1 \\
a_{21} & a_{22} & \cdots & a_{2n} & b_2 \\
\cdot & \cdot & \cdot & \cdot & \cdot \\
a_{m1} & a_{m2} & \cdots & a_{mn} & b_m
\end{array}
\right\| .
$$

B is called the *augmented matrix* and is the same as A except for the additional column of b_i's.

We can now present the general theorem.

THEOREM. Consider the system of Equation (13), where A and B have been defined as above:

(i) If $r(A) \neq r(B)$, then there exist no solutions to Equations (13); that is, the equations are *inconsistent*.

(ii) If $r(A) = r(B) = \beta$, then the values of $n - \beta$ of the x_i's may be assigned at pleasure (provided only that the rank of the matrix of the coefficients of the remaining β unknowns is β) and the remaining β x_i's will be uniquely determined.

Proof. Clearly $r(A)$ cannot be greater than $r(B)$, since every minor which occurs in A also occurs in B. Hence there arise but two cases:

Case (i): $r(A) < r(B)$.

Case (ii): $r(A) = r(B)$.

We proceed to treat these two cases.

Case (i): Let $r(B) = \alpha > r(A)$. Assume for definiteness that a nonvanishing determinant of order α is located in the upper right-hand corner of B. Such a determinant must exist and contain the b_i column. For simplicity in notation, let

$$\lambda_i(x) = a_{i1}x_1 + a_{i2}x_2 + \cdots + a_{in}x_n \quad , \quad i = 1, 2, \cdots, m$$

and

$$L_i(x) = \lambda_i(x) + b_i \quad , \quad i = 1, 2, \cdots, m \quad .$$

Since $r(A) < \alpha$, there must exist constants c_i not all zero such that

$$c_1\lambda_1 + c_2\lambda_2 + \cdots + c_\alpha\lambda_\alpha = 0 \quad ;$$

hence

$$\sum_{i=1}^{\alpha} c_i L_i = \sum_{i=1}^{\alpha} c_i(\lambda_i + b_i) = \sum_{i=1}^{\alpha} c_i b_i = C \quad .$$

Since $r(B) = \alpha$ the L_i are linearly independent and hence $C \neq 0$. The equations are therefore inconsistent, for, if they were not, there would exist values of the x_i, say x_i', such that

$$L_i(x') = 0$$

and hence

$$\sum_{i=1}^{\alpha} c_i L_i = 0 = C \neq 0 \quad ,$$

a contradiction.

Case (ii): Let $r(A) = r(B) = \beta$. Let a determinant of rank β appear in the upper left-hand corner of the matrix B. Since all $(\beta + 1)$ rowed determinants vanish, there must exist constants c_i not all zero such that

$$c_1L_1 + c_2L_2 + \cdots + c_\beta L_\beta + c_{\beta+1}L_{\beta+1} = 0 \quad ;$$

that is, $L_1, L_2, \cdots, L_{\beta+1}$ are linearly dependent. In particular, $c_{\beta+1} \neq 0$, for, if it were equal to zero, the rank of the matrix would be less than or equal to $\beta - 1$; that is, the $L_1, L_2, \cdots, L_\beta$ would be linearly dependent, contrary to hypothesis. Hence we may write

$$L_{\beta+1} = k_{11}L_1 + k_{21}L_2 + \cdots + k_{\beta 1}L_\beta \quad .$$

Similarly, for every $L_{\beta+r}$ with $1 \leq r \leq m - \beta$,

$$L_{\beta+r} = k_{1r}L_1 + k_{2r}L_2 + \cdots + k_{\beta r}L_\beta \quad .$$

If $L_1, L_2, \cdots, L_\beta$ vanish for $x_i = x_i^*$, $i = 1, 2, \cdots, n$, then $L_{\beta+1}, L_{\beta+2}, \cdots, L_m$ also vanish. Let $x_{\beta+1}, x_{\beta+2}, \cdots, x_n$ have any numerical values, say $x_{\beta+1}^*, x_{\beta+2}^*, \cdots, x_n^*$, respectively. We may then write the equations in the form

$$a_{11}x_1 + a_{12}x_2 + \cdots + a_{1\beta}x_\beta = -a_{1,\beta+1}x_{\beta+1}^* - a_{1,\beta+2}x_{\beta+2}^* - \cdots - a_{1n}x_n^* - b_1$$
$$a_{21}x_1 + a_{22}x_2 + \cdots + a_{2\beta}x_\beta = -a_{2,\beta+1}x_{\beta+1}^* - a_{2,\beta+2}x_{\beta+2}^* - \cdots - a_{2n}x_n^* - b_2$$
$$\cdots \cdots \cdots \cdots \cdots \cdots \cdots \cdots \cdots \cdots \cdots \cdots \cdots \cdots \cdots \cdots \cdots \cdots$$
$$a_{\beta 1}x_1 + a_{\beta 2}x_2 + \cdots + a_{\beta\beta}x_\beta = -a_{\beta,\beta+1}x_{\beta+1}^* - a_{\beta,\beta+2}x_{\beta+2}^* - \cdots - a_{\beta n}x_n^* - b_\beta$$

and apply Cramer's rule.

EXERCISES

1. Investigate completely and find all solutions of the following system of equations

$$2x - 3y + z = -1$$
$$5x + 2y - 3z = 0$$
$$x + 8y - 5z = 2 \quad .$$

2. If each of the three equations in Exercise 1 is considered as a plane in three-dimensional space, interpret the solution geometrically.

3. Solve completely the following system of equations

$$2x + 3y + z = 4$$
$$x - 2y + 4z = -5$$
$$3x + 8y - 2z = 13$$
$$4x - y + 9z = -6 \quad .$$

REFERENCES

Birkhoff, Garrett, and Saunders MacLane, *A Survey of Modern Algebra*. New York: The Macmillan Company, 1951.

Bôcher, Maxime, *Introduction to Higher Algebra*. New York: The Macmillan Company, 1907.

Halmos, P. R., *Finite Dimensional Vector Spaces*. Princeton, N.J.: Princeton University Press, 1942.

Margenau, Henry, and G. M. Murphy, *The Mathematics of Physics and Chemistry*. New York: D. Van Nostrand Company, Inc., 1943.

Salvadori, M. G., and K. S. Miller, *The Mathematical Solution of Engineering Problems*. New York: Columbia University Press, 1953.

Waerden, B. L. van der, *Modern Algebra*. New York: Frederick Ungar Publishing Company, 1949, Vol. 1.

1. Introduction

In almost every mathematical problem of a practical nature certain "special" functions appear. For example, it would be difficult to formulate a problem whose solution did not involve polynomials or trigonometric functions or exponentials or a combination of these "elementary functions." As we progress to more difficult problems, other more advanced functions appear. For example, the solution may appear as an integral or as a "non-elementary function" such as a Bessel function. In the present chapter we wish to collect and discuss a few of the more common functions defined by integrals. From the point of view of differential equations, the problem of finding y where

$$y = \int f(x) \, dx$$

can be considered equivalent to solving the first-order differential equation

$$y' = f(x) \quad .$$

Besides the special integrals such as Gamma function, Beta function, the error function and elliptic integrals, we shall consider certain results which depend on these formulas, for example, Stirling's approximation to the factorial and Euler's constant. *All* these special results will be used in future chapters in connection with the solution of various engineering problems and are not presented merely as interesting mathematical sidelights. In addition to the special functions, certain techniques which are useful in evaluating integrals, such as differentiation with respect to a parameter and Simpson's rule, will appear. These methods will frequently be of use to the reader in solving other problems that he may encounter in his work.

Throughout the book other special formulas and methods will appear. For example, Bessel functions, Hermite functions, Legendre polynomials will be discussed at length in Chapter 3. Various applications of these functions will be given in that chapter as well as in future chapters.

2. Gamma Function

Perhaps the best known nonelementary function is the *Gamma function,* written $\Gamma(\alpha)$ and defined by the equation

$$\Gamma(\alpha) = \int_0^\infty x^{\alpha-1}e^{-x}dx \tag{1}$$

for all positive α. The reader has probably already encountered this formula in earlier work; nevertheless, we shall briefly discuss its salient features. The Gamma function is sometimes called the *factorial function* because it has the property that

$$\Gamma(\alpha) = (\alpha - 1)! \tag{2}$$

when α is a positive integer. Formula (2) is readily deduced by integrating Equation (1) by parts; namely,

$$\Gamma(\alpha) = \int_0^\infty x^{\alpha-1}d(-e^{-x}) = -x^{\alpha-1}e^{-x}\Big|_0^\infty + \int_0^\infty (\alpha-1)x^{\alpha-2}e^{-x}dx$$

$$= 0 + (\alpha-1)\int_0^\infty x^{\alpha-2}e^{-x}dx$$

$$= (\alpha-1)\Gamma(\alpha-1) \quad, \quad \alpha > 1 \quad.$$

Repeated applications of this formula yield

$$\Gamma(\alpha) = (\alpha - 1)\Gamma(\alpha - 1)$$
$$= (\alpha - 1)[(\alpha - 2)\Gamma(\alpha - 2)]$$
$$= \cdot \quad \cdot \quad \cdot \quad \cdot \quad \cdot \quad \cdot \quad \cdot \quad \cdot \quad \cdot$$
$$= (\alpha - 1)(\alpha - 2)\cdots 2 \cdot 1\Gamma(1) \quad.$$

But

$$\Gamma(1) = \int_0^\infty e^{-x}dx = 1 \quad;$$

hence Equation (2) is established.

We note, however, that $\Gamma(\alpha)$ is also defined when α is *not* an integer, and therefore can be considered as a generalization of $\alpha!$ when α is not an integer.

The integral representation of $\Gamma(\alpha)$ given by Equation (1) is meaningful only when α is *positive*. To show this, write

$$\Gamma(\alpha) = \int_0^A x^{\alpha-1} e^{-x} dx + \int_A^\infty x^{\alpha-1} e^{-x} dx \quad ,$$

where A is any positive number. Now by the mean-value theorem for integrals,

$$\int_0^A x^{\alpha-1} e^{-x} dx = e^{-\theta} \int_0^A x^{\alpha-1} dx = \frac{e^{-\theta} x^\alpha}{\alpha}\Big|_0^A$$

where θ is some number between 0 and A. Hence, if $\alpha > 0$, $x^\alpha \to 0$ as $x \to 0$ and

$$\frac{e^{-\theta} x^\alpha}{\alpha}\Big|_0^A = \frac{e^{-\theta} A^\alpha}{\alpha} - 0$$

is a finite number. If $\alpha < 0$, then $x^\alpha \to \infty$ as $x \to 0$; hence

$$\frac{e^{-\theta} x^\alpha}{\alpha}\Big|_0^A = \frac{e^{-\theta} A^\alpha}{\alpha} + \infty$$

does not have a finite value. (If $\alpha = 0$,

$$e^{-\theta} \int_0^A x^{\alpha-1} dx = e^{-\theta} \log x \Big|_0^A \quad ,$$

and $-\log x$ also approaches infinity as $x \to 0$.) We leave it to the reader to show that no matter what the value of α,

$$\int_A^\infty x^{\alpha-1} e^{-x} dx$$

is always a finite quantity.

Since $\Gamma(\alpha)$ as given by Equation (1) only makes sense when $\alpha > 0$, and since in certain applications (cf. Chap. 3) it is convenient to use $\Gamma(\alpha)$ with $\alpha \leq 0$, we *define* $\Gamma(\alpha)$ for $\alpha < 0$ by the formula

$$\Gamma(\alpha) = \frac{\Gamma(\alpha + 1)}{\alpha} \quad ., \quad -(n+1) < \alpha < -n \tag{3}$$

for $n = 0, 1, 2, \cdots$. This formula and Equation (1) then define $\Gamma(\alpha)$ for all α not zero or a negative integer. When $\alpha = 0$, we write

$$\Gamma(0) = \lim_{\alpha \to 0} \Gamma(\alpha) = \lim_{\alpha \to 0} \frac{\Gamma(\alpha + 1)}{\alpha} = \infty$$

and from Equation (3), if N is a positive integer,

$$\Gamma(-N) = \frac{1}{(-N)(-N+1)\cdots(-1)} \Gamma(0) = \frac{(-1)^N}{N!} \Gamma(0) = \pm \infty \quad .$$

Thus the function $\Gamma(\alpha)$ has been defined for all values of the argument α, positive or negative, integral or nonintegral. A graph of $\Gamma(\alpha)$ appears in Figure 2.1.

EXERCISES

1. Prove that $\int_A^\infty x^{\alpha-1}e^{-x}dx$ has a finite value for $A > 0$ no matter what the value of α. HINT: Write $x^{\alpha-1}e^{-x} = x^{\alpha-1}/e^x$, and expand e^x in a Maclaurin series.

2. In Section 3 we shall show that $\Gamma(\tfrac{1}{2}) = \sqrt{\pi}$. Use this result to prove that

$$\Gamma(n + \tfrac{1}{2}) = \frac{(2n)!}{n!2^{2n}} \sqrt{\pi} \quad ,$$

   where n is a positive integer.

3. Tabulated values of $\Gamma(\alpha)$ are given for $1 \leqq \alpha \leqq 2$ in various tables.† Prove that if α is any number, positive, negative, or zero, that one can numerically evaluate $\Gamma(\alpha)$ with these tables. Calculate the numerical value of $\Gamma(4.70)$ and $\Gamma(-1.30)$ given that $\Gamma(1.70) = 0.90864$.

4. Prove that

$$\int_0^\infty x^\alpha e^{-x^2}dx = \tfrac{1}{2}\Gamma\left(\frac{\alpha+1}{2}\right) \quad .$$

3. Error Function

The function e^{-x^2} and its integral $\int e^{-x^2}dx$ frequently appear in engineering problems. For example, we may mention probability theory (cf. Chap. 7) and the Fourier integral (cf. Chap. 4). When the particular constant $2/\sqrt{\pi}$ is appended before the integral, namely,

$$\frac{2}{\sqrt{\pi}} \int_0^x e^{-x^2}dx \quad ,$$

then we call this expression the *error function*, and write

$$\operatorname{erf} x = \frac{2}{\sqrt{\pi}} \int_0^x e^{-x^2}dx \quad .$$

---

† For example, C.R.C., *Standard Mathematical Tables*, p. 300.

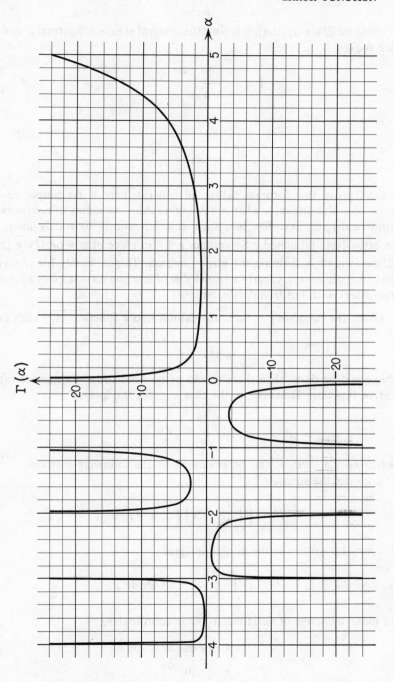

Fig. 2.1

The constant $2/\sqrt{\pi}$ appearing before the integral sign is a "normalizing factor" which makes

$$\text{erf } \infty = \frac{2}{\sqrt{\pi}} \int_0^\infty e^{-x^2} dx = 1 \quad ;$$

that is,

$$\int_0^\infty e^{-x^2} dx = \frac{\sqrt{\pi}}{2} \quad .$$

We shall prove this formula below. In general there is no simple analytical method of evaluating erf x when x has a finite value. One may of course evaluate it numerically (cf. Sec. 10), but, since this function is so widely used, it has been extensively tabulated.[†] Sometimes $e^{-x^2/2}$ in place of e^{-x^2} or $1/\sqrt{\pi}$ in place of $2/\sqrt{\pi}$ is used in defining the error function. This is merely for convenience in certain applications. Clearly a knowledge of any one form implies a knowledge of the others with but trivial calculations.

Given the function $\int_0^x e^{-x^2} dx$, one cannot find a function $\psi(x)$ such that

$$\psi'(x) = e^{-x^2} \quad .$$

If this could be done, then there would be no need to have extensive tables of the error function. However, in the case $x = \infty$, the integral

$$I = \int_0^\infty e^{-x^2} dx \quad ,$$

which is now a *number*, can be evaluated by the following method:

Consider the square of I,

$$I^2 = \left(\int_0^\infty e^{-x^2} dx \right) \left(\int_0^\infty e^{-y^2} dy \right) \quad ,$$

which may be written as the double integral

$$I^2 = \int_0^\infty \int_0^\infty e^{-(x^2+y^2)} dx\, dy \quad . \tag{4}$$

If we make a change of variables to polar coordinates,

$$x = r \cos \theta$$

$$y = r \sin \theta \quad ,$$

---

† See, for example, C.R.C., *Standard Mathematical Tables*, p. 234.

then

$$x^2 + y^2 = r^2 \quad,$$

and the differential product becomes

$$dx\,dy = r\,dr\,d\theta \quad.$$

Also, as x and y vary from 0 to ∞, r varies from 0 to ∞ and θ from 0 to $\pi/2$. Equation (4) thus becomes

$$I^2 = \int_0^{\pi/2} d\theta \int_0^{\infty} re^{-r^2}dr = \frac{\pi}{2}\left[\frac{e^{-r^2}}{-2}\right]\Big|_0^{\infty} = \frac{\pi}{4} \quad,$$

and

$$I = \frac{\sqrt{\pi}}{2} \quad,$$

as we wished to prove.

This result will be used many times in future applications. For the present, let us use it to evaluate $\Gamma(\tfrac{1}{2})$. In the expression for $\Gamma(\alpha)$ let $\alpha = 1/2$; then

$$\Gamma(\tfrac{1}{2}) = \int_0^{\infty} x^{-\frac{1}{2}}e^{-x}dx \quad.$$

If we make the change of variable $x = y^2$, then $dx = 2y\,dy$, $x^{-\frac{1}{2}} = 1/y$, and

$$\Gamma(\tfrac{1}{2}) = \int_0^{\infty} \frac{1}{y}e^{-y^2}2y\,dy = 2\int_0^{\infty} e^{-y^2}dy = \sqrt{\pi} \quad,$$

as we asserted in Exercise 2 of the previous section.

We shall also have occasion in our future work to use the *co-error function* cerf x. It is defined as one minus the error function. Thus

$$\text{cerf } x = 1 - \text{erf } x = 1 - \frac{2}{\sqrt{\pi}}\int_0^x e^{-\xi^2}d\xi = \frac{2}{\sqrt{\pi}}\int_x^{\infty} e^{-\xi^2}d\xi \quad.$$

EXERCISE

Show that if $\phi(x) = (1/\sigma\sqrt{2\pi})\exp[-x^2/2\sigma^2]$ then

(i) $\displaystyle\int_{-\infty}^{\infty} \phi(x)dx = 1$ (ii) $\displaystyle\int_{-\infty}^{\infty} x\phi(x)dx = 0$ (iii) $\displaystyle\int_{-\infty}^{\infty} x^2\phi(x)dx = \sigma^2 \quad.$

4. Jacobians

In the previous section we made a change of variable (to polar coordinates) in the double integral of Equation (4). This change introduced the factor "r" in the integrand. More generally, if we wished to evaluate the integral of $f(x, y)$ over the region R by changing to polar coordinates, we would write

$$\iint_R f(x, y)dx\,dy = \iint_R f(r\cos\theta, r\sin\theta)r\,dr\,d\theta \quad . \tag{5}$$

Suppose, however, we wished to change our variables not to polar coordinates, but to some other variables u and v where u and v are related to x and y by the reversable equations

$$x = \phi(u, v)$$
$$y = \psi(u, v) \quad . \tag{6}$$

Then what factor J analogous to the "r" in Equation (5) must we introduce to make

$$\iint_R f(x, y)dx\,dy = \iint_R f(\phi(u, v), \psi(u, v))J\,du\,dv \tag{7}$$

a true equation?

We shall now compute the J that appears in Equation (7). It is called the *Jacobian of the transformation* of Equation (6). Consider then a small differential area in the u, v coordinate system (cf. Fig. 2.2). The values of the coordinates $x_1, x_2, x_3, y_1, y_2, y_3$ are given by the formulas:

$$x_1 = \phi(u, v)$$

$$x_2 = \phi(u + du, v) = \phi(u, v) + \frac{\partial\phi}{\partial u}\,du$$

$$x_3 = \phi(u, v + dv) = \phi(u, v) + \frac{\partial\phi}{\partial v}\,dv$$

$$y_1 = \psi(u, v)$$

$$y_2 = \psi(u + du, v) = \psi(u, v) + \frac{\partial\psi}{\partial u}\,du$$

$$y_3 = \psi(u, v + dv) = \psi(u, v) + \frac{\partial\psi}{\partial v}\,dv \quad .$$

The element of area shaded in Figure 2.2 is, for small *du* and *dv*, approximately a quadrilateral; and its area is therefore approximately twice the area of the triangle with coordinates (x_1, y_1), (x_2, y_2), (x_3, y_3). By analytic geometry, the area of this triangle is given by one-half the absolute value of the determinant

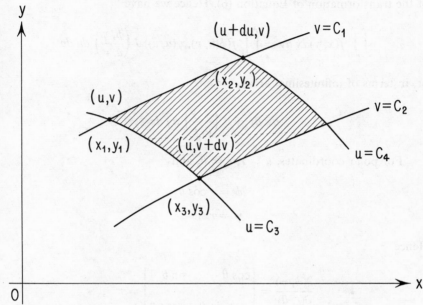

Fig. 2.2

$$\begin{vmatrix} x_1 & y_1 & 1 \\ x_2 & y_2 & 1 \\ x_3 & y_3 & 1 \end{vmatrix} = \begin{vmatrix} \phi & \psi & 1 \\ \phi + \dfrac{\partial \phi}{\partial u} du & \psi + \dfrac{\partial \psi}{\partial u} du & 1 \\ \phi + \dfrac{\partial \phi}{\partial v} dv & \psi + \dfrac{\partial \psi}{\partial v} dv & 1 \end{vmatrix} = \begin{vmatrix} \dfrac{\partial \phi}{\partial u} & \dfrac{\partial \psi}{\partial u} \\ \dfrac{\partial \phi}{\partial v} & \dfrac{\partial \psi}{\partial v} \end{vmatrix} du\, dv \ .$$

The determinant

$$\begin{vmatrix} \dfrac{\partial \phi}{\partial u} & \dfrac{\partial \psi}{\partial u} \\ \dfrac{\partial \phi}{\partial v} & \dfrac{\partial \psi}{\partial v} \end{vmatrix}$$

is called a *functional determinant* and is usually written symbolically as $\dfrac{\partial(\phi, \psi)}{\partial(u, v)}$.

Its absolute value is called the *Jacobian J*,

$$J\left(\frac{\phi, \psi}{u, v}\right) = \left|\frac{\partial(\phi, \psi)}{\partial(u, v)}\right|$$

of the transformation of Equation (6). Hence we have

$$\iint_R f(x, y)dx\, dy = \iint_R f(\phi(u, v), \psi(u, v))\, J\left(\frac{\phi, \psi}{u, v}\right) du\, dv \quad,$$

or, in terms of infinitesimal areas,

$$dx\, dy = J\left(\frac{x, y}{u, v}\right) du\, dv \quad.$$

For polar coordinates, $u = r$, $v = \theta$, and

$$\phi = r \cos \theta$$
$$\psi = r \sin \theta \quad.$$

Hence

$$\frac{\partial(\phi, \psi)}{\partial(r, \theta)} = \begin{vmatrix} \cos \theta & \sin \theta \\ -r \sin \theta & r \cos \theta \end{vmatrix} = r \quad,$$

and

$$J\left(\frac{\phi, \psi}{r, \theta}\right) = \left|\frac{\partial(\phi, \psi)}{\partial(r, \theta)}\right| = r \quad,$$

as we previously knew from our elementary calculus. Other applications of Jacobians will be presented in the next section and in future chapters of the book.

EXERCISES

1. Generalize the definition of the Jacobian to triple integrals.
2. If Equation (6) can be uniquely solved for u and v in terms of x and y, say

$$u = \xi(x, y)$$
$$v = \eta(x, y) \quad,$$

show that the Jacobian of this transformation is the reciprocal of $J\left(\dfrac{\xi, \eta}{x, y}\right)$. That is, show that

$$J\left(\frac{x, y}{u, v}\right) J\left(\frac{u, v}{x, y}\right) = 1 \quad.$$

5. Beta Function

Another function closely allied to the Gamma function that frequently appears in engineering applications is the *Beta function*. The Beta function is a function of *two* variables and is defined by the equation

$$B(u, v) = \int_0^1 x^{u-1}(1 - x)^{v-1} dx \tag{8}$$

for positive u and v. The Beta function is a *symmetric function* of the two variables u and v; that is,

$$B(u, v) = B(v, u) \quad,$$

as can easily be seen by letting $x = 1 - y$ in Equation (8).

By various simple transformations one can convert $B(u, v)$ into other equivalent forms which are frequently more convenient for use in applications than the one given by Equation (8). One of the most useful is to let $x = \sin^2 \theta$. Then

$$x^{u-1} = \sin^{2u-2}\theta$$

$$(1 - x)^{v-1} = \cos^{2v-2}\theta$$

$$dx = 2 \sin \theta \cos \theta \, d\theta \quad,$$

and when $x = 0$, $\theta = 0$, when $x = 1$, $\theta = \pi/2$. Hence

$$B(u, v) = 2 \int_0^{\pi/2} \sin^{2u-1}\theta \cos^{2v-1}\theta \, d\theta \tag{9}$$

To show the relation between the Gamma and Beta functions, we consider the product of Gamma functions $\Gamma(u)\Gamma(v)$,

$$\Gamma(u)\Gamma(v) = \int_0^\infty x^{u-1}e^{-x}dx \int_0^\infty y^{v-1}e^{-y}dy$$

$$= \int_0^\infty \int_0^\infty x^{u-1}y^{v-1}e^{-(x+y)}dx \, dy$$

In this double integral make the change of variable

$$x = r \sin^2 \theta$$
$$y = r \cos^2 \theta \quad .$$

The Jacobian J of this transformation is the absolute value of the determinant

$$\begin{vmatrix} \dfrac{\partial x}{\partial r} & \dfrac{\partial y}{\partial r} \\[2ex] \dfrac{\partial x}{\partial \theta} & \dfrac{\partial y}{\partial \theta} \end{vmatrix} = \begin{vmatrix} \sin^2 \theta & \cos^2 \theta \\[2ex] 2r \sin \theta \cos \theta & -2r \cos \theta \sin \theta \end{vmatrix}$$

$$= -2r \sin \theta \cos \theta \quad ,$$

and

$$J = 2r \sin \theta \cos \theta \quad .$$

Hence

$$\Gamma(u)\Gamma(v) = 2 \int_0^{\pi/2} \int_0^\infty r^{(u+v)-1} e^{-r} \sin^{2u-1}\theta \cos^{2v-1}\theta \; dr \; d\theta$$

$$= \left[2 \int_0^{\pi/2} \sin^{2u-1}\theta \cos^{2v-1}\theta \; d\theta \right] \left[\int_0^\infty r^{(u+v)-1} e^{-r} \; dr \right]$$

$$= B(u, v)\Gamma(u + v) \quad ,$$

or

$$B(u, v) = \frac{\Gamma(u)\Gamma(v)}{\Gamma(u + v)} \quad . \tag{10}$$

One can use this result, for example, to evaluate such integrals as

$$\int_0^{\pi/2} \cos^\alpha \theta \; d\theta \quad ,$$

where α is any positive number. For, from Equation (9),

$$B\left(\frac{1}{2}, \frac{\alpha + 1}{2}\right) = 2 \int_0^{\pi/2} \cos^\alpha \theta \; d\theta \quad ,$$

and from Equation (10)

$$B\left(\frac{1}{2}, \frac{\alpha + 1}{2}\right) = \frac{\Gamma\left(\dfrac{1}{2}\right)\Gamma\left(\dfrac{\alpha + 1}{2}\right)}{\Gamma\left(\dfrac{\alpha}{2} + 1\right)}.$$

Hence

$$\int_0^{\pi/2} \cos^\alpha \theta \, d\theta = \frac{\sqrt{\pi}}{2} \frac{\Gamma\left(\dfrac{\alpha+1}{2}\right)}{\Gamma\left(\dfrac{\alpha}{2}+1\right)} \quad . \tag{11}$$

The above formula can be used to derive *Wallis' product* which expresses the number π as a certain limit. Our immediate purpose in deducing this formula—besides illustrating an application of the Beta function—is because of its use in establishing Stirling's formula (cf. the following section).

If α is an odd integer, say $\alpha = 2n+1$, then Equation (11) may be written

$$\int_0^{\pi/2} \cos^{2n+1} \theta \, d\theta = \frac{1}{2} \frac{2^{2n+1}(n!)^2}{(2n+1)(2n)!} \quad , \tag{12}$$

while, if α is an even integer, say $\alpha = 2n$, then Equation (11) becomes

$$\int_0^{\pi/2} \cos^{2n} \theta \, d\theta = \frac{1}{2} \frac{(2n)!\pi}{(n!)^2 2^{2n}} \quad . \tag{13}$$

Dividing Equation (13) by Equation (12) and letting

$$I_\alpha = \int_0^{\pi/2} \cos^\alpha \theta \, d\theta$$

for simplicity in notation, we obtain

$$\pi = \frac{2^{4n+1}(n!)^4}{[(2n)!]^2(2n+1)} \frac{I_{2n}}{I_{2n+1}} \quad .$$

Now, if $0 < \theta < \pi/2$,

$$\cos^{2n-1} \theta > \cos^{2n} \theta > \cos^{2n+1} \theta > 0 \quad ;$$

hence

$$I_{2n-1} > I_{2n} > I_{2n+1} > 0 \quad ,$$

or

$$\frac{I_{2n-1}}{I_{2n+1}} > \frac{I_{2n}}{I_{2n+1}} > 1 \quad .$$

But

$$\frac{I_{2n-1}}{I_{2n+1}} = \frac{1}{2} \frac{[(n-1)!]^2 2^{2n-1}}{(2n-1)(2n-2)!} \frac{2(2n+1)(2n)!}{(n!)^2 2^{2n+1}} = \frac{2n+1}{2n} \quad .$$

Since this implies

$$\lim_{n \to \infty} \frac{I_{2n}}{I_{2n+1}} = \lim_{n \to \infty} \frac{2n+1}{2n} = 1 \quad ,$$

we may write

$$\pi = \lim_{n \to \infty} \frac{2^{4n}(n!)^4}{[(2n)!]^2(n + \frac{1}{2})} \quad .$$

Further, since

$$\lim_{n \to \infty} \frac{n}{n + \frac{1}{2}} = 1 \quad ,$$

we may write, for symmetry, that

$$\pi = \lim_{n \to \infty} \frac{2^{4n}(n!)^4}{[(2n)!]^2 n} \quad .$$

The above equation is *Wallis' formula* which may also be written as

$$\frac{\pi}{2} = \frac{2 \cdot 2}{1 \cdot 3} \frac{4 \cdot 4}{3 \cdot 5} \frac{6 \cdot 6}{5 \cdot 7} \frac{8 \cdot 8}{7 \cdot 9} \cdots \quad .$$

EXERCISES

1. If n is a positive odd integer, show that

$$\int_0^1 \frac{x^n \, dx}{\sqrt{1 - x^2}} = \frac{2^{n-1}\left[\left(\frac{n-1}{2}\right)!\right]^2}{n!} \quad .$$

Establish a similar formula for n even.

2. Evaluate

$$\int_0^1 \frac{x^2 \, dx}{\sqrt{1 - x^4}} \quad .$$

3. Prove that

$$B(u, u) = \frac{2^{1-2u}\sqrt{\pi}\,\Gamma(u)}{\Gamma(u + \frac{1}{2})} \quad .$$

4. Establish the identity

$$\int_0^n s^{u-1}\left(1-\frac{s}{n}\right)^n ds = \frac{n!n^u}{u(u+1)\cdots(u+n)} \quad , \quad (u>0) \quad .$$

5. Using the result of Exercise 4, show that

$$\Gamma(u) = \lim_{n\to\infty} \frac{n!n^u}{u(u+1)\cdots(u+n)} \quad .$$

6. Stirling's Formula

The evaluation of $n!$ can be conveniently carried out when n is a small integer. However, the evaluation of such a number as even 100! would be very laborious. In other applications (cf. Chap. 7) one must also use $n!$ in certain theoretical derivations. Both of these considerations make it desirable to have a formula for $n!$ which is convenient to manipulate both practically and theoretically. Such an expression is *Stirling's formula* which states that

$$n! = n^n\sqrt{2\pi n}\, e^{-n}(1+\theta_n) \quad , \tag{14}$$

where θ_n approaches zero as $n \to \infty$. Such a formula is called an *asymptotic formula*, since the larger n, the more closely $n^n\sqrt{2\pi n}\, e^{-n}$ approximates $n!$.

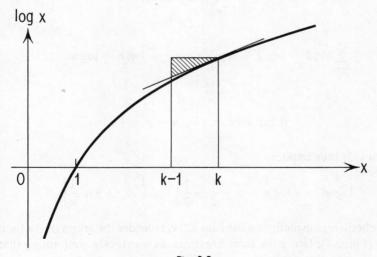

Fig. 2.3

To derive Stirling's formula, let us first sketch the graph of the function $y = \log x$ (cf. Fig. 2.3). The area of the rectangle between the two consecutive integers $k - 1$ and k is $[k - (k - 1)] \log k = \log k$. The tangent to the curve at the point $x = k$ has slope

$$\left.\frac{dy}{dx}\right|_{x=k} = \frac{1}{k} \ ;$$

hence the area of the shaded triangle is

$$\frac{1}{2}[k - (k - 1)] \cdot \frac{1}{k} = \frac{1}{2k} \ .$$

On the other hand, the area under the curve $y = \log x$ between the points $x = k - 1$ and $x = k$ is of course

$$\int_{k-1}^{k} \log x \, dx \ .$$

Hence, referring to Figure 2.3, we see that

$$\log k - \frac{1}{2k} > \int_{k-1}^{k} \log x \, dx$$

and, summing this inequality from $k = 2$ to $k = n$,

$$\sum_{k=2}^{n} \log k - \frac{1}{2} \sum_{k=2}^{n} \frac{1}{k} > \int_{1}^{n} \log x \, dx \ . \tag{15}$$

But

$$\sum_{k=2}^{n} \log k = \log 2 + \log 3 + \cdots + \log n = \log n! \ ,$$

and

$$\int_{1}^{n} \log x \, dx = n \log n - n + 1 \ .$$

Equation (15) thus implies

$$\log n! > n \log n - n + \frac{1}{2} + \frac{1}{2}\left[1 + \frac{1}{2} + \cdots + \frac{1}{n}\right] \ . \tag{16}$$

To obtain an inequality on the sum $\Sigma 1/k$, consider the graph of the function $y = 1/x$ (Fig. 2.4). Using the same argument as previously, and noting that the area of the shaded triangle is

$$\frac{1}{2}\left(\frac{1}{k} - \frac{1}{k+1}\right) ,$$

we have

$$1 + \frac{1}{2} + \cdots + \frac{1}{n} > \int_1^{n+1} \frac{dx}{x} + \frac{1}{2}\left[\frac{1}{2} + \left(\frac{1}{2} - \frac{1}{3}\right)\right.$$
$$\left. + \left(\frac{1}{3} - \frac{1}{4}\right) + \cdots + \left(\frac{1}{n} - \frac{1}{n+1}\right)\right]$$

or

$$\sum_{k=1}^n \frac{1}{k} > \log(n+1) + \frac{1}{2} - \frac{1}{2(n+1)} \quad .$$

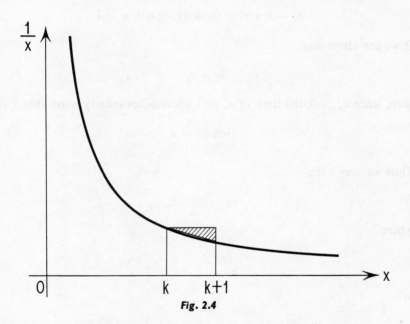

Fig. 2.4

Combining this result with Equation (16),

$$\log n! > n \log n - n + \frac{1}{2} + \frac{1}{2}\left[\log(n+1) + \frac{1}{2} - \frac{1}{2(n+1)}\right] \quad (17)$$

$$= \left(n + \frac{1}{2}\right)\log n - n + \frac{1}{2} + \frac{1}{2}\log\left(\frac{n+1}{n}\right) + \frac{1}{4} - \frac{1}{4(n+1)} \quad .$$

But for $n \geq 1$,

$$\log\left(\frac{n+1}{n}\right) > 0 \quad ,$$

and

$$\frac{1}{4}\left[1 - \frac{1}{n+1}\right] > 0 \ .$$

Hence, if these terms are neglected in Equation (17), the inequality will be strengthened:

$$\log n! > (n + \tfrac{1}{2}) \log n - n + \tfrac{1}{2} \ .$$

Now let

$$a_n = \log n! - (n + \tfrac{1}{2}) \log n + n - \tfrac{1}{2} \ .$$

If we can show that

$$a_1 > a_2 > a_3 > \cdots \ ,$$

then, since $a_n > 0$, the limit of a_n as n approaches infinity must exist,[†] say

$$\lim_{n\to\infty} a_n = a \ .$$

Thus we may write

$$a_n - a = Z_n \ ,$$

where

$$\lim_{n\to\infty} Z_n = 0 \ ,$$

or

$$\log n! = (n + \tfrac{1}{2}) \log n - n + \tfrac{1}{2} + a + Z_n \ . \tag{18}$$

Before we proceed further with Equation (18), let us prove our assertion regarding the a_n. All we need do is to prove $a_n - a_{n+1} > 0$. Now

$$a_n - a_{n+1} = \log n! - \log (n+1)! - (n + \tfrac{1}{2}) \log n + (n + \tfrac{3}{2}) \log (n+1)$$
$$+ n - (n+1)$$
$$= \left(n + \frac{1}{2}\right) \log \left(\frac{n+1}{n}\right) - 1 \ .$$

---

† This follows from the mathematical theorem: "A nonincreasing sequence of positive numbers has a limit."

Using the Maclaurin expansion of $\log(1+x)$, we may write

$$a_n - a_{n+1} = \left(n + \frac{1}{2}\right)\left(\frac{1}{n} - \frac{1}{2n^2} + \frac{1}{3n^3} - \frac{1}{4n^4} + \cdots\right) - 1 \quad .$$

Since the series for $\log(1+x)$ is an alternating series and each term is less than its predecessor (for $n > 1$), we conclude that

$$a_n - a_{n+1} > \left(n + \frac{1}{2}\right)\left(\frac{1}{n} - \frac{1}{2n^2} + \frac{1}{3n^3} - \frac{1}{4n^4}\right) - 1$$

or

$$a_n - a_{n+1} > \frac{1}{12n^2} - \frac{1}{12n^3} - \frac{1}{8n^4} \quad .$$

One can readily verify that

$$\frac{1}{12n^2} - \frac{1}{12n^3} - \frac{1}{8n^4} > 0$$

for $n = 2, 3, \cdots$, while for $n = 1$, we have directly:

$$a_1 - a_2 = \tfrac{3}{2}\log 2 - 1 > 0 \quad .$$

(Recall that all logarithms are to the base e.)

Returning to Equation (18), let us take the antilog of both sides of the expression. Then

$$n! = An^n\sqrt{n}\,e^{-n}(1 + \theta_n) \quad , \tag{19}$$

where $A = e^{a+\frac{1}{2}}$ and $e^{Z_n} = 1 + \theta_n$. (Since $\lim_{n\to\infty} e^{Z_n} = 1$, we conclude that $\lim_{n\to\infty} \theta_n = 0$.)

To find the numerical value of A we use Wallis' formula derived in the previous section. It is

$$\pi = \lim_{n\to\infty} \frac{2^{4n}(n!)^4}{[(2n)!]^2 n} \quad .$$

If we replace $n!$ and $(2n)!$ by Equation (19), we obtain, after some simple algebraic manipulations,

$$\pi = \lim_{n\to\infty} \frac{A^2}{2} \frac{(1 + \theta_n)^4}{(1 + \theta_{2n})^2} = \frac{A^2}{2} \quad ,$$

or

$$A = \sqrt{2\pi} \quad.$$

Thus, substituting this value of A in Equation (19), we have established Stirling's formula

$$n! = n^n \sqrt{2\pi n}\, e^{-n}(1 + \theta_n) \quad.$$

We sometimes write

$$n! \sim n^n \sqrt{2\pi n}\, e^{-n}$$

to indicate that $n!$ is asymptotic to $n^n \sqrt{2\pi n}\, e^{-n}$.

EXERCISE

Evaluate 10! exactly and compare it with the value obtained from Stirling's formula.

7. Euler's Constant

The familiar numerical constants π and e appear in a great many places in mathematics. However, when the original definition of e was first given in the differential calculus as

$$e = \lim_{n \to 0} (1 + n)^{1/n} \quad,$$

the reader probably did not anticipate its great usefulness. Another constant that appears in certain more advanced portions of mathematics (cf., for example, Chap. 3) is *Euler's constant*.

We recall from the calculus that the *harmonic series*

$$1 + \tfrac{1}{2} + \tfrac{1}{3} + \cdots$$

is a divergent series; that is,

$$\lim_{n \to \infty} \sum_{k=1}^{n} \frac{1}{k} = \infty \quad.$$

Also,

$$\lim_{n \to \infty} \log n = \infty$$

Now the difference

$$\lim_{n \to \infty} \left[\sum_{k=1}^{n} \frac{1}{k} - \log n \right]$$

is indeterminate, $\infty - \infty$. It turns out that the above limit *does* exist. This limit is called *Euler's constant*, γ, and has the numerical value of approximately, $\gamma = 0.5772157 \cdots$.

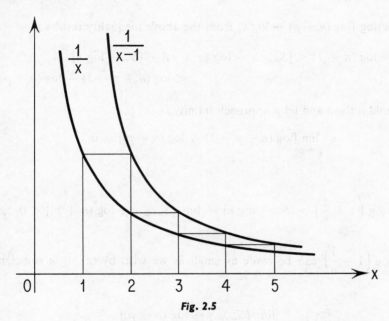

Fig. 2.5

Our first task is to show that the limit actually exists. From a simple geometric argument similar to the one used in deriving Stirling's formula we see that (cf. Fig. 2.5)

$$\int_{n+1}^{n+p} \frac{dx}{x} < \frac{1}{n+1} + \frac{1}{n+2} + \cdots + \frac{1}{n+p-1} < \int_{n+1}^{n+p} \frac{dx}{x-1}$$

or

$$\log (n + p) - \log (n + 1) < \frac{1}{n+1} + \cdots + \frac{1}{n+p-1} < \log (n + p - 1) \\ - \log n \quad . \quad (20)$$

For convenience in notation, let

$$S_\alpha = 1 + \frac{1}{2} + \cdots + \frac{1}{\alpha} \quad .$$

Then

$$\frac{1}{n+1} + \cdots + \frac{1}{n+p-1} = S_{n+p-1} - S_n \quad ,$$

and Equation (20) may be written

$$\log(n+p) - \log(n+1) < S_{n+p-1} - S_n < \log(n+p-1) - \log n \quad .$$

Subtracting $[\log(n+p) - \log n]$ from the above inequality results in

$$\log n - \log(n+1) < [S_{n+p-1} - \log(n+p)] - [S_n - \log n]$$
$$< \log(n+p-1) - \log(n+p) \quad .$$

If we hold n fixed and let p approach infinity,

$$\lim_{p \to \infty} [\log(n+p-1) - \log(n+p)] = 0$$

and

$$\log\left(1 + \frac{1}{n}\right) > [S_n - \log n] - \lim_{p \to \infty} [S_{n+p-1} - \log(n+p)] < 0 \quad . \quad (21)$$

Since $\log\left(1 + \frac{1}{n}\right)$ can be made as small as we wish by taking n sufficiently large,

$$\lim_{p \to \infty} [S_{n+p-1} - \log(n+p)]$$

exists. As we have indicated above, this limit is called *Euler's constant* γ.

Equation (21) also gives us bounds for the numerical computation of γ, namely,

$$[S_n - \log(n+1)] < \gamma < [S_n - \log n] \quad .$$

If, for example, $n = 10$,

$$S_{10} = 2.928968 \quad ,$$

and

$$0.53107 < \gamma < 0.62638 \quad .$$

Using a larger value of n will, of course, give us a better approximation to γ.

EXERCISES

1. Using the expression for $\Gamma(u)$ given in Exercise 5 of Section 5, show that

$$\Gamma(u) = \frac{1}{ue^{\gamma u} \prod_{n=1}^{\infty} \left(1 + \frac{u}{n}\right) e^{-u/n}} \quad,$$

where γ is Euler's constant.

2. Prove that

$$\frac{d}{dx} \Gamma(x) \Big|_{x=1} = -\gamma \quad.$$

8. Sine-Integral Function

Another function defined by an integral which appears in such applications as Fourier transforms and the response of an ideal low-pass filter to a step-function input (cf. Chap. 6) is the *sine-integral function*. This function is written Si (x) and is defined by the integral

$$\text{Si}\,(x) = \int_0^x \frac{\sin x}{x}\, dx \quad.$$

As in the case of the error function, there is no way of finding a function $\psi(x)$ such that

$$\psi'(x) = \frac{\sin x}{x} \quad.$$

However, because of its frequent occurrence in practical problems it has been extensively tabulated.† In the special case $x = \infty$, however, we can calculate

$$\int_0^{\infty} \frac{\sin x}{x}\, dx$$

without finding the primitive $\psi(x)$.

The method we shall use is one which can be applied to a variety of other problems (cf. the exercises at the end of this section). We begin by considering the integral

$$I(\alpha) = \int_0^{\infty} \frac{e^{-\alpha x} \sin x}{x}\, dx \quad, \quad \alpha \geqq 0 \quad.$$

---

† For example, see C.R.C., *Standard Mathematical Tables*, p. 304.

Now $I(0)$ is the desired integral we are seeking. Also, note that $I(\infty) = 0$. If we *differentiate*† $I(\alpha)$ with respect to α,

$$I'(\alpha) = -\int_0^\infty e^{-\alpha x} \sin x \, dx \quad,$$

and integrating this expression,

$$I'(\alpha) = -\left[\frac{e^{-\alpha x}}{1 + \alpha^2}(-\alpha \sin x - \cos x)\right]\Bigg|_0^\infty = -\frac{1}{1 + \alpha^2} \quad.$$

We thus have a simple differential equation on $I(\alpha)$ whose solution is

$$I(\alpha) = c - \arctan \alpha \quad,$$

c being the constant of integration. But

$$I(\infty) = 0 = c - \arctan \infty = c - \frac{\pi}{2} \quad,$$

and $c = \pi/2$. Thus

$$I(\alpha) = \frac{\pi}{2} - \arctan \alpha \quad.$$

So actually we have proved more than we set out to accomplish, namely, that

$$\int_0^\infty \frac{e^{-\alpha x} \sin x}{x} \, dx = \frac{\pi}{2} - \arctan \alpha \quad.$$

In the particular case $\alpha = 0$, we have

$$\text{Si}\,(\infty) = \int_0^\infty \frac{\sin x}{x} \, dx = \frac{\pi}{2} \quad,$$

since $\arctan 0 = 0$.

EXERCISES

1. Show that

$$\int_0^\infty \frac{\sin \alpha x}{x} \, dx = \begin{cases} \dfrac{\pi}{2} & \alpha > 0 \\[2mm] 0 & \alpha = 0 \\[2mm] -\dfrac{\pi}{2} & \alpha < 0 \end{cases} \quad.$$

---

† See, for example, Chap. 6 of Carslaw, *Introduction to the Theory of Fourier's Series and Integrals*, for a statement of the mathematical conditions under which an infinite integral can be differentiated with respect to a parameter.

2. The integral

$$I = \int_0^\infty e^{-a^2x^2} \cos bx \, dx$$

appears in certain boundary value problems in the theory of partial differential equations. Show, by differentiation with respect to the parameter b, that

$$I = \frac{\sqrt{\pi}}{2a} e^{-b^2/4a^2} \quad .$$

3. Establish the formula

$$\int_0^1 \frac{x^\alpha - x^\beta}{\log x} \, dx = \log \frac{\alpha + 1}{\beta + 1} \quad , \quad \alpha, \beta > 0 \quad .$$

4. Prove that

(i) $\displaystyle\int_0^\pi \log(5 - 4\cos x)dx = \pi \log 4$.

(ii) $\displaystyle\int_0^{\pi/2} \log(\sin x)dx = -\frac{\pi}{2}\log 2$.

5. Show that

$$\int_0^\infty \frac{\cos \alpha x}{1 + x^2} \, dx = \frac{\pi}{2} e^{-|\alpha|} \quad .$$

6. Prove that

$$\int_0^\infty \frac{\sin^4 ax}{x^2} \, dx = \frac{\pi}{4}|a| \quad .$$

7. Prove that

$$\int_{-\infty}^\infty \frac{e^{-a^2x^2}}{b^2 + x^2} \, dx = \frac{\pi}{b} e^{a^2b^2} \operatorname{cerf}|ab| \quad .$$

8. Establish the formulas

$$\int_0^{\pi/2} e^{-\alpha^2 \tan^2 x} \, dx = \int_0^{\pi/2} e^{-\alpha^2 \cot^2 x} \, dx = \frac{\pi}{2} e^{\alpha^2} \operatorname{cerf}|\alpha| \quad .$$

9. Elliptic Integrals

The equation of motion of a simple pendulum is a familiar result to every-one who has had a course in college physics. One considers a bob of mass m at the end of a rigid, weightless bar of length L (cf. Fig. 2.6). If length of path s

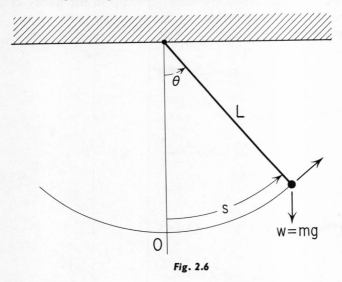

Fig. 2.6

is measured from the point 0, then $s = L\theta$, and, taking the sum of forces in the tangential direction,

$$- (mg) \sin \theta = m \frac{d^2s}{dt^2} = mL \frac{d^2\theta}{dt^2} \quad .$$

Canceling m, we have the equation of motion

$$\frac{d^2\theta}{dt^2} = - \frac{g}{L} \sin \theta \quad . \tag{22}$$

In the elementary theory one assumes that the swing of the pendulum is small compared to its length L and hence that θ is a good approximation to $\sin \theta$. Equation (22) then assumes the form

$$\frac{d^2\theta}{dt^2} + \frac{g}{L} \theta = 0 \quad ,$$

whose general solution is

$$\theta(t) = A \cos\sqrt{\frac{g}{L}} t + B \sin\sqrt{\frac{g}{L}} t \quad ,$$

where A and B are constants of integration. If the string is initially released when $\theta = \alpha$, then at $t = 0$, $\theta = \alpha$, $d\theta/dt = 0$, and one immediately sees that

$$\theta(t) = \alpha \cos\sqrt{\frac{g}{L}}\, t$$

is the equation of motion of the simple pendulum. The *period* is of course the value T of t, which makes

$$\sqrt{\frac{g}{L}}\, t = 2\pi \quad ;$$

that is,

$$T = 2\pi\sqrt{\frac{L}{g}} \quad .$$

Now let us suppose that the oscillations are not necessarily small and hence the assumption $\sin \theta = \theta$ is no longer valid. Returning to Equation (22), we can perform one integration by multiplying both sides of this equation by $d\theta/dt$ and noting that

$$\frac{d}{dt}\left(\frac{d\theta}{dt}\right)^2 = 2\frac{d\theta}{dt}\frac{d^2\theta}{dt^2} \quad ,$$

$$\frac{1}{2}\frac{d}{dt}\left(\frac{d\theta}{dt}\right)^2 = -\frac{g}{L}\sin\theta\frac{d\theta}{dt} = \frac{d}{dt}\left(\frac{g}{L}\cos\theta\right)$$

or

$$\left(\frac{d\theta}{dt}\right)^2 = \frac{2g}{L}\cos\theta + C \quad . \tag{23}$$

If the pendulum is released when $\theta = \alpha$, then $d\theta/dt = 0$ and

$$0 = \frac{2g}{L}\cos\alpha + C \quad ,$$

or

$$C = -\frac{2g}{L}\cos\alpha \quad ,$$

and Equation (23) becomes

$$\left(\frac{d\theta}{dt}\right)^2 = \frac{2g}{L}(\cos\theta - \cos\alpha)$$

Thus

$$\frac{dt}{d\theta} = \sqrt{\frac{L}{2g}} \frac{1}{\sqrt{\cos \theta - \cos \alpha}} \quad ,$$

and

$$t = \sqrt{\frac{L}{2g}} \int \frac{d\theta}{\sqrt{\cos \theta - \cos \alpha}} \quad . \tag{24}$$

The integral appearing in Equation (24) is essentially the *elliptic integral of the first kind.* If we rewrite Equation (24) in terms of half angles,

$$t = \frac{1}{2} \sqrt{\frac{L}{g}} \int \frac{d\theta}{\sqrt{\sin^2 \dfrac{\alpha}{2} - \sin^2 \dfrac{\theta}{2}}} \quad ,$$

introduce the change of variable $\sin \dfrac{\theta}{2} = \sin \dfrac{\alpha}{2} \sin \phi$, and let $k = \sin \frac{1}{2}\alpha$; then

$$t = \sqrt{\frac{L}{g}} \int \frac{d\phi}{\sqrt{1 - k^2 \sin^2 \phi}} \quad .$$

The integral

$$K(k, \phi) = \int_0^\phi \frac{d\phi}{\sqrt{1 - k^2 \sin^2 \phi}} \tag{25}$$

is known as the *elliptic integral of the first kind.* The number k is called the *modulus*; note that $|k| \leq 1$, while ϕ is called the *amplitude.* If $\phi = \pi/2$, then

$$K\left(k, \frac{\pi}{2}\right) = \int_0^{\pi/2} \frac{d\phi}{\sqrt{1 - k^2 \sin^2 \phi}}$$

depends only on k and is called the *complete elliptic integral of the first kind.* Sometimes we refer to Equation (25) as an *incomplete elliptic integral.*

One sometimes has occasion to deal with the integral

$$E(k, \phi) = \int_0^\phi \sqrt{1 - k^2 \sin^2 \phi} \, d\phi \quad ,$$

which is known as the *elliptic integral of the second kind.* Both types of elliptic integrals are tabulated functions.†

---

† See, for example, C.R.C., *Standard Mathematical Tables*, p. 250.

If we allow large swings of the pendulum, then it is possible that the motion will no longer be oscillatory, but will become rotary; that is, the pendulum will travel in a complete circle. We shall investigate these two types of motion. First, we note that the total energy of the pendulum remains constant since we have no damping. The kinetic energy, K.E., equals

$$\tfrac{1}{2}mV^2 = \tfrac{1}{2}mL^2\dot\theta^2 \quad ,\dagger$$

where V is the velocity of the bob, and the potential energy, P.E., is $mgL(1 - \cos\theta)$. Hence, if at time t the angular velocity of the bob is $\dot\theta(t)$ and is displaced the angle $\theta(t)$ from the vertical, then the total energy E is

$$E = \text{K.E.} + \text{P.E.} = \tfrac{1}{2}mL^2\dot\theta^2 + mgL(1 - \cos\theta) \quad .$$

(We are assuming that the potential energy is zero when the bob is at its lowest point, namely, point 0 of Figure 2.6.) Now, if the pendulum is to travel in circular motion, it must have at least enough energy to reach the top of its swing, namely, $mg(2L)$. We shall call this the *critical energy E_c,*

$$E_c = 2mgL \quad .$$

We see, therefore, that if

$$E < E_c$$

we have oscillatory motion, while if

$$E > E_c$$

we have rotary motion.

The period T_0 of the pendulum, in the oscillatory case, is equal to four times the time necessary for the pendulum to travel from its lowest point to its maximum excursion, $\theta = \alpha$. Hence

$$T_0 = 4\sqrt{\frac{L}{g}} \int_0^{\pi/2} \frac{d\phi}{\sqrt{1 - k^2\sin^2\phi}} = 4\sqrt{\frac{L}{g}}\,K\!\left(k, \frac{\pi}{2}\right) \quad , \tag{26}$$

since $\theta = \alpha$ implies $\phi = \pi/2$.

To investigate the case of rotary motion it is convenient to adopt the following point of view. At any time, t, the total energy of the pendulum is

$$E = \tfrac{1}{2}mL^2\dot\theta^2 + mgL(1 - \cos\theta) \quad . \tag{27}$$

---

† We are using a conventional notation, viz.: $\dot\theta \equiv \dfrac{d\theta}{dt}$. Similarly, $\ddot\theta$ would represent $\dfrac{d^2\theta}{dt^2}$.

If we let h be the distance one would have to drop the bob in order to acquire the energy E, then we may also write

$$E = mgh \quad . \tag{28}$$

Equating Equations (27) and (28), we obtain

$$\tfrac{1}{2}mL^2\dot{\theta}^2 = mgh - mgL(1 - \cos\theta) \quad ;$$

hence

$$t = \int_0^\theta \frac{d\theta}{\dot{\theta}} = \int_0^\theta \frac{d\theta}{\sqrt{\dfrac{2g}{L^2}[h - L(1 - \cos\theta)]}} \quad . \tag{29}$$

If we let

$$k^2 = \frac{2L}{h} < 1$$

and introduce the change of variable $\psi = \theta/2$, Equation (29) assumes the form

$$t = k\sqrt{\frac{L}{g}} \int_0^\psi \frac{d\psi}{\sqrt{1 - k^2\sin^2\psi}} \quad ,$$

and the period T_r in the rotary case becomes twice the time it takes the pendulum to get from its lowest point to $\theta = \pi$; that is, $\psi = \pi/2$. Hence

$$T_r = 2k\sqrt{\frac{L}{g}}\, K\left(k, \frac{\pi}{2}\right) \quad .$$

EXERCISES

1. Consider a simple pendulum. Let $T = 2\pi\sqrt{L/g}$ be the period of the pendulum for small oscillations. Plot T_0/T or T_r/T versus E/E_c (as the independent variable) for values of E/E_c from 0 to 4.

2. In Equation (25) for $K(k, \phi)$, introduce the transformation

$$\tan\phi = \frac{\sin 2\psi}{k + \cos 2\psi}$$

(called *Landen's transformation*) to show that

$$K(k, \phi) = \frac{2}{1 + k}\, K(m, \psi) \quad ,$$

where

$$m = \frac{2\sqrt{k}}{1 + k} \; .$$

Show that $m \leqq 1$.

10. Simpson's Rule

Generally the most convenient way to evaluate a definite integral, say

$$\int_a^b f(x)dx \; ,$$

is to find a function $F(x)$ such that $F'(x) = f(x)$. Then

$$\int_a^b f(x)dx = F(b) - F(a) \; .$$

However, sometimes even if $F(x)$ exists it may be extremely difficult to evaluate, and sometimes $F(x)$ cannot be found at all (as in the case of

$$\int e^{x^2} dx \;).$$

When these states of affair arise we must resort to some method of approximately evaluating

$$\int_a^b f(x)dx \; .$$

Two of the most common are the *trapezoidal rule* and *Simpson's rule*.

The trapezoidal rule consists in approximating the integral

$$\int_a^b f(x)dx \; ,$$

by a sequence of trapezoids. We divide the interval $[a, b]$ into n equal segments by the points of subdivision $x_0, x_1, \cdots, x_n$ (cf. Fig. 2.7). Let the length of each segment $x_k - x_{k-1}$ be h,

$$h = \frac{b - a}{n} \; .$$

If we call y_k the ordinate corresponding to x_k, the area T_k of the kth trapezoid (the shaded area of Figure 2.7) is

$$T_k = \frac{h}{2}(y_{k-1} + y_k) \quad ;$$

hence

$$T = \sum_{k=1}^{n} T_k \tag{30}$$

is an approximation to $\int_a^b f(x)dx$. Expanding Equation (30),

$$T = \sum_{k=1}^{n} \frac{h}{2}(y_{k-1} + y_k) = \frac{h}{2}(y_0 + 2y_1 + 2y_2 + \cdots + 2y_{n-1} + y_n) \quad .$$

The smaller h the better we would expect T to approximate $\int_a^b f(x)dx$.

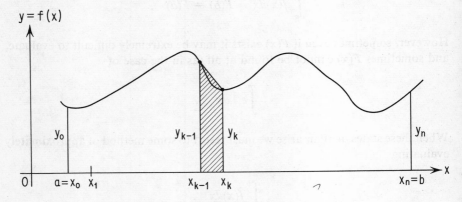

Fig. 2.7

The other common method of numerical integration consists in passing a *parabola* through every consecutive triplet of points P_{k-1}, P_k, P_{k+1}, as in Figure 2.8. One would expect, in general, that such an approximation would be more accurate than the trapezoidal rule. Theoretically, of course, we could use a cubic or higher degree polynomials as approximating curves rather than quadratics (as in Simpson's rule) or linear functions (as in the trapezoidal rule).

An elementary calculation shows that the area under the parabola passing through the three points P_{k-1}, P_k, P_{k+1} is

$$\frac{h}{3}(y_{k-1} + 4y_k + y_{k+1}) \quad ,$$

where

$$h = x_k - x_{k-1} = x_{k+1} - x_k \quad .$$

Hence, if we divide the interval $[a, b]$ into an even number of equal segments, say, $2n$, each of length

$$h = \frac{b - a}{2n} \quad ,$$

and pass parabolas through the points P_0, P_1, P_2; the points $P_2, P_3, P_4; \cdots$; the points $P_{2n-2}, P_{2n-1}, P_{2n}$, then the sum of the areas under these parabolas, S, will be

$$S = \frac{h}{3} (y_0 + 4y_1 + 2y_2 + 4y_3 + 2y_4 + \cdots + 2y_{2n-2} + 4y_{2n-1} + y_{2n}) \quad .$$

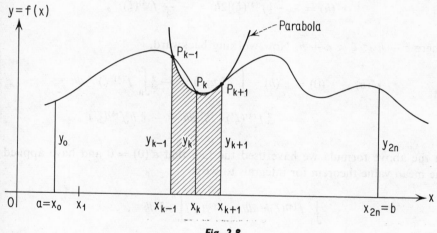

Fig. 2.8

Again, intuition tells us that the smaller h the better the approximation of S to $\int_a^b f(x)dx$. However, let us investigate more closely this difference,

$$\varepsilon(h) = \int_a^b f(x)dx - S \quad ,$$

and see if we can form some estimate of ε. It turns out that this is possible in much the same way that the remainder theorem in Taylor's series was derived.

To obtain the basic formula, we first assume that $n = 2$; then

$$\varepsilon(h) = \int_{c-h}^{c+h} f(x)dx - \frac{h}{3}[f(c-h) + 4f(c) + f(c+h)] \quad ,$$

where c is the midpoint of $[a, b]$ and hence $c + h = b$, $c - h = a$. If we call $F(x)$ the indefinite integral of $f(x)$, that is, $F(x) = \int f(x)dx$, then

$$\varepsilon(h) = F(c + h) - F(c - h) - \frac{h}{3}[f(c - h) + 4f(c) + f(c + h)] \quad .$$

A necessary step in our evaluation of ε is to calculate the third derivative of $\varepsilon(h)$ with respect to h. It is

$$\varepsilon'''(h) = \frac{h}{3}[-f'''(c + h) + f'''(c - h)] \quad .$$

If we apply the law of the mean for derivatives to the difference $f'''(c + h) - f'''(c - h)$, we obtain

$$\varepsilon'''(h) = -\frac{h}{3}[f^{(4)}(\zeta)]2h = -\frac{2h^2}{3}f^{(4)}(\zeta) \quad ,$$

where $c - h < \zeta < c + h$. Now working backward,

$$\varepsilon''(h) - \varepsilon''(0) = \varepsilon''(h) = \int_0^h \varepsilon'''(h)dh = -\tfrac{2}{3}\int_0^h f^{(4)}(\zeta)h^2\, dh$$

$$= -\tfrac{2}{3}f^{(4)}(\zeta')\int_0^h h^2\, dh = -\tfrac{2}{9}h^3 f^{(4)}(\zeta') \quad .$$

In the above formula we have used the fact that $\varepsilon''(0) = 0$ and have applied the mean value theorem for integrals to write

$$\int_0^h f^{(4)}(\zeta)h^2\, dh = f^{(4)}(\zeta')\int_0^h h^2\, dh \quad ,$$

where again $c - h < \zeta' < c + h$. If we proceed in the same manner,

$$\varepsilon'(h) - \varepsilon'(0) = \varepsilon'(h) = \int_0^h \varepsilon''(h)dh = -\tfrac{1}{18}h^4 f^{(4)}(\zeta'') \quad ,$$

and

$$\varepsilon(h) = -\tfrac{1}{90}h^5 f^{(4)}(\zeta''') \quad . \tag{31}$$

Equation (31) was derived on the assumption that we divided $[a, b]$ into two intervals. Now, if we use $2n$ intervals, then the total error E will be the sum of terms of the form of Equation (31) for each pair of intervals. Hence

$$E = -\tfrac{1}{90}h^5[f^{(4)}(\zeta_1''') + f^{(4)}(\zeta_2''') + \cdots + f^{(4)}(\zeta_n''')] \quad , \tag{32}$$

where the subscript on the ζ''' refers to the subintervals. But the average

$$\frac{f^{(4)}(\zeta_1''') + f^{(4)}(\zeta_2''') + \cdots + f^{(4)}(\zeta_n''')}{n}$$

lies somewhere between the maximum and minimum of the $f^{(4)}(\zeta_k''')$. Hence, if we let

$$f^{(4)}(\xi) = \frac{f^{(4)}(\zeta_1''') + f^{(4)}(\zeta_2''') + \cdots + f^{(4)}(\zeta_n''')}{n} \quad ,$$

where $a < \xi < b$, we may write Equation (32) as

$$E = -n \tfrac{1}{90} h^5 f^{(4)}(\xi)$$
$$= -\tfrac{1}{180} h^4 (b - a) f^{(4)}(\xi) \quad , \tag{33}$$

since $2nh = b - a$.

Of course, in deriving the above formula we have tacitly assumed that the fourth derivative of $f(x)$ existed.

Suppose we wished to evaluate

$$I = \int_1^2 (\log x)^2 dx$$

by Simpson's rule. What would be the error if ten subintervals were used? To solve this problem we must first compute the fourth derivative of $f(x) = (\log x)^2$,

$$f'(x) = \frac{2 \log x}{x}$$

$$f''(x) = \frac{2(1 - \log x)}{x^2}$$

$$f'''(x) = 2 \left(\frac{-3 + 2 \log x}{x^3} \right)$$

$$f^{(4)}(x) = 2 \left(\frac{11 - 6 \log x}{x^4} \right) \quad .$$

Then, since $b - a = 1$, $2n = 10$, $h = \dfrac{b - a}{2n} = \dfrac{1}{10}$, and

$$E = -\frac{1}{180} \left(\frac{1}{10} \right)^4 (1) 2 \left(\frac{11 - 6 \log \xi}{\xi^4} \right)$$

$$= 1.111 \times 10^{-6} \left(\frac{6 \log \xi - 11}{\xi^4} \right) \quad ,$$

where ξ is some number between 1 and 2. Of course we cannot find the *exact* value of ξ, but we can find an *overestimate*. That is, for ξ in the range from 1 to 2, certainly

$$\left| \frac{6 \log \xi - 11}{\xi^4} \right| < \left| \frac{6 \log 1 - 11}{1^4} \right| = 11 \quad ;$$

hence

$$|E| < (1.111 \times 10^{-6})(11) = 1.222 \times 10^{-5} \quad .$$

Thus the approximation using Simpson's rule will differ from the actual value of the integral I by less than $1\frac{1}{4}$ parts in 100,000.

EXERCISES

1. Evaluate

$$\int_0^4 e^{-x^2}\, dx$$

by Simpson's rule (using 8 subintervals), and evaluate the error, using the error formula of Equation (33).

2. Evaluate

$$\int_0^1 \frac{\sin x}{x}\, dx$$

by Simpson's rule, using 10 subintervals. Compare it with the exact value obtainable from the tables.

3. Derive a modified form of Simpson's rule that would be applicable to infinite integrals, that is, to integrals of the form $\displaystyle\int_a^\infty f(x)\, dx$.

REFERENCES

Carslaw, H. S., *Introduction to the Theory of Fourier's Series and Integrals*, 3rd ed. New York: Dover Publications, 1930.

Courant, Richard, *Differential and Integral Calculus*, 2nd rev. ed. New York: Interscience Publishers, Inc., 1951, Vols. 1 and 2.

C.R.C., *Standard Mathematical Tables*, 10th ed. Cleveland, Ohio: Chemical Rubber Publishing Company, 1954.

Woods, F. S., *Advanced Calculus*, rev. ed. Boston: Ginn & Co., 1934.

| *Chapter Three* | # LINEAR DIFFERENTIAL EQUATIONS |

1. Introduction

Differential equations, with all their ramifications and generalizations, are undoubtedly the most powerful tool in applied mathematics. We presume that the reader has had some acquaintance with the elements of ordinary differential equations; hence we need not discourse at length on their utility in treating physical phenomena such as the flow of heat, mechanics, electricity, hydrodynamics, and so forth. However, the application of differential equations extends far beyond the methods usually treated in an introductory course. One of our objectives in this book will be to present some of the more advanced techniques associated with differential equations.

As an introduction, let us consider a simple physical problem which gives rise to a differential equation. We shall suppose that we have a mass m_0 attached to a spring which in turn is fastened to the ceiling of a room (cf. Fig. 3.1). The positive direction of the y axis will be taken downward. Further, it will be supposed that the mass is submerged in some liquid (which will give rise to a frictional force). Our problem will be to determine the differential equation satisfied by the displacement y of the mass m_0. If the spring obeys Hooke's law, that is, the restoring force F is proportional to the displacement y, then we have

$$F = -ky \quad , \qquad (1)$$

where k is the constant of proportionality. We shall assume that the frictional force f is proportional to the velocity dy/dt,

$$f = -k' \frac{dy}{dt} \qquad (2)$$

where k' is another constant of proportionality.

From elementary mechanics we have the result: $\Sigma F = ma$. That is, the sum of the forces in any direction is equal to the mass times the acceleration in that direction. Using the y direction, we have

$$F + f = m_0 a_y \quad ,$$

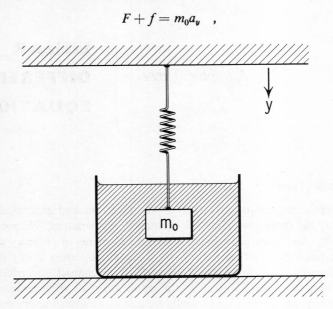

Fig. 3.1

where a_y is the acceleration in the y direction. But $a_y = d^2y/dt^2$, and, if we use Equations (1) and (2), this becomes

$$- ky - k' \frac{dy}{dt} = m_0 \frac{d^2y}{dt^2}$$

or

$$m_0 \frac{d^2y}{dt^2} + k' \frac{dy}{dt} + ky = 0 \quad . \tag{3}$$

(We have neglected the force due to gravity.) Of course Equation (3) is trivial to solve. One considers the indicial equation

$$m_0 \lambda^2 + k'\lambda + k = 0 \quad .$$

If the roots λ_1 and λ_2 of this algebraic equation are real and distinct, then the general solution of Equation (3) is

$$y(t) = C_1 e^{\lambda_1 t} + C_2 e^{\lambda_2 t} \quad ,$$

where C_1 and C_2 are arbitrary constants. If the roots are equal, $\lambda = \lambda_1 = \lambda_2$, then

$$y(t) = C_1 e^{\lambda t} + C_2 t e^{\lambda t} \quad ;$$

and, finally, if the roots are complex, $\lambda_1 = \alpha + j\beta$, $\lambda_2 = \alpha - j\beta$, then

$$y(t) = C_1 e^{\alpha t} \cos \beta t + C_2 e^{\alpha t} \sin \beta t$$

is the general solution.

In other physical problems† linear differential equations of order higher than the second occur. The reader has probably considered such equations in an elementary course on differential equations, but for completeness we shall briefly indicate the results here before passing on to more advanced topics.

The general n^{th}-order linear differential equation with constant coefficients may be written

$$a_0 y^{(n)} + a_1 y^{(n-1)} + \cdots + a_n y = 0 \quad , \tag{4}$$

where the a_i, $i = 0, 1, 2, \cdots, n$ are constants. We sometimes write Equation (4) symbolically as

$$Ly = 0 \quad ,$$

where L is the *linear differential operator*

$$L \equiv a_0 \frac{d^n}{dx^n} + a_1 \frac{d^{n-1}}{dx^{n-1}} + \cdots + a_n \cdot \quad .$$

The adjectives "n^{th} order" and "with constant coefficients" are evident. We call the equation *linear*, since if $f(x)$ and $g(x)$ are any two functions of x, whose n^{th} derivatives exist, then

$$L[af + bg] = aLf + bLg \quad ,$$

where a and b are any constants. The equation $(y')^2 + 2y = 0$ is *not* a linear equation, since

$$(af + bg)'^2 + 2(af + bg) = (af' + bg')^2 + 2(af + bg) \neq a(f')^2 + 2af + b(g')^2 + 2bg \quad .$$

The adjective *homogeneous* is frequently appended to the description of Equation (4) since the right-hand member is zero. An equation such as

$$Ly(x) = r(x)$$

would be called *nonhomogeneous* if $r(x) \not\equiv 0$.

---

† Compare Salvadori and Schwarz, *Differential Equations in Engineering Problems*, Chap. 3.

To solve Equation (4) we consider a function e^{mx} and substitute it into Ly. We thus obtain

$$Le^{mx} = (a_0 m^n + a_1 m^{n-1} + \cdots + a_n)e^{mx} \quad .$$

If this is to be zero,

$$a_0 m^n + a_1 m^{n-1} + \cdots + a_n$$

must vanish, since e^{mx} is never zero. Hence, if m' is any root of the *indicial equation*

$$a_0 m^n + a_1 m^{n-1} + \cdots + a_n = 0 \quad , \tag{5}$$

then $e^{m'x}$ is a solution of $Ly = 0$. The only complications that must be considered are those that arise when the roots of Equation (5) are complex or repeated or both.

An nth-degree algebraic equation such as Equation (5) has n roots which may or may not be distinct. We can briefly summarize the situation as follows:

(i) If λ is a distinct real root of Equation (5), then $e^{\lambda x}$ is a solution of Equation (4).

(ii) If λ is a real root of multiplicity r of Equation (5), then

$$e^{\lambda x} \quad , \quad xe^{\lambda x} \quad , \quad x^2 e^{\lambda x} \quad , \cdots, \quad x^{r-1}e^{\lambda x}$$

are r solutions of Equation (4).

(iii) If $\lambda = \alpha + j\beta$ and $\bar{\lambda} = \alpha - j\beta$ are a pair of distinct complex roots of Equation (5), then

$$e^{\alpha x}\cos\beta x \quad , \quad e^{\alpha x}\sin\beta x$$

are two solutions of Equation (4).

(iv) If λ and $\bar{\lambda}$ are a pair of complex roots of multiplicity s, then

$$e^{\alpha x}\cos\beta x \quad , \quad xe^{\alpha x}\cos\beta x \quad , \quad \cdots \quad , \quad x^{s-1}e^{\alpha x}\cos\beta x$$
$$e^{\alpha x}\sin\beta x \quad , \quad xe^{\alpha x}\sin\beta x \quad , \quad \cdots \quad , \quad x^{s-1}e^{\alpha x}\sin\beta x$$

are $2s$ solutions of Equation (4).

For example, consider the eleventh-order linear differential equation whose indicial equation has the roots

$$\lambda_1 = 0$$
$$\lambda_2 = -1$$
$$\lambda_3 = \lambda_4 = \lambda_5 = -2$$
$$\lambda_6 = j \quad , \quad \lambda_7 = \bar{\lambda}_6 = -j$$
$$\lambda_8 = \lambda_9 = -1 + 2j \quad , \quad \lambda_{10} = \lambda_{11} = \bar{\lambda}_8 = \bar{\lambda}_9 = -1 - 2j \quad .$$

Then the general solution of this differential equation is

$$y(x) = C_1 + C_2 e^{-x} + C_3 e^{-2x} + C_4 x e^{-2x} + C_5 x^2 e^{-2x} + C_6 \cos x$$
$$+ C_7 \sin x + C_8 e^{-x} \cos 2x + C_9 e^{-x} \sin 2x + C_{10} x e^{-x} \cos 2x$$
$$+ C_{11} x e^{-x} \sin 2x \quad,$$

where $C_1, C_2, \cdots, C_{11}$ are arbitrary constants.

2. The General Linear Differential Equation

We now wish to consider some fundamental features in the mathematical theory of linear differential equations. The general n^{th}-order, homogeneous, linear differential equation may be written

$$p_0(x) y^{(n)} + p_1(x) y^{(n-1)} + \cdots + p_n(x) y = 0 \quad, \tag{6}$$

where the coefficients $p_i(x)$ are functions of the independent variable x. The case where all the $p_i(x)$ are constant is a special case which we have just disposed of in the previous section. For the general variable coefficient equation of Equation (6) the situation is more involved. Let us first see if we can define what is meant by a *solution* of Equation (6). First, if the function $y = \phi(x)$ is to be a solution of Equation (6) it must satisfy Equation (6); that is,

$$L\phi(x) \equiv 0 \quad,$$

where we have used L to denote the differential operator

$$p_0(x) \frac{d^n}{dx^n} + p_1(x) \frac{d^{n-1}}{dx^{n-1}} + \cdots + p_n(x)\cdot \quad.$$

Also, the values of $\phi(x)$ and its first $n - 1$ derivatives must be specified at some point, say $x = x_0$. Thus, by a *solution* of Equation (6), we mean a function $\phi(x)$ such that $L\phi(x) \equiv 0$ and

$$\phi(x_0) = y_0$$
$$\phi^{(k)}(x_0) = y_k \quad, \quad k = 1, 2, \cdots, n - 1 \quad, \tag{7}$$

where $y_0, y_1, \cdots, y_{n-1}$ are numbers which are assigned in advance. The conditions stated in Equation (7) are called *boundary conditions*, or *initial conditions*. In the mathematical theory of differential equations† one can show that under suitable conditions the function $\phi(x)$ described above *exists* and is *unique*. That

---

† See, for example, Murray and Miller, *Existence Theorems for Ordinary Differential Equations*, Chap. 6.

is, there is one and only one function $\phi(x)$ which satisfies Equation (6) and the boundary conditions of Equation (7). The "suitable conditions" are easy enough to state: The coefficients $p_0(x), p_1(x), \cdots, p_n(x)$ must be continuous on some interval I of the x axis containing the point $x = x_0$, and $p_0(x)$ must be unequal to zero on I. Unfortunately, the proof of the theorem given in detail in Murray and Miller,† is beyond the scope of this book and hence will be omitted.

We can illustrate this result, however. For example, let us find the solution $\phi(x)$ to the differential equation

$$4y'' + y = 0 \tag{8}$$

which at the point $x = 0$ satisfies the boundary conditions

$$\begin{aligned} \phi(0) &= 0 \\ \phi'(0) &= 1 \end{aligned} \tag{9}$$

Since 4 and 1 (the coefficients of the derivatives of y) are constants, they are continuous, and certainly, $4 \neq 0$. Hence the general theorem described above asserts that there exists a unique function $\phi(x)$. Using elementary techniques, we find that

$$\phi(x) = 2 \sin \tfrac{1}{2}x \quad .$$

Looking at the example of Equation (8), we know that $\cos \tfrac{1}{2}x$ satisfies Equation (8) [but not the boundary conditions of Equation (9)]. Hence, if we asked the question, find the solution $\psi(x)$ of Equation (8) which satisfies the boundary conditions

$$\begin{aligned} \psi(0) &= 1 \\ \psi'(0) &= 0 \quad , \end{aligned} \tag{10}$$

then

$$\psi(x) = \cos \tfrac{1}{2}x$$

would be the desired function. Recalling (cf. Sec. 6 of Chap. 1) that $\phi(x)$ and $\psi(x)$ are linearly independent, we see that we have found two *linearly independent* solutions of Equation (8)—one satisfying the boundary conditions of Equation (9) and the other the boundary conditions of Equation (10). This is a general property of linear differential equations. Combining all the statements we have made, we may summarize them in the following theorem.

---

† See, for example, Murray and Miller, *loc. cit.*

Theorem. Let

$$p_0(x)y^{(n)} + p_1(x)y^{(n-1)} + \cdots + p_n(x)y = 0 \tag{11}$$

be a linear differential equation whose coefficients $p_i(x)$ are continuous on some interval $[a, b]$ of the x axis and $p_0(x) \neq 0$ on $[a, b]$. Let x_0 be any point in $[a, b]$. Then there exist n functions $\phi_1(x), \phi_2(x), \cdots, \phi_n(x)$ with the following properties:

(i) Every $\phi_i(x)$ satisfies Equation (11).

(ii) The functions $\phi_i(x)$ satisfy the boundary conditions

$$\phi_i(x_0) = 0 \ , \quad \phi_i'(x_0) = 0 \ , \quad \cdots, \phi_i^{(i-1)}(x_0) = 1 \ , \quad \cdots, \phi_i^{(n-1)}(x_0) = 0 \ .$$

(iii) The $\phi_i(x)$ functions are unique.

(iv) The $\phi_i(x)$ are linearly independent.

To prove (i), (ii) and (iii) we must appeal to the general existence theorem.† However, we shall prove the linear independence of the $\phi_i(x)$. If we are to show that the $\phi_1(x), \phi_2(x), \cdots, \phi_n(x)$ are linearly independent, we must show that if there exists for all x in $[a, b]$ an identical relationship of the form

$$c_1\phi_1(x) + c_2\phi_2(x) + \cdots + c_n\phi_n(x) = 0 \ , \tag{12}$$

where the c_i are constants, then

$$c_1 = c_2 = \cdots = c_n = 0 \ .$$

To show that the c_i are all zero we shall use portions of our theory of determinants. Since Equation (12) is an identity, we can differentiate it with respect to x and still have a true equation, namely,

$$c_1\phi_1'(x) + c_2\phi_2'(x) + \cdots + c_n\phi_n'(x) = 0 \ .$$

Similarly, we can differentiate Equation (12) $(n - 2)$ more times, thus obtaining the system of equations

$$
\begin{aligned}
c_1\phi_1(x) \quad &+ c_2\phi_2(x) \quad + \cdots + c_n\phi_n(x) \quad = 0 \\
c_1\phi_1'(x) \quad &+ c_2\phi_2'(x) \quad + \cdots + c_n\phi_n'(x) \quad = 0 \\
&\ \cdot \ \cdot \ \cdot \ \cdot \ \cdot \ \cdot \ \cdot \ \cdot \ \cdot \ \cdot \ \cdot \ \cdot \\
c_1\phi_1^{(n-1)}(x) &+ c_2\phi_2^{(n-1)}(x) + \cdots + c_n\phi_n^{(n-1)}(x) = 0 \ .
\end{aligned} \tag{13}
$$

Now, if we consider the c_i's as the *unknowns* and the $\phi_i^{(j)}(x)$ as coefficients, we

---

† Compare Murray and Miller, *loc. cit.*

can solve Equations (13) by Cramer's rule provided that the determinant of the coefficients is not zero. The determinant of the coefficients is

$$W(x) = \begin{vmatrix} \phi_1(x) & \phi_2(x) & \cdots & \phi_n(x) \\ \phi_1'(x) & \phi_2'(x) & \cdots & \phi_n'(x) \\ \cdots & \cdots & \cdots & \cdots \\ \phi_1^{(n-1)}(x) & \phi_2^{(n-1)}(x) & \cdots & \phi_n^{(n-1)}(x) \end{vmatrix} . \tag{14}$$

Hence, if $W(x) \neq 0$, the corollary to Cramer's rule implies $c_1 = c_2 = \cdots = c_n = 0$. Thus, to establish the linear independence of the solutions $\phi_1(x)$, $\phi_2(x), \cdots, \phi_n(x)$, we must show that $W(x) \neq 0$ for all x in $[a, b]$.

To prove this result we shall first show that $W(x)$ satisfies a first-order linear differential equation. The nonvanishing of $W(x)$ will be an immediate consequence of this fact. If we differentiate $W(x)$ with respect to x and apply the rule for differentiating determinants (cf. Exercise 3, Sec. 1, Chap. 1),

$$W'(x) = \begin{vmatrix} \phi_1' & \cdots & \phi_n' \\ \phi_1' & \cdots & \phi_n' \\ \phi_1'' & \cdots & \phi_n'' \\ \cdots & \cdots & \cdots \\ \phi_1^{(n-1)} & \cdots & \phi_n^{(n-1)} \end{vmatrix} + \begin{vmatrix} \phi_1 & \cdots & \phi_n \\ \phi_1'' & \cdots & \phi_n'' \\ \phi_1'' & \cdots & \phi_n'' \\ \cdots & \cdots & \cdots \\ \phi_1^{(n-1)} & \cdots & \phi_n^{(n-1)} \end{vmatrix}$$

$$+ \cdots + \begin{vmatrix} \phi_1 & \cdots & \phi_n \\ \phi_1' & \cdots & \phi_n' \\ \cdots & \cdots & \cdots \\ \phi_1^{(n-2)} & \cdots & \phi_n^{(n-2)} \\ \phi_1^{(n)} & \cdots & \phi_n^{(n)} \end{vmatrix} . \tag{15}$$

The first $n - 1$ determinants on the right of Equation (15) are zero, since they all have two identical rows. The last determinant on the right-hand side of Equation (15) can be simplified by noting that every $\phi_i(x)$, $i = 1, 2, \cdots, n$ satisfies Equation (11):

$$\phi_i^{(n)}(x) = -\frac{1}{p_0(x)} [p_1(x)\phi_i^{(n-1)}(x) + \cdots + p_n(x)\phi_i(x)] , \tag{16}$$

$$i = 1, 2, \cdots, n .$$

[Note that since we have assumed $p_0(x) \neq 0$ on $[a, b]$ we may divide by p_0.]

If we substitute $\phi_i^{(n)}(x)$ as given by Equation (16) into the last row of the last determinant in Equation (15), we obtain

$$W'(x) = \begin{vmatrix} \phi_1 & \cdots & \phi_n \\ \phi_1' & \cdots & \phi_n' \\ \cdots & \cdots & \cdots \\ \phi_1^{(n-2)} & \cdots & \phi_n^{(n-2)} \\ -\dfrac{1}{p_0}\sum_i p_i \phi_1^{(n-i)} & \cdots & -\dfrac{1}{p_0}\sum_i p_i \phi_n^{(n-i)} \end{vmatrix} . \tag{17}$$

Now, using the theorems of Section 2 of Chapter 1, we can factor a $-1/p_0$ from the last row. Also, if we multiply the first row by p_n and subtract from the last row, multiply the second row by p_{n-1} and subtract from the last row, etc., until we multiply the $(n-1)^{\text{st}}$ row by p_2 and subtract from the last row, Equation (17) takes on the form

$$W'(x) = -\frac{1}{p_0} \begin{vmatrix} \phi_1 & \cdots & \phi_n \\ \phi_1' & \cdots & \phi_n' \\ \cdots & \cdots & \cdots \\ \phi_1^{(n-2)} & \cdots & \phi_n^{(n-2)} \\ p_1 \phi_1^{(n-1)} & \cdots & p_1 \phi_n^{(n-1)} \end{vmatrix}$$

Factoring p_1 from the last row of the above determinant yields

$$W'(x) = -\frac{p_1}{p_0} W(x) ,$$

or

$$p_0 W'(x) + p_1 W(x) = 0 \tag{18}$$

is the differential equation satisfied by $W(x)$. The solution of this equation is

$$W(x) = W(x_0) e^{-\int_{x_0}^{x} \frac{p_1(x)}{p_0(x)} dx} .$$

But from Equation (14),

$$W(x_0) = \begin{vmatrix} 1 & 0 & \cdots & 0 \\ 0 & 1 & \cdots & 0 \\ \cdots & \cdots & \cdots & \cdots \\ 0 & 0 & \cdots & 1 \end{vmatrix} = 1$$

by (ii) of the theorem; hence

$$W(x) = e^{-\int_{x_0}^{x} \frac{p_1(x)}{p_0(x)} dx} \, .$$

Since the exponential is never zero, $W(x)$ is never zero, and therefore $\phi_1, \phi_2, \cdots, \phi_n$ are linearly independent. This completes the proof of the linear independence of the $\phi_i(x)$ functions.

A set of n linearly independent solutions is called a *fundamental system of solutions*. By an argument similar to the above, we can see that $W(x) \neq 0$ for these n solutions. The function $W(x)$ is called the *Wronskian* of the fundamental system and plays a prominent role in the theory of linear differential equations.

3. Green's Function

If in the linear differential equation

$$Ly = p_0(x)y^{(n)} + p_1(x)y^{(n-1)} + \cdots + p_n(x)y = r(x) \tag{19}$$

the function $r(x)$ is identically zero, we call the equation *homogeneous*, and we have shown in the last section the existence of n linearly independent solutions of Equation (19). Now suppose $r(x)$ is *not* identically zero. Then the above results are not immediately applicable. In the present section we shall show how Equation (19) can be conveniently solved if only the *homogeneous* equation can be solved.

We might add parenthetically that finding the solution of the homogeneous equation is invariably the most difficult part of the problem. In later sections of this chapter we shall exhibit practical methods for explicitly finding these solutions (generally as infinite series). Lest the reader be misled, the methods are at best lengthy and cumbersome. There exists no general, short, easy method of finding solutions of linear differential equations with *non*constant coefficients.

If we assume that the homogeneous equation

$$Ly = p_0(x)y^{(n)} + p_1(x)y^{(n-1)} + \cdots + p_n(x)y = 0$$

corresponding to Equation (19) has been solved, then there exist n linearly independent functions $\phi_1(x), \cdots, \phi_n(x)$ which satisfy $Ly = 0$ and take on assigned initial conditions. To solve the nonhomogeneous equation $Ly = r$, we use the method of *variation of parameters*. This method consists in assuming a solution of Equation (19) in the form

$$\Phi(x) = \phi_1(x)\psi_1(x) + \phi_2(x)\psi_2(x) + \cdots + \phi_n(x)\psi_n(x) \, , \tag{20}$$

where the $\psi_i(x)$ are as yet unspecified functions. Now, if $\Phi(x)$ as given by Equation (20) is to satisfy Equation (19), certain conditions must be imposed on the $\psi_i(x)$. To see what these conditions are, let us calculate the derivatives of $\Phi(x)$. First,

$$\Phi'(x) = \phi_1'\psi_1 + \cdots + \phi_n'\psi_n + [\phi_1\psi_1' + \cdots + \phi_n\psi_n'] \quad,$$

and as our first condition on the ψ_i's we shall require that

$$\phi_1\psi_1' + \cdots + \phi_n\psi_n' = 0 \quad.$$

If this be the case,

$$\Phi''(x) = \phi_1''\psi_1 + \cdots + \phi_n''\psi_n + [\phi_1'\psi_1' + \cdots + \phi_n'\psi_n'] \quad,$$

and as our second condition on the ψ_i's we shall require that

$$\phi_1'\psi_1' + \cdots + \phi_n'\psi_n' = 0 \quad.$$

Continuing in this fashion, we find

$$\Phi^{(n-1)}(x) = \phi_1^{(n-1)}\psi_1 + \cdots + \phi_n^{(n-1)}\psi_n + [\phi_1^{(n-2)}\psi_1' + \cdots + \phi_n^{(n-2)}\psi_n']$$

and require

$$\phi_1^{(n-2)}\psi_1' + \cdots + \phi_n^{(n-2)}\psi_n' = 0 \quad.$$

Finally, we compute

$$\Phi^{(n)}(x) = \phi_1^{(n)}\psi_1 + \cdots + \phi_n^{(n)}\psi_n + [\phi_1^{(n-1)}\psi_1' + \cdots + \phi_n^{(n-1)}\psi_n']$$

and require

$$\phi_1^{(n-1)}\psi_1' + \cdots + \phi_n^{(n-1)}\psi_n' = +\frac{r(x)}{p_0(x)} \quad.$$

Now, substituting $\Phi(x)$ into Equation (19) and collecting coefficients of $\psi_i(x)$, we find

$$L\Phi = \psi_1 L\phi_1 + \psi_2 L\phi_2 + \cdots + \psi_n L\phi_n + p_0\left[+\frac{r(x)}{p_0(x)}\right] = r(x) \quad,$$

since $L\phi_i = 0$. Hence, if the $\psi_i(x)$ satisfy the n algebraic equations

$$\begin{aligned}
\phi_1\psi_1' \quad + \phi_2\psi_2' \quad + \cdots + \phi_n\psi_n' \quad &= 0 \\
\phi_1'\psi_1' \quad + \phi_2'\psi_2' \quad + \cdots + \phi_n'\psi_n' \quad &= 0 \\
\cdots \cdots \cdots \cdots \cdots \cdots \cdots \cdots & \\
\phi_1^{(n-1)}\psi_1' + \phi_2^{(n-1)}\psi_2' + \cdots + \phi_n^{(n-1)}\psi_n' &= +\frac{r(x)}{p_0(x)} \quad,
\end{aligned} \qquad (21)$$

then the function $\Phi(x)$ is a solution to the nonhomogeneous equation, $Ly = r$. Considering Equation (21) as a system of n equations on the n unknowns $\psi_i'(x)$, we may apply Cramer's rule to write

$$\psi_1'(x) = -(-1)^n \frac{r(x)}{p_0(x)} \frac{1}{W(x)} \begin{vmatrix} \phi_2(x) & \phi_3(x) & \cdots & \phi_n(x) \\ \phi_2'(x) & \phi_3'(x) & \cdots & \phi_n'(x) \\ \cdot & \cdot & \cdots & \cdot \\ \phi_2^{(n-2)}(x) & \phi_3^{(n-2)}(x) & \cdots & \phi_n^{(n-2)}(x) \end{vmatrix} \quad (22)$$

with similar expressions for $\psi_2'(x)$, $\psi_3'(x)$, $\cdots$, $\psi_n'(x)$. Note that the determinant of the ψ_i' is precisely the Wronskian $W(x)$.

Now, if we integrate the above equation,

$$\psi_1(x) = A_1 + \int_{x_0}^x \frac{r(\xi) D_1(\xi)}{p_0(\xi) W(\xi)} \, d\xi \quad , \quad (23)$$

where $D_1(\xi)$ is $(-1)^{n+1}$ times the determinant appearing in Equation (22). Writing expressions for $\psi_2, \cdots, \psi_n$ similar to Equation (23) results in

$$\Phi(x) = \sum_{i=1}^n A_i \phi_i(x) + \sum_{i=1}^n \phi_i(x) \int_{x_0}^x \frac{r(\xi) D_i(\xi)}{p_0(\xi) W(\xi)} \, d\xi \quad , \quad (24)$$

the solution of the nonhomogeneous equation of Equation (19), where the A_i are constants of integration. We wish to simplify Equation (24) in two respects. First, we wish to write the integral term in a more compact form, and, second, we wish to evaluate the A_i by imposing specific boundary conditions on $\Phi(x)$.

Consider, then, the integral term of Equation (24), which we write as

$$\sum_{i=1}^n \phi_i(x) \int_{x_0}^x \frac{r(\xi) D_i(\xi)}{p_0(\xi) W(\xi)} \, d\xi = \int_{x_0}^x \left[\sum_{i=1}^n \frac{\phi_i(x) D_i(\xi)}{p_0(\xi) W(\xi)} \right] r(\xi) \, d\xi \quad . \quad (25)$$

The expression $\sum_{i=1}^n \phi_i(x) D_i(\xi)$ is merely the expanded form of the determinant

$$D(x, \xi) = (-1)^{n-1} \begin{vmatrix} \phi_1(x) & \phi_2(x) & \cdots & \phi_n(x) \\ \phi_1(\xi) & \phi_2(\xi) & \cdots & \phi_n(\xi) \\ \phi_1'(\xi) & \phi_2'(\xi) & \cdots & \phi_n'(\xi) \\ \cdot & \cdot & \cdots & \cdot \\ \phi_1^{(n-2)}(\xi) & \phi_2^{(n-2)}(\xi) & \cdots & \phi_n^{(n-2)}(\xi) \end{vmatrix} \quad . \quad (26)$$

If we let

$$H(x, \xi) = \frac{D(x, \xi)}{p_0(\xi)W(\xi)} \quad , \qquad (27)$$

then Equation (24) may be written

$$\Phi(x) = \sum_{i=1}^{n} A_i \phi_i(x) + \int_{x_0}^{x} H(x, \xi) r(\xi) d\xi \quad . \qquad (28)$$

The function $H(x, \xi)$ is called the *one-sided Green's function* of the linear differential operator L. We see that if we can construct H we can immediately write down the solution to the nonhomogeneous equation. Note that the last $n - 1$ rows of $D(x, \xi)$ are identical with the first $n - 1$ rows of the Wronskian. This fact makes it particularly simple to remember the form of H.

Now we turn to evaluating the A_i. If we take as initial conditions for Φ,

$$\Phi^{(\alpha)}(x_0) = 0 \quad , \quad \alpha = 0, 1, \cdots, n - 1 \quad , \qquad (29)$$

then from Equation (28)

$$\Phi^{(\alpha)}(x) = \sum_{i=1}^{n} A_i \phi_i^{(\alpha)}(x) + \int_{x_0}^{x} \frac{\partial^\alpha}{\partial x^\alpha} H(x, \xi) r(\xi) d\xi + \frac{\partial^{\alpha-1}}{\partial x^{\alpha-1}} H(x, \xi) \bigg|_{x=\xi} r(\xi)$$

for $\alpha = 1, 2, \cdots, n - 1$, since

$$\frac{\partial^{\alpha-1}}{\partial x^{\alpha-1}} H(x, \xi) \bigg|_{x=\xi} = 0 \quad \text{for} \quad \alpha = 1, 2, \cdots, n - 1 \quad .$$

[Note that the $D(x, \xi)$ determinant has two identical rows in these cases; cf. Equation (26)]. Hence

$$\Phi^{(\alpha)}(x_0) = \sum_{i=1}^{n} A_i \phi_i^{(\alpha)}(x_0) \quad , \quad \alpha = 0, 1, \cdots, n - 1 \quad , \qquad (30)$$

since

$$\int_{x_0}^{x_0} \frac{\partial^\alpha H}{\partial x^\alpha} r(\xi) d\xi = 0 \quad .$$

The boundary conditions of Equation (29) which we have imposed on Φ imply [from Equations (30)] that

$$\sum_{i=1}^{n} A_i \phi_i^{(\alpha)}(x_0) = 0 \quad , \quad \alpha = 0, 1, \cdots, n - 1$$

and by the corollary to Cramer's rule, $A_1 = A_2 = \cdots = A_n = 0$, since the determinant of the coefficients of the A_i is the Wronskian $W(x_0)$.

Summarizing our results, we may state the following theorem:

THEOREM. Let

$$Ly \equiv p_0 y^{(n)} + p_1 y^{(n-1)} + \cdots + p_n y = r(x)$$

be a nonhomogeneous linear differential equation and let $\phi_1, \phi_2, \cdots, \phi_n$ be n linearly independent solutions of the homogeneous equation $Ly = 0$. Then $\Phi(x)$,

$$\Phi(x) = \int_{x_0}^{x} H(x, \xi) r(\xi) d\xi$$

is a solution of the nonhomogeneous linear differential equation $Ly = r(x)$, where $H(x, \xi)$ is the one-sided Green's function for L, that is,

$$H(x, \xi) = \frac{(-1)^{n-1}}{p_0(\xi) W(\xi)} \begin{vmatrix} \phi_1(x) & \phi_2(x) & \cdots & \phi_n(x) \\ \phi_1(\xi) & \phi_2(\xi) & \cdots & \phi_n(\xi) \\ \phi_1'(\xi) & \phi_2'(\xi) & \cdots & \phi_n'(\xi) \\ \cdot & \cdot \cdot \cdot \cdot \cdot \cdot \cdot \cdot \cdot & \cdot \\ \phi_1^{(n-2)}(\xi) & \phi_2^{(n-2)}(\xi) & \cdots & \phi_n^{(n-2)}(\xi) \end{vmatrix},$$

where $W(\xi)$ is the Wronskian of the fundamental system $\phi_1, \phi_2, \cdots, \phi_n$. Further, $\Phi(x)$ satisfies the boundary conditions

$$\Phi^{(\alpha)}(x_0) = 0 \quad , \quad \alpha = 0, 1, \cdots, n-1 \quad .$$

If we wish to find a function $\Psi(x)$ which satisfies the *nonhomogeneous* boundary conditions

$$\Psi^{(\alpha)}(x_0) = C_\alpha \quad , \quad \alpha = 0, 1, \cdots, n-1 \quad ,$$

then all we have to do is write

$$\Psi(x) = \sum_{k=0}^{n-1} a_k \phi_{k+1}(x) + \Phi(x) \quad ,$$

where $\phi_k(x)$ is a fundamental set of solutions. Then

$$\Psi^{(\alpha)}(x_0) = \sum_{k=0}^{n-1} a_k \phi_{k+1}^{(\alpha)}(x_0) + 0 = C_\alpha$$

for $\alpha = 0, 1, 2, \cdots, n-1$ represents a system of n linear algebraic equations on the a_k. Since the determinant of the coefficients is the Wronskian evaluated at x_0, it is unequal to zero, and hence we may solve for the a_k by Cramer's rule.

As an example of the Green's function method, consider the following problem: An emf of $E(t)$ volts is applied to the simple RLC circuit of Figure 3.2. If initially the condenser has no charge, $q(0) = 0$ and $q'(0) = 0$, find the charge q at any time t.

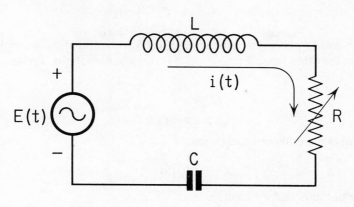

Fig. 3.2

It is shown in Salvadori and Schwarz† that the charge q satisfies the differential equation

$$\frac{d^2q}{dt^2} + \frac{R}{L}\frac{dq}{dt} + \frac{1}{LC}q = \frac{1}{L}E(t) \quad .$$

If $L = 1\,h.$, $C = \frac{1}{2}f.$, and $R = 3\,\Omega.$, then the above equation becomes, numerically,

$$q'' + 3q' + 2q = E(t) \quad .$$

Two linearly independent solutions of the homogeneous equation

$$q'' + 3q' + 2q = 0$$

are

$$\phi_1(t) = e^{-t} \quad \text{and} \quad \phi_2(t) = e^{-2t} \quad .$$

The Green's function $H(t, \xi)$ is

$$H(t, \xi) = -\frac{\begin{vmatrix} \phi_1(t) & \phi_2(t) \\ \phi_1(\xi) & \phi_2(\xi) \end{vmatrix}}{\begin{vmatrix} \phi_1(\xi) & \phi_2(\xi) \\ \phi_1'(\xi) & \phi_2'(\xi) \end{vmatrix}} = -\frac{\begin{vmatrix} e^{-t} & e^{-2t} \\ e^{-\xi} & e^{-2\xi} \end{vmatrix}}{\begin{vmatrix} e^{-\xi} & e^{-2\xi} \\ -e^{-\xi} & -2e^{-2\xi} \end{vmatrix}}$$

$$= e^{\xi-t} - e^{2(\xi-t)} \quad .$$

---

† Salvadori and Schwarz, *loc. cit.*

The solution of the nonhomogeneous equation with the boundary conditions $q(0) = 0$, $q'(0) = 0$ is therefore

$$q(t) = \int_0^t (e^{\xi-t} - e^{2(\xi-t)})E(\xi)d\xi \quad . \tag{31}$$

Hence, given any particular value of $E(\xi)$, $q(t)$ can be found by a simple quadrature. On the other hand, Equation (31) represents the solution for an *arbitrary* emf $E(t)$.

EXERCISES

1. Solve the differential equation

$$y'' - 2y' + y = e^x$$

   with the boundary conditions

$$y(0) = 0 \quad , \quad y'(0) = 0 \quad .$$

2. Find the function $y(x)$ which satisfies the differential equation

$$\frac{d^2y}{dx^2} - 4\frac{dy}{dx} + 5y = 7e^{2x}$$

   and assumes the initial values $y(\pi) = 0$, $y'(\pi) = 0$.

3. Solve the differential system

$$y''' + 5y'' + 4y' = 4 \quad ,$$

$$y(1) = 2 \quad , \quad y'(1) = 0 \quad , \quad y''(1) = 1 \quad .$$

4. Find the solution of the differential equation

$$x^2y'' - 2xy' + 2y = 4x^3 \sin x$$

   which satisfies the boundary conditions

$$y(\tfrac{1}{2}\pi) = -2\pi \quad \text{and} \quad y'(\tfrac{1}{2}\pi) = -4 \quad .$$

4. Solutions in Series

In Section 1 we rapidly disposed of constant coefficient linear differential equations, while Sections 2 and 3 were devoted to some theoretical remarks concerning linear differential equations in general. If we can solve the homogeneous equation, the solution of the nonhomogeneous equation becomes simply a matter of a single integration using the Green's function method. But, as we remarked earlier, the main task is to solve the *homogeneous equation.* While it is comforting to know that the differential equation has solutions (cf. the existence theorem of Sec. 2), it is not much help if we actually wish explicitly to find these solutions. The remainder of this chapter will be devoted to the problem of actually finding such explicit solutions.

Before we start such a program, let us give at least one example to show how differential equations with nonconstant coefficients arise. Returning to the example considered at the beginning of this chapter (cf. Fig. 3.1), suppose that the liquid in which the mass is suspended is a copper sulfate solution and that, as time progresses, copper is deposited on the mass m_0. Then the mass can no longer be regarded as a constant but varies with the time. Let us assume that this is a linear variation, that is,

$$m = m_0 + \alpha t \quad ,$$

where α is a constant and m_0 is the mass at $t = 0$. Equation (3) then becomes

$$(m_0 + \alpha t)\frac{d^2y}{dt^2} + k'\frac{dy}{dt} + ky = 0 \quad . \tag{32}$$

If we replace t by the new independent variable $x = m_0 + \alpha t$, then Equation (32) assumes the form

$$x\frac{d^2y}{dx^2} + \frac{k'}{\alpha}\frac{dy}{dx} + \frac{ky}{\alpha^2} = 0 \quad . \tag{33}$$

The crucial difference between this equation and Equation (3) is that the coefficients of the derivatives of y are no longer constants, but are functions of the independent variable x. Of course Equation (33) is still a *linear* differential equation, but the technique of considering the indicial equation is no longer applicable. As we shall see later in this chapter as well as in future chapters, differential equations with nonconstant coefficients arise in a great number of physical problems. However, for the present, let us see if we can devise a practical method for solving Equation (33).

One method is to *assume* a solution in terms of powers of x, say,

$$y(x) = \sum_{n=0}^{\infty} a_n x^n \quad , \tag{34}$$

and endeavor to determine the coefficients a_n such as to satisfy the given differential equation. One could of course use this method even with *constant coefficient* differential equations such as Equation (3), but there is no necessity for doing this, since in this case we already have a much simpler method available.

For convenience in numerical computation, let us assume that $\alpha = 2$ and $k = k' = 1$. Then Equation (33) becomes

$$4xy'' + 2y' + y = 0 \quad . \tag{35}$$

In order to solve Equation (35) let us first compute y' and y''. From Equation (34),

$$y'(x) = \sum_{n=0}^{\infty} na_n x^{n-1} = \sum_{n=1}^{\infty} na_n x^{n-1}$$

$$y''(x) = \sum_{n=0}^{\infty} n(n-1)a_n x^{n-2} = \sum_{n=2}^{\infty} n(n-1)a_n x^{n-2} \quad .$$

Substituting these formulas and Equation (34) into Equation (35), we obtain

$$4x \sum_{n=2}^{\infty} n(n-1)a_n x^{n-2} + 2\sum_{n=1}^{\infty} na_n x^{n-1} + \sum_{n=0}^{\infty} a_n x^n = 0 \quad . \tag{36}$$

To collect powers of x, it is convenient to let $n = m + 1$ in the first two sums and $n = m$ in the last sum. Then

$$4x \sum_{n=2}^{\infty} n(n-1)a_n x^{n-2} = \sum_{n=2}^{\infty} 4n(n-1)a_n x^{n-1} = \sum_{m=1}^{\infty} 4(m+1)m a_{m+1} x^m \quad ,$$

$$2\sum_{n=1}^{\infty} na_n x^{n-1} = \sum_{m=0}^{\infty} 2(m+1)a_{m+1} x^m \quad ,$$

and Equation (36) becomes

$$\sum_{m=1}^{\infty} 4m(m+1)a_{m+1} x^m + \sum_{m=0}^{\infty} 2(m+1)a_{m+1} x^m + \sum_{m=0}^{\infty} a_m x^m = 0 \quad .$$

When the first term of each of the last two sums is explicitly written out, the above equation becomes

$$\sum_{m=1}^{\infty} 4m(m+1)a_{m+1} x^m + \left[2a_1 x^0 + \sum_{m=1}^{\infty} 2(m+1)a_{m+1} x^m \right] + \left[a_0 x^0 + \sum_{m=1}^{\infty} a_m x^m \right] = 0 \quad ,$$

and, collecting like powers of x, we have

$$(a_0 + 2a_1)x^0 + \sum_{m=1}^{\infty} [4m(m+1)a_{m+1} + 2(m+1)a_{m+1} + a_m]x^m = 0 \quad .$$

Hence, if our trial function, Equation (34), is to satisfy the differential equation, Equation (35), the coefficients of the powers of x in the above expression must vanish; that is,

$$a_0 + 2a_1 = 0 \quad ,$$

and

$$[4m(m + 1) + 2(m + 1)]a_{m+1} + a_m = 0 \quad , \quad m = 1, 2, \cdots \; .$$

Hence we let

$$a_1 = -\frac{a_0}{2} \; ,$$

and from the second equation,

$$a_{m+1} = \frac{-a_m}{(2m + 1)(2m + 2)} \quad , \quad m = 1, 2, \cdots \; ,$$

we see that the a_{m+1} coefficient can be determined in terms of the a_m coefficient. Since $a_1 = -a_0/2$, all the coefficients can be determined in terms of a_0. For example, setting $m = 1$ in the above equation,

$$a_2 = \frac{-a_1}{3 \cdot 4} = +\frac{a_0}{2 \cdot 3 \cdot 4} \; .$$

Letting $m = 2$, we see that

$$a_3 = \frac{-a_2}{5 \cdot 6} = -\frac{a_0}{2 \cdot 3 \cdot 4 \cdot 5 \cdot 6} \; .$$

In general, it is easy to see that

$$a_m = \frac{(-1)^m a_0}{(2m)!} \quad ;$$

hence

$$y(x) = a_0 \left[1 - \frac{1}{2}x + \frac{1}{4!}x^2 - \frac{1}{6!}x^3 + \cdots + (-1)^m \frac{1}{(2m)!}x^m + \cdots \right] \quad (37)$$

is a solution of Equation (35). The constant a_0 is an arbitrary constant of integration which can be made explicit by assuming particular boundary conditions.

Now we know that a second-order linear differential equation has two linearly independent solutions. How, then, shall we obtain the second solution to Equation (35)? By a method which is by no means obvious, assume a solution of the form

$$y(x) = \sum_{n=0}^{\infty} b_n x^{n+\frac{1}{2}} \; . \quad (38)$$

The reason for choosing this particular form will be discussed in detail later in this chapter. If all the solutions of a differential equation with variable coefficients could be determined from an expression of the form of Equation (34), then the theory would be quite simple.

Using Equation (38), we determine y' and y'' as before:

$$y'(x) = \sum_{n=0}^{\infty} (n + \tfrac{1}{2}) b_n x^{n-\frac{1}{2}}$$

$$y''(x) = \sum_{n=0}^{\infty} (n + \tfrac{1}{2}) (n - \tfrac{1}{2}) b_n x^{n-\frac{3}{2}} \quad .$$

If these are substituted into Equation (35), there results

$$\sum_{n=0}^{\infty} (2n + 1)(2n - 1)b_n x^{n-\frac{1}{2}} + \sum_{n=0}^{\infty} (2n + 1)b_n x^{n-\frac{1}{2}} + \sum_{n=0}^{\infty} b_n x^{n+\frac{1}{2}} = 0 \quad .$$

In order to collect like powers of x we substitute $m + 1$ for n in the first two sums, and, on writing out the first term of each of these sums explicitly, we have

$$\left[- b_0 x^{-\frac{1}{2}} + \sum_{m=0}^{\infty} (2m + 3)(2m + 1)b_{m+1}x^{m+\frac{1}{2}} \right] + \left[b_0 x^{-\frac{1}{2}} + \sum_{m=0}^{\infty} (2m + 3)b_{m+1}x^{m+\frac{1}{2}} \right]$$

$$+ \sum_{m=0}^{\infty} b_m x^{m+\frac{1}{2}} = 0$$

or

$$(- b_0 + b_0)x^{-\frac{1}{2}} + \sum_{m=0}^{\infty} [(2m + 3)(2m + 1)b_{m+1} + (2m + 3)b_{m+1} + b_m]x^{m+\frac{1}{2}} = 0 \quad ,$$

which we may write as

$$\sqrt{x} \sum_{m=0}^{\infty} [(2m + 2)(2m + 3)b_{m+1} + b_m]x^m = 0 \quad .$$

In order that $y(x)$ as given by Equation (38) satisfy the original differential equation, we must have

$$(2m + 2)(2m + 3)b_{m+1} + b_m = 0 \quad , \quad m = 0, 1, \cdots$$

or

$$b_{m+1} = \frac{- b_m}{(2m + 2)(2m + 3)} \quad .$$

Letting b_0 be arbitrary, we have, on letting $m = 0$ in the above equation,

$$b_1 = \frac{- b_0}{2 \cdot 3} \quad .$$

Letting $m = 1$, we have

$$b_2 = \frac{-b_1}{4 \cdot 5} = +\frac{b_0}{2 \cdot 3 \cdot 4 \cdot 5} \quad,$$

and, in general, we find that

$$b_m = \frac{(-1)^m b_0}{(2m+1)!} \quad, \quad m = 1, 2, \cdots .$$

Hence

$$y(x) = b_0 \left[x^{\frac{1}{2}} - \frac{x^{\frac{3}{2}}}{3!} + \frac{x^{\frac{5}{2}}}{5!} + \cdots + \frac{(-1)^m x^{\frac{2m+1}{2}}}{(2m+1)!} + \cdots \right] . \tag{39}$$

If we call the term in brackets in Equation (37), $y_1(x)$ and call the term in brackets in Equation (39) above, $y_2(x)$, then $y_1(x)$ and $y_2(x)$ are two linearly independent solutions of Equation (35), and its general solution may be written

$$y(x) = a_0 y_1(x) + b_0 y_2(x) \quad,$$

where a_0 and b_0 are arbitrary constants.

Having completed the somewhat laborious task of finding $y_1(x)$ and $y_2(x)$, let us survey the situation and see what we have accomplished. First, we have solved a differential equation with nonconstant coefficients, the solutions being the infinite series $y_1(x)$ and $y_2(x)$. However, we must find for what values of x these series converge, since, if for example, the series do not converge at some point $x = x'$, then $y_1(x')$ would not be meaningful and hence certainly not a solution of the differential equation. The reader will recall from his treatment of power series in the calculus that there exist various tests to determine whether a series converges or not. Perhaps the most familiar is the *Ratio Test*,[†] which works in a great many examples. For convenience we state it here:

RATIO TEST. Let

$$a_0 + a_1 x + a_2 x^2 + \cdots$$

be a power series. Let

$$L = \lim_{n \to \infty} \left| \frac{a_{n+1}}{a_n} \right| .$$

Then $R = 1/L$ is the radius of convergence of the power series; that is, the

---

† Salvadori and Miller, *The Mathematical Solution of Engineering Problems*, p. 176.

power series converges for all x with $|x| < R$ and diverges for all x with $|x| > R$. If $|x| = R$, the series may diverge or converge.†

In the problem just solved,

$$y_1(x) = \sum_{n=0}^{\infty} \frac{(-1)^n}{(2n)!} x^n$$

and

$$\frac{1}{R} = L = \lim_{n\to\infty}\left|\frac{a_{n+1}}{a_n}\right| = \lim_{n\to\infty}\frac{(2n)!}{(2n+2)!} = \lim_{n\to\infty}\frac{1}{(2n+2)(2n+1)} = 0 \ .$$

Hence the radius of convergence of $y_1(x)$ is infinite, and $y_1(x)$ is a solution of Equation (35) valid for all values of x. The reader has probably already recognized $y_1(x)$ as

$$y_1(x) = \cos \sqrt{x} \ , \quad x \geqq 0$$
$$= \cosh \sqrt{-x} \ , \quad x < 0 \ . \tag{40}$$

The fact that $y_1(x)$ turns out to be an elementary function is the exception rather than the rule; however, it in no way invalidates our conclusions. If we write

$$y_2(x) = \sqrt{x} \sum_{n=0}^{\infty} \frac{(-1)^n x^n}{(2n+1)!} = \sqrt{x}\phi_2(x) \ ,$$

then we also see that $\phi_2(x)$ has an infinite radius of convergence; moreover, it can be represented in terms of elementary functions.

Having convinced ourselves that $y_1(x)$ and $y_2(x)$ are indeed solutions of Equation (35) for all x, we still leave unanswered the reason for introducing

---

† While discussing the theoretical properties of power series, we might state the following theorem (a proof of which will be found, for example, in Woods, *Advanced Calculus*) that will be frequently used.

THEOREM. Let

$$f(x) = \sum_{n=0}^{\infty} a_n x^n$$

have a positive radius of convergence, R. Let s be a positive number less than R. Then for all x, $-s \leqq x \leqq s$, term-by-term differentiation of the series is valid. That is,

$$\frac{d}{dx}f(x) = \sum_{n=0}^{\infty} na_n x^{n-1} \ , \quad -s \leqq x \leqq s \ .$$

Also, one can integrate a power series term by term in the interval $-s \leqq x \leqq s$. That is,

$$\int_0^{\xi} f(x)\,dx = \sum_{n=0}^{\infty} \frac{a_n}{n+1}\xi^{n+1} \ , \quad -s \leqq \xi \leqq s$$

is a true equation.

the factor $\sqrt{x}$ in Equation (38). After all, if we are to systematically solve differential equations with nonconstant coefficients, we must have some general rule which satisfactorily settles this dilemma. Such a rule will be developed in the next section, when we consider the *method of Frobenius*. After developing this method we shall apply it to a number of important equations of mathematical physics, in particular, Legendre's equation, Hermite's equation, and Bessel's equations.

5. The Method of Frobenius

Before starting on the systematic solution of linear differential equations we wish to state another existence theorem. If we look at Equation (35), we see that the condition $p_0(x) \neq 0$ of the existence theorem of Section 2 is not fulfilled, for in this case $p_0(x) = 4x$, which vanishes at $x = 0$. The modified theorem which takes care of such difficulties reads† :

THEOREM. Let

$$x^2 y'' + x p_1(x) y' + p_2(x) y = 0 \tag{41}$$

be a linear differential equation of the second order where the coefficients $p_1(x)$ and $p_2(x)$ are analytic‡ in some neighborhood N of the point $x = 0$. Then there exist two linearly independent solutions $\phi(x)$ and $\psi(x)$ of Equation (41) which are of the form

$$\phi(x) = x^{s_1} \phi_1(x)$$

$$\psi(x) = x^{s_2} \psi_1(x) + A x^{s_1} \phi_1(x) \log x \quad,$$

where $\phi_1(x)$ and $\psi_1(x)$ are analytic in N. s_1, s_2 and A are constants. If s_1 and s_2 do not differ by an integer, then $A = 0$.

Just how to find s_1, s_2, A, ϕ_1, and ψ_1 will be the main content of the present section. If we allow the coefficients of the earlier existence theorem (cf. Sec. 2) to be analytic, which certainly implies that they are continuous, then this earlier result becomes a special case of the above theorem. For if we write the equation of this earlier section for $n = 2$ as

$$P_0(x) y'' + P_1(x) y' + P_2(x) y = 0 \quad,$$

then, since $P_0(x) \neq 0$, we can divide by P_0, obtaining

$$y'' + q_1(x) y' + q_2(x) y = 0 \quad,$$

---

† Compare Ince, *Ordinary Differential Equations*.

‡ We say that a function $f(x)$ is "analytic in some neighborhood of the point $x = a$" if it can be developed about the point $x = a$ in a power series which has a positive radius of convergence. If, for example, the radius of convergence is R, then the "neighborhood of the point $x = a$" is the totality of points x satisfying the inequalities $-R < x - a < R$.

where $q_1 = P_1/P_0$, $q_2 = P_2/P_0$. Multiplying the above equation by x^2 yields

$$x^2 y'' + x^2 q_1(x) y' + x^2 q_2(x) y = 0 \quad ,$$

and we can then identify $x q_1(x)$ and $x^2 q_2(x)$ with $p_1(x)$ and $p_2(x)$, respectively, of Equation (41).

The method we shall expound for solving Equation (41) is due to G. Frobenius and dates back to the latter part of the nineteenth century. Let us assume that the solution to Equation (41) may be written in the form

$$y(x) = \sum_{n=0}^{\infty} a_n x^{n+s} \quad , \tag{42}$$

where the a_n, $n = 0, 1, \cdots$ and s are as yet undetermined constants. First we compute y' and y'',

$$y'(x) = \sum_{n=0}^{\infty} (n + s) a_n x^{n+s-1}$$

$$y''(x) = \sum_{n=0}^{\infty} (n + s)(n + s - 1) a_n x^{n+s-2}$$

and substitute in Equation (41), obtaining

$$\sum_{n=0}^{\infty} a_n [(n + s)(n + s - 1) + (n + s) p_1(x) + p_2(x)] x^{n+s} = 0 \quad . \tag{43}$$

By hypothesis, $p_1(x)$ and $p_2(x)$ are analytic functions and hence can be expanded into power series with positive radii of convergence, say

$$p_1(x) = \sum_{m=0}^{\infty} \alpha_m x^m \quad , \quad p_2(x) = \sum_{m=0}^{\infty} \beta_m x^m \quad , \tag{44}$$

where the α_m and β_m are *known* constants. Substituting $p_1(x)$ and $p_2(x)$ as given by Equations (44) into Equation (43), we obtain

$$\sum_{n=0}^{\infty} a_n [(n + s)(n + s - 1) + (n + s) \sum_{m=0}^{\infty} \alpha_m x^m + \sum_{m=0}^{\infty} \beta_m x^m] x^{n+s} = 0 \quad . \tag{45}$$

Now, if we are to follow the same general line of reasoning established in Section 4, we must first collect coefficients of like powers of x. If we can do this, then the above equation will be of the form

$$x^s \sum_{n=0}^{\infty} A_n x^n \equiv 0 \quad . \tag{46}$$

If we assume that the power series has a positive radius of convergence, it is an analytic function which equals zero. By the uniqueness of the expansion, every

A_n must be zero. Hence, if we can write Equation (45) in the form of Equation (46), then we can equate to zero the coefficients of all powers of x. To do this, let us write

$$\sum_{n=0}^{\infty} a_n \left[(n+s) \sum_{m=0}^{\infty} \alpha_m x^m \right] x^{n+s}$$

as

$$\sum_{p=0}^{\infty} \left[\sum_{m=0}^{p} a_{p-m}(p-m+s)\alpha_m x^{p+s} \right] \quad,$$

where we have introduced the new variable $p = m + n$ in place of n. Similarly,

$$\sum_{n=0}^{\infty} a_n \left[\sum_{m=0}^{\infty} \beta_m x^m \right] x^{n+s} = \sum_{p=0}^{\infty} \left[\sum_{m=0}^{p} a_{p-m}\beta_m x^{p+s} \right] \quad,$$

and Equation (45) becomes

$$\sum_{p=0}^{\infty} \left[a_p(p+s)(p+s-1) + \sum_{m=0}^{p} a_{p-m}(p-m+s)\alpha_m + \sum_{m=0}^{p} a_{p-m}\beta_m \right] x^{p+s} = 0$$

or

$$x^s \sum_{p=0}^{\infty} \left\{ a_p(p+s)(p+s-1) + \sum_{m=0}^{p} a_{p-m}[(p-m+s)\alpha_m + \beta_m] \right\} x^p = 0 \quad . \quad (47)$$

Equating coefficients of powers of x to zero, we have

$$a_0[s(s-1) + s\alpha_0 + \beta_0] = 0 \qquad (48)$$

$$a_p(p+s)(p+s-1) + \sum_{m=0}^{p} a_{p-m}[(p-m+s)\alpha_m + \beta_m] = 0 \quad,$$

$$p = 1, 2, \cdots \quad .$$

In order to express a_p in terms of a_m, $m < p$, write out the zeroth term in the last sum, namely,

$$a_p(p+s)(p+s-1) + a_p[(p+s)\alpha_0 + \beta_0] + \sum_{m=1}^{p} a_{p-m}[(p-m+s)\alpha_m + \beta_m] = 0 \quad,$$

which, if we let $q = p - m$, gives

$$a_p[(p+s)(p+s-1) + (p+s)\alpha_0 + \beta_0] + \sum_{q=0}^{p-1} a_q[(q+s)\alpha_{p-q} + \beta_{p-q}] = 0 \quad,$$

$$p = 1, 2, \cdots \quad . \quad (49)$$

If the coefficients of Equation (47) are to vanish identically, the coefficients a_p must be determined by Equations (48) and (49). To make these expressions more tractable, we introduce the following notation. Let

$$f_0(s) = s(s - 1) + s\alpha_0 + \beta_0 \quad ,$$

which is called the *indicial equation* of the original Equation (41) and plays an important role in determining the exponents s_1 and s_2 mentioned in the theorem. Also let

$$f_r(s) = s\alpha_r + \beta_r \quad , \quad r = 1, 2, \cdots \quad .$$

Then Equations (48) and (49) can be compactly and symmetrically written as

$$a_0 f_0(s) = 0$$
$$a_1 f_0(s + 1) + a_0 f_1(s) = 0$$
$$a_2 f_0(s + 2) + a_1 f_1(s + 1) + a_0 f_2(s) = 0 \tag{50}$$
$$\cdot \; \cdot \; \cdot \; \cdot \; \cdot \; \cdot \; \cdot \; \cdot \; \cdot \; \cdot \; \cdot \; \cdot \; \cdot \; \cdot \; \cdot \; \cdot$$
$$a_p f_0(s + p) + a_{p-1} f_1(s + p - 1) + \cdots + a_0 f_p(s) = 0$$
$$\cdot \; \cdot \; \cdot \; \cdot \; \cdot \; \cdot \; \cdot \; \cdot \; \cdot \; \cdot \; \cdot \; \cdot \; \cdot \; \cdot \; \cdot \; \cdot$$

If we set $f_0(s)$ equal to zero we can in general determine $a_1, a_2, \cdots$ in terms of a_0 by Equations (50) and thus obtain a solution of Equation (41). Let us make this situation more precise. From the second of Equations (50), assuming $f_0(s + 1) \neq 0$, we have

$$a_1 = -a_0 \frac{f_1(s)}{f_0(s + 1)} \quad .$$

From the third of Equations (50), assuming $f_0(s + 2) \neq 0$, we have

$$a_2 = \frac{-a_0 f_2(s) + a_0 f_1(s)\dfrac{f_1(s + 1)}{f_0(s + 1)}}{f_0(s + 2)}$$
$$= -a_0 \left[\frac{f_0(s + 1)f_2(s) - f_1(s)f_1(s + 1)}{f_0(s + 1)f_0(s + 2)} \right] \quad ,$$

and, in general,

$$a_n = \frac{a_0 F_n(s)}{f_0(s + 1)f_0(s + 2) \cdots f_0(s + n)} \quad , \quad n = 1, 2, 3, \cdots \quad , \tag{51}$$

where $F_n(s)$,

$$F_n(s) = (-1)^n \begin{vmatrix} f_1(s) & f_0(s+1) & 0 & \cdots & 0 \\ f_2(s) & f_1(s+1) & f_0(s+2) & \cdots & 0 \\ \cdot & \cdot \cdot \cdot \cdot \cdot \cdot \cdot \cdot \cdot \cdot \cdot \cdot \cdot & & & \cdot \\ f_{n-1}(s) & f_{n-2}(s+1) & f_{n-3}(s+2) & \cdots & f_0(s+n-1) \\ f_n(s) & f_{n-1}(s+1) & f_{n-2}(s+2) & \cdots & f_1(s+n-1) \end{vmatrix}$$

is a polynomial in s and we are assuming that the denominator is unequal to zero. We also write

$$y(x, s) = \sum_{n=0}^{\infty} a_n(s)x^{n+s} \quad , \tag{52}$$

where the $a_n(s)$ are determined from Equation (51).

Now let s_1 and s_2 be the roots of the indicial equation

$$f_0(s) \equiv s(s-1) + s\alpha_0 + \beta_0 = (s - s_1)(s - s_2) = 0 \quad ;$$

that is, $f_0(s_1) = 0 = f_0(s_2)$. If s_1 and s_2 do not differ by an integer, we assert that $f_0(s_1 + p) \neq 0$, $f_0(s_2 + p) \neq 0$. For, suppose $f_0(s_1 + p) = 0$ for $p \geq 1$. Then $s_1 + p$ must equal s_1 or s_2. Since $p > 0$, $s_1 + p \neq s_1$ and since $s_1 - s_2$ is not an integer, $s_1 + p \neq s_2$. Similarly, $f_0(s_2 + p) \neq 0$ for any positive integer p. Thus

$$a_n(s_1) = \frac{a_0 F_n(s_1)}{f_0(s_1 + 1)f_0(s_1 + 2) \cdots f_0(s_1 + n)}$$

is finite, since the denominator is unequal to zero and

$$y(x, s_1) = \sum_{n=0}^{\infty} a_n(s_1)x^{n+s_1}$$

is a solution of Equation (41). Also, since $f_0(s_2 + 1)f_0(s_2 + 2) \cdots f_0(s_2 + n) \neq 0$,

$$y(x, s_2) = \sum_{n=0}^{\infty} a_n(s_2)x^{n+s_2}$$

is another distinct solution of Equation (41). By the theorem stated at the beginning of this section,

$$\sum_{n=0}^{\infty} a_n(s_1)x^n \quad \text{and} \quad \sum_{n=0}^{\infty} a_n(s_2)x^n$$

are analytic in a neighborhood of $x = 0$, the radius of convergence extending at least as far as the smaller of the radii of convergence of $p_1(x)$ and $p_2(x)$.

So we see that in the case the roots of the indicial equation differ by a number which is not an integer, we can readily obtain two distinct solutions of the differential equation. There remain the cases when $s_1 = s_2$ and when s_1 and s_2 differ by an integer.

If s_1 and s_2 are equal, then by the methods of the preceding paragraphs we can obtain *one* solution of the differential equation; namely,

$$y(x, s_1) = \sum_{n=0}^{\infty} a_n(s_1)x^{n+s_1} = x^{s_1}\sum_{n=0}^{\infty} a_n(s_1)x^n \equiv x^{s_1}\phi_1(x) \quad ,$$

where the a_n are given by Equation (51) and $\phi_1(x) \equiv \sum_{n=0}^{\infty} a_n(s_1)x^n$ is analytic in the neighborhood of the origin. But $y(x, s_2) \equiv y(x, s_1)$, since $s_1 = s_2$ and hence is not a distinct solution. To obtain the second linearly independent solution we use the following artifice.

Consider Equation (41), which we write symbolically as

$$Ly = 0 \quad ,$$

L being the differential operator,

$$L = x^2 \frac{d^2}{dx^2} + xp_1(x)\frac{d}{dx} + p_2(x)\cdot \quad .$$

Then, if we substitute $y(x, s)$ as given by Equation (52) into Equation (41), we obtain Equation (47), which upon utilizing the relations of Equation (49) reduces to

$$Ly(x, s) = a_0 f_0(s)x^s \quad .$$

Note that we are substituting $y(x, s)$ in the equation *before* letting s be a root of the indicial equation. Now

$$\frac{\partial}{\partial s}[Ly(x, s)] = a_0 f_0'(s)x^s + a_0 f_0(s)x^s \log x \tag{53}$$

$$= (s - s_1)a_0 x^s[2 + (s - s_1)\log x]$$

since $f_0(s) = (s - s_1)^2$, the roots of the indicial equation being equal. Equation (53) then implies

$$\frac{\partial}{\partial s}[Ly(x, s)]\bigg|_{s=s_1} = 0 \quad . \tag{54}$$

But

$$\frac{\partial}{\partial s}[Ly(x, s)] = L\left[\frac{\partial}{\partial s}y(x, s)\right] \quad ,$$

and by virtue of Equation (54)

$$\frac{\partial}{\partial s} y(x, s)\Big|_{s=s_1}$$

is also a solution of Equation (41). Now

$$\frac{\partial}{\partial s} y(x, s) = \frac{\partial}{\partial s} \sum_{n=0}^{\infty} a_n(s)x^{n+s}$$

$$= \log x \sum_{n=0}^{\infty} a_n(s)x^{n+s} + \sum_{n=0}^{\infty} \frac{\partial a_n}{\partial s} x^{n+s} \quad,$$

and

$$\frac{\partial}{\partial s} y(x, s)\Big|_{s=s_1} = x^{s_1}(\log x)\phi_1(x) + x^{s_1}\phi_2(x)$$

is a solution of Equation (41), where

$$\phi_2(x) = \sum_{n=0}^{\infty} \left(\frac{\partial a_n}{\partial s}\right)_{s=s_1} x^n \quad.$$

Thus the two distinct solutions of Equation (41), when the roots of the indicial equation are repeated, that is, $s_1 = s_2$, are

$$y_1(x) = x^{s_1}\phi_1(x)$$
$$y_2(x) = x^{s_1}\phi_1(x) \log x + x^{s_1}\phi_2(x) \quad,$$

where

$$\phi_1(x) = \sum_{n=0}^{\infty} a_n(s_1)x^n$$

and

$$\phi_2(x) = \sum_{n=0}^{\infty} \left(\frac{\partial a_n}{\partial s}\right)_{s=s_1} x^n$$

are analytic functions of x in the neighborhood of $x = 0$.

There remains but one case to consider, namely, when the roots s_1 and s_2 of the indicial equation differ by a nonzero integer. Let us assume without loss of generality that $s_1 > s_2$ and

$$s_1 - s_2 = \sigma \quad,$$

where σ is a positive integer.

Now $f_0(s_1) = 0$, since it is a root of the indicial equation. We assert

$$f_0(s_1 + p) \neq 0$$

for $p = 1, 2, \cdots$. For suppose $f_0(s_1 + p) = 0$. Then

$$s_1 + p = s_1 \text{ or } s_2 \quad.$$

The equation $s_1 + p = s_1$ is impossible, since $p > 0$, and the equation $s_1 + p = s_2$ is also impossible, since $s_1 > s_2$ and $p > 0$. Thus the coefficients $a_n(s_1)$ given by Equation (51) are finite and

$$y(x, s_1) = \sum_{n=0}^{\infty} a_n(s_1)x^{n+s_1}$$

is a solution of the differential equation.

However, for the second root $f_0(s_2) = 0$; but $f_0(s_2 + p)$ also equals zero when $p = \sigma$, since $s_2 + \sigma = s_1$ and $f_0(s_1) = 0$. Hence we have no guarantee that $a_n(s_2)$ with $n \geqq \sigma$ is finite. We can treat this difficulty as follows. Consider the function

$$y^*(x, s) = (s - s_2)y(x, s) = (s - s_2)\sum_{n=0}^{\infty} a_n(s)x^{n+s} = \sum_{n=0}^{\infty} b_n(s)x^{n+s} \quad.$$

Then all the coefficients $(s - s_2)a_n(s) = b_n(s)$ are finite at $s = s_2$, $b_n(s_2) = 0$ for $n = 0, 1, \cdots, \sigma - 1$, and the series $y^*(x, s_2)$ is just a constant multiple of $y(x, s_1)$, say

$$y^*(x, s_2) = Ay(x, s_1) \quad. \tag{55}$$

Hence $y^*(x, s_2)$ is not a distinct solution. To get this second linearly independent solution we proceed as in the multiple root case:

$$Ly^*(x, s) = (s - s_2)a_0 f_0(s)x^s = (s - s_2)a_0[(s - s_1)(s - s_2)]x^s \quad,$$

and

$$\frac{\partial}{\partial s}[Ly^*(x, s)] = a_0(s - s_2)x^s[(s - s_2) + 2(s - s_1) + (s - s_1)(s - s_2)\log x]$$

from which follows

$$\frac{\partial}{\partial s}[Ly^*(x, s)]\bigg|_{s=s_2} = 0 \quad.$$

Thus

$$\frac{\partial}{\partial s}y^*(x, s)\bigg|_{s=s_2}$$

is a solution of Equation (41), since

$$\frac{\partial}{\partial s}[Ly^*(x, s)] = L\left[\frac{\partial}{\partial s}y^*(x, s)\right] .$$

Now

$$y^*(x, s) = \sum_{n=0}^{\infty} b_n(s)x^{n+s} ,$$

and

$$\frac{\partial y^*}{\partial s} = \log x \sum_{n=0}^{\infty} b_n(s)x^{n+s} + \sum_{n=0}^{\infty} \frac{\partial b_n}{\partial s} x^{n+s}$$

$$= (\log x)y^*(x, s) + \sum_{n=0}^{\infty} \frac{\partial b_n}{\partial s} x^{n+s} .$$

But from Equation (55)

$$y^*(x, s_2) = Ay(x, s_1) .$$

Thus

$$\left(\frac{\partial y^*}{\partial s}\right)_{s=s_2} = (\log x)Ay(x, s_1) + \sum_{n=0}^{\infty} \left(\frac{\partial b_n}{\partial s}\right)_{s=s_2} x^{n+s_2} .$$

Summarizing, if s_1 and s_2 are roots of the indicial equation and $s_1 - s_2 = \sigma$ where σ is a positive integer, then the two linearly independent solutions of Equation (41) are

$$y_1(x) = x^{s_1}\phi_1(x)$$

$$y_2(x) = x^{s_2}\phi_2(x) + A(\log x)x^{s_1}\phi_1(x) ,$$

where

$$\phi_1(x) = \sum_{n=0}^{\infty} a_n(s_1)x^n$$

and

$$\phi_2(x) = \sum_{n=0}^{\infty} \left(\frac{\partial b_n}{\partial s}\right)_{s=s_2} x^n$$

are analytic functions of x in the neighborhood of $x = 0$; $[b_n(s) = (s - s_2)a_n(s)]$.

We have now found the solution of Equation (41) under all possible conditions. The next few sections will be devoted to the application of these techniques to various concrete problems.

6. Solution of Introductory Problem

As our first example, let us consider again our original problem, namely, Equation (35) of Section 4. It is

$$4xy'' + 2y' + y = 0 \quad . \tag{56}$$

In order to put it into the standard form to which the method of Frobenius applies, we multiply by $\dfrac{x}{4}$,

$$x^2 y'' + x \left[\frac{1}{2} \right] y' + \left[\frac{x}{4} \right] y = 0 \quad ,$$

where $1/2$ is the $p_1(x)$ of Equation (41) and $p_2(x) = x/4$. The indicial equation is

$$f_0(s) = s(s-1) + \tfrac{1}{2}s = 0 \quad ,$$

since $\alpha_0 = \tfrac{1}{2}$ and $\beta_0 = 0$. The roots of this equation are

$$s_1 = \tfrac{1}{2} \quad \text{and} \quad s_2 = 0 \quad .$$

Since they are distinct and do not differ by an integer, both solutions can be determined immediately by the use of Equations (50). We also have

$$f_1(s) = \tfrac{1}{4}$$
$$f_r(s) = 0 \quad , \quad r = 2, 3, \cdots \quad ;$$

hence the equations for the coefficients become

$$a_0 \left[s \left(s - \frac{1}{2} \right) \right] = 0$$

$$a_1 \left[(s+1) \left(s + \frac{1}{2} \right) \right] + a_0 \left[\frac{1}{4} \right] = 0$$

$$a_2 \left[(s+2) \left(s + \frac{3}{2} \right) \right] + a_1 \left[\frac{1}{4} \right] = 0$$

$$a_3 \left[(s+3) \left(s + \frac{5}{2} \right) \right] + a_2 \left[\frac{1}{4} \right] = 0$$

$$a_4 \left[(s+4) \left(s + \frac{7}{2} \right) \right] + a_3 \left[\frac{1}{4} \right] = 0$$

$$\cdot \quad \cdot \quad \cdot \quad \cdot \quad \cdot \quad \cdot \quad \cdot \quad \cdot \quad \cdot \quad \cdot \quad \cdot \quad \cdot \quad \cdot$$

or

$$a_1(s) = \frac{-a_0}{4(s+1)(s+\frac{1}{2})}$$

$$a_2(s) = \frac{a_0}{4^2(s+2)(s+1)(s+\frac{1}{2})(s+\frac{3}{2})}$$

$$a_3(s) = \frac{-a_0}{4^3(s+3)(s+2)(s+1)(s+\frac{1}{2})(s+\frac{3}{2})(s+\frac{5}{2})}$$

$$a_4(s) = \frac{a_0}{4^4(s+4)(s+3)(s+2)(s+1)(s+\frac{1}{2})(s+\frac{3}{2})(s+\frac{5}{2})(s+\frac{7}{2})}$$

$$\cdots \cdots \cdots \cdots \cdots \cdots \cdots \cdots \cdots \cdots \cdots \cdots$$

Our two distinct solutions are

$$y(x, s_1) = \sum_{n=0}^{\infty} a_n(s_1) x^{n+s_1}$$

and

$$y(x, s_2) = \sum_{n=0}^{\infty} a_n(s_2) x^{n+s_2} \quad .$$

But, with $s_1 = \frac{1}{2}$,

$$a_1(s_1) = \frac{-a_0}{3 \cdot 2}$$

$$a_2(s_1) = \frac{a_0}{5 \cdot 4 \cdot 3 \cdot 2}$$

$$a_3(s_1) = \frac{-a_0}{7 \cdot 6 \cdot 5 \cdot 4 \cdot 3 \cdot 2}$$

$$a_4(s_1) = \frac{a_0}{9 \cdot 8 \cdot 7 \cdot 6 \cdot 5 \cdot 4 \cdot 3 \cdot 2}$$

$$\cdots \cdots \cdots \cdots \cdots \cdots \cdots \cdots \cdots \cdots \cdots$$

Hence

$$y(x, \tfrac{1}{2}) = \sum_{n=0}^{\infty} a_n(\tfrac{1}{2}) x^{n+\frac{1}{2}} = a_0(\tfrac{1}{2}) \sqrt{x} \sum_{n=0}^{\infty} \frac{(-1)^n}{(2n+1)!} x^n \quad ,$$

which is identical with Equation (39).

Similarly, using the second solution $s_2 = 0$ of the indicial equation, we obtain from Equations (50)

$$a_1(0) = \frac{-a_0}{2}$$

$$a_2(0) = \frac{a_0}{4 \cdot 3 \cdot 2}$$

$$a_3(0) = \frac{-a_0}{6 \cdot 5 \cdot 4 \cdot 3 \cdot 2}$$

$$a_4(0) = \frac{a_0}{8 \cdot 7 \cdot 6 \cdot 5 \cdot 4 \cdot 3 \cdot 2}$$

. . . .

and

$$y(x, 0) = \sum_{n=0}^{\infty} a_n(0)x^{n+0} = a_0(0) \sum_{n=0}^{\infty} \frac{(-1)^n}{(2n)!} x^n \quad ,$$

which is identical with Equation (37).

7. Legendre's Equation

In certain problems that arise in electromagnetic theory it is necessary to determine the electrostatic potential u inside a given sphere S when the distribution of potential is known only on the surface of S. If the sphere is considered to have its center at the origin of a three-dimensional cartesian coordinate system, x, y, z, then it can be shown† that the potential u satisfies the partial differential equation

$$\sin \theta \frac{\partial}{\partial r} \left(r^2 \frac{\partial u}{\partial r} \right) + \frac{\partial}{\partial \theta} \left(\sin \theta \frac{\partial u}{\partial \theta} \right) = 0 \quad , \tag{57}$$

where θ is the angle measured from the z-axis, r is the distance from the origin to any point in the sphere, and we have assumed that the potential is symmetric about the z-axis. One method of solving the above partial differential equation is to assume that the solution $u = u(r, \theta)$ can be expressed as a function of r times a function of θ, say

$$u(r, \theta) = R(r)\Theta(\theta) \quad .$$

---

† Compare, for example, Miller, *Partial Differential Equations in Engineering Problems*, p. 177.

If we substitute this expression into Equation (57), there results

$$\Theta \sin \theta \frac{d}{dr} (r^2 R') + R \frac{d}{d\theta} (\Theta' \sin \theta) = 0 \quad,$$

where the primes indicate differentiation with respect to the only variable present. If we divide by $R\Theta \sin \theta$ and transpose,

$$\frac{1}{\Theta \sin \theta} \frac{d}{d\theta} (\Theta' \sin \theta) = - \frac{1}{R} \frac{d}{dr} (r^2 R') \quad . \tag{58}$$

Since the left-hand side is independent of r and the right-hand side is independent of θ, their common ratio must be a constant, say λ. Thus Equation (58) reduces to the two ordinary differential equations

$$\frac{1}{\sin \theta} \frac{d}{d\theta} (\Theta' \sin \theta) - \lambda \Theta = 0 \quad . \tag{59}$$

and

$$\frac{d}{dr} (r^2 R') + \lambda R = 0 \quad . \tag{60}$$

The first of these equations is *Legendre's equation*. If we make the substitution $x = \cos \theta$, $\Theta(\theta) = y(x)$ and introduce $-\nu(\nu + 1)$ in place of λ, then Equation (59) assumes the form

$$\frac{d}{dx} \left[(1 - x^2) \frac{dy}{dx} \right] + \nu(\nu + 1)y = 0 \quad . \tag{61}$$

This is the standard form of Legendre's equation. Carrying out the indicated differentiations, we may also write Equation (61) as

$$(1 - x^2)y'' - 2xy' + \nu(\nu + 1)y = 0 \quad , \tag{62}$$

which is the form we shall consider in our present investigations.

We see, therefore, that the solution of the original partial differential equation has been reduced to the study of two ordinary differential equations. Our main interest in this chapter, however, is to solve Equation (62) and examine the properties of its solutions. [For completeness: Equation (60) is a Cauchy equation which when $\lambda = - \nu(\nu + 1)$ has the two distinct solutions $c_1 r^\nu$ and $c_2 r^{-(\nu+1)}$ where c_1 and c_2 are constants.]

If we write Equation (62) as

$$x^2 y'' + x \left[\frac{-2x^2}{1 - x^2} \right] y' + \frac{\nu(\nu + 1)x^2}{1 - x^2} y = 0 \quad,$$

we see that it is in a form to which the Frobenius method applies. Here

$$p_1(x) = \frac{-2x^2}{1-x^2} = \sum_{m=0}^{\infty} -2x^{2m+2}$$

$$p_2(x) = \frac{\nu(\nu+1)x^2}{1-x^2} = \sum_{m=0}^{\infty} \nu(\nu+1)x^{2m+2} \quad,$$

and these series have radii of convergence one. The indicial equation is

$$f_0(s) = s(s-1)$$

whose roots are

$$s_1 = 1 \quad \text{and} \quad s_2 = 0 \quad.$$

As suggested by the general theory, we assume a solution of the form

$$y(x, s) = \sum_{n=0}^{\infty} a_n(s)x^{n+s} \quad,$$

where the $a_n(s)$ are given by Equation (50). In particular, we know that

$$y(x, s_1) = \sum_{n=0}^{\infty} a_n(s_1)x^{n+s_1}$$

is one solution of Legendre's equation. We shall obtain this solution and then further use the Frobenius method to determine the second solution (cf. Sec. 5),

$$\frac{\partial}{\partial s} y^*(x, s)\bigg|_{s=s_2} \quad, \tag{63}$$

where

$$y^*(x, s) = \sum_{n=0}^{\infty} sa_n(s)x^{n+s} \quad.$$

Let us turn, then, to the computation of the $a_n(s)$. If we use the notation of Section 5,

$$f_r(s) = -2s + \nu(\nu+1) \quad, \quad r = 2, 4, 6, \cdots$$

$$f_r(s) = 0 \quad\quad\quad\quad , \quad r = 1, 3, 5, \cdots \quad,$$

and Equations (50) of Section 5 become

$$a_0[s(s-1)] = 0$$

$$a_1[(s+1)s] = 0$$

$$a_2[(s+2)(s+1)] + a_0[\nu(\nu+1) - 2s] = 0$$

$$a_3[(s+3)(s+2)] + a_1[\nu(\nu+1) - 2(s+1)] = 0$$

$$a_4[(s+4)(s+3)] + a_2[\nu(\nu+1) - 2(s+2)] + a_0[\nu(\nu+1) - 2s] = 0$$

$$a_5[(s+5)(s+4)] + a_3[\nu(\nu+1) - 2(s+3)] + a_1[\nu(\nu+1) - 2(s+1)] = 0$$

$$a_6[(s+6)(s+5)] + a_4[\nu(\nu+1) - 2(s+4)] + a_2[\nu(\nu+1) - 2(s+2)]$$
$$+ a_0[\nu(\nu+1) - 2s] = 0$$

. . . .

When $s = s_1 = 1$, our first conclusion is that $a_1 = 0$, which implies $a_3 = 0$, which implies $a_5 = 0$, etc. That is, all the a_n with n odd are zero. The even coefficients are

$$a_2 = \frac{-a_0[\nu(\nu+1) - 2s]}{(s+1)(s+2)}$$

$$a_4 = \frac{a_0[\nu(\nu+1) - 2s]\{[\nu(\nu+1) - 2(s+2)] - (s+1)(s+2)\}}{(s+1)(s+2)(s+3)(s+4)} \tag{64}$$

$$a_6 = \frac{-a_0[\nu(\nu+1) - 2s]\{[\nu(\nu+1) - (s+2)(s+3)][\nu(\nu+1) - 2(s+4)] - [\nu(\nu+1) - 2(s+2)](s+3)(s+4) + (s+1)(s+2)(s+3)(s+4)\}}{(s+1)(s+2)(s+3)(s+4)(s+5)(s+6)}$$

. . . .

Letting $s = 1$, these coefficients become

$$a_2 = -a_0 \frac{(\nu+2)(\nu-1)}{3!}$$

$$a_4 = a_0 \frac{(\nu+4)(\nu+2)(\nu-1)(\nu-3)}{5!}$$

$$a_6 = -a_0 \frac{(\nu+6)(\nu+4)(\nu+2)(\nu-1)(\nu-3)(\nu-5)}{7!}$$

. . . . ,

and

$$y(x, 1) = a_0(1)\left[x - \frac{(\nu-1)(\nu+2)}{3!}x^3 + \frac{(\nu-3)(\nu-1)(\nu+2)(\nu+4)}{5!}x^5 \right.$$
$$\left. - \frac{(\nu-5)(\nu-3)(\nu-1)(\nu+2)(\nu+4)(\nu+6)}{7!}x^7 + \cdots \right] \tag{65}$$

is one solution of Legendre's equation.

To find the second solution we construct

$$y^*(x, s) = \sum_{n=0}^{\infty} sa_n(s)x^{n+s} \quad .$$

Then the second solution is given by Equation (63); namely,

$$\frac{\partial}{\partial s} y^*(x, s)\bigg|_{s=0} = \sum_{n=0}^{\infty} \frac{\partial}{\partial s} sa_n(s)\bigg|_{s=0} x^{n+0} + \log x \sum_{n=0}^{\infty} sa_n(s)\bigg|_{s=0} x^{n+0} \quad .$$

Now the $a_n(s)$ terms [Equation (64)] have no s factor in their denominators; hence

$$sa_n(s)\bigg|_{s=0} = 0 \quad .$$

So here is an example in which the roots of the indicial equation differ by an integer, but the log term is not present. Also

$$\frac{\partial}{\partial s} sa_n(s) = s\frac{\partial}{\partial s} a_n + a_n(s) \quad ,$$

and, evaluated at $s = 0$,

$$\frac{\partial}{\partial s} sa_n(s)\bigg|_{s=0} = a_n(0) \quad .$$

The second distinct solution $\frac{\partial}{\partial s} y^*(x, 0)$ of Legendre's equation is therefore given by

$$\frac{\partial}{\partial s} y^*(x, 0) = \sum_{n=0}^{\infty} a_n(0)x^n \quad .$$

The $a_n(0)$ coefficients can be determined from Equation (64) by setting s equal to zero in these expressions. They are

$$a_2(0) = - a_0 \frac{\nu(\nu + 1)}{2!}$$

$$a_4(0) = a_0 \frac{(\nu + 3)(\nu + 1)(\nu)(\nu - 2)}{4!}$$

$$a_6(0) = - a_0 \frac{(\nu + 5)(\nu + 3)(\nu + 1)(\nu)(\nu - 2)(\nu - 4)}{6!}$$

$$\cdot \quad \cdot \quad \cdot \quad \cdot \quad \cdot \quad \cdot \quad \cdot \quad \cdot \quad \cdot \quad \cdot \quad \cdot \quad \cdot \quad \cdot \quad \cdot \quad \cdot \quad \cdot \quad \cdot \quad \cdot \quad \cdot \quad ,$$

and the second distinct solution of Legendre's equation is given by

$$\frac{\partial}{\partial s} y^*(x, 0) = a_0(0) \left[1 - \frac{\nu(\nu + 1)}{2!} x^2 + \frac{(\nu - 2)(\nu)(\nu + 1)(\nu + 3)}{4!} x^4 \right.$$
$$\left. - \frac{(\nu - 4)(\nu - 2)(\nu)(\nu + 1)(\nu + 3)(\nu + 5)}{6!} x^6 + \cdots \right] \quad . \quad (66)$$

By our general existence theorem, or by the Ratio Test, we see that Equations (65) and (66) converge for all x, $|x| < 1$, that is, the radius of convergence is one, the same as that of $p_1(x)$ and $p_2(x)$.

There are a number of interesting results associated with Equations (65) and (66). We note that if ν is a positive odd integer, then $y(x, 1)$ is a finite series, since all the terms after the $\frac{\nu + 1}{2}$ vanish; and if ν is a positive even integer, $\frac{\partial}{\partial s} y^*(x, 0)$ is a finite series, since all terms after the $\frac{\nu + 2}{2}$ vanish. Similar remarks apply if ν is a negative integer, with the roles of y and $\frac{\partial y^*}{\partial s}$ reversed. Hence, if ν is an integer, one of $y(x, 1)$ and $\frac{\partial}{\partial x} y^*(x, 0)$ is a finite series, that is, a polynomial. Of course, in this special case, these series have infinite radii of convergence.

Let us now assume for the remainder of this section that ν *is* an integer. Then, when suitable values are assigned to $a_0(1)$ and $a_0(0)$, the $y(x, 1)$ and $\frac{\partial}{\partial s} y^*(x, 0)$ functions become the *Legendre polynomials*. [When ν is odd we use $y(x, 1)$, and when ν is even we use $\frac{\partial}{\partial s} y^*(x, 0)$.] The appropriate choice, when ν is odd, say $\nu = 2N + 1$, is to set

$$a_0(1) = \frac{(- 1)^N (2N + 1)!}{(N!)^2 2^{2N}} \quad .$$

Then $y(x, 1)$ becomes the *Legendre polynomial $P_{2N+1}(x)$*,

$$P_{2N+1}(x) = \sum_{\alpha=0}^{N} \frac{(- 1)^{N+\alpha} (2N + 2\alpha + 1)!}{(N - \alpha)!(N + \alpha)!(2\alpha + 1)! 2^{2N}} x^{2\alpha+1} \quad . \quad (67)$$

When ν is even, say $\nu = 2N$, we set

$$a_0(0) = \frac{(- 1)^N (2N)!}{(N!)^2 2^{2N}} \quad ,$$

and $\dfrac{\partial}{\partial s} y^*(x, 0)$ becomes the *Legendre polynomial* $P_{2N}(x)$,

$$P_{2N}(x) = \sum_{\alpha=0}^{N} \frac{(-1)^{N+\alpha}(2N+2\alpha)!}{(N-\alpha)!(N+\alpha)!(2\alpha)!2^{2N}} x^{2\alpha} \quad . \tag{68}$$

Hence for ν, even or odd, we have a Legendre polynomial. The first few are

$$P_0(x) = 1$$

$$P_1(x) = x$$

$$P_2(x) = \frac{3}{2} x^2 - \frac{1}{2}$$

$$P_3(x) = \frac{5}{2} x^3 - \frac{3}{2} x \tag{69}$$

$$P_4(x) = \frac{35}{8} x^4 - \frac{15}{4} x^2 + \frac{3}{8}$$

$$P_5(x) = \frac{63}{8} x^5 - \frac{35}{4} x^3 + \frac{15}{8} x \quad .$$

There exist many formulas involving Legendre functions, some of which are mentioned in the Exercises at the end of this section. Perhaps one of the most useful is *Rodrigues' formula*:

$$P_n(x) = \frac{1}{2^n n!} \frac{d^n}{dx^n} (x^2 - 1)^n \quad , \tag{70}$$

which we shall now establish.

By the binomial theorem

$$(x^2 - 1)^n = \sum_{k=0}^{n} \binom{n}{k} (-1)^{n-k} x^{2k} \quad ,$$

where $\dbinom{n}{k} = \dfrac{n!}{k!(n-k)!}$ is the binomial coefficient. Also, from elementary calculus,

$$\frac{d^n}{dx^n} x^{2k} = 0 \quad \text{if} \quad k < \frac{n}{2}$$

$$\frac{d^n}{dx^n} x^{2k} = (2k)(2k-1)(2k-2)\cdots(2k-n+1)x^{2k-n} \quad \text{if} \quad k \geq \frac{n}{2} \quad .$$

Let us assume that n is odd, say $n = 2N + 1$. Then define $R_{2N+1}(x)$ by:

$$R_{2N+1}(x) = \frac{1}{2^{2N+1}(2N+1)!} \frac{d^{2N+1}}{dx^{2N+1}} (x^2 - 1)^{2N+1}$$

$$= \frac{1}{2^{2N+1}(2N+1)!} \frac{d^{2N+1}}{dx^{2N+1}} \sum_{k=0}^{2N+1} \binom{2N+1}{k} (-1)^{2N+1-k} x^{2k}$$

$$= \frac{1}{2^{2N+1}(2N+1)!} \sum_{k=N+1}^{2N+1} \binom{2N+1}{k} (-1)^{k+1}(2k)(2k-1) \cdots$$
$$(2k - 2N)x^{2k-2N-1} \quad .$$

Now, if we change the dummy variable of summation k by setting

$$\alpha = k - N - 1 \quad ,$$

then the above formula becomes

$$R_{2N+1}(x) = \frac{1}{2^{2N+1}(2N+1)!} \sum_{\alpha=0}^{N} \frac{(2N+1)!(-1)^{\alpha+N}(2\alpha+2N+2)!}{(\alpha+N+1)!(N-\alpha)!\,(2\alpha+1)!} x^{2\alpha+1} \quad ,$$

and, if we write

$$2^{2N+1}(\alpha + N + 1)! = 2^{2N}(2\alpha + 2N + 2)(\alpha + N)!$$

in the denominator and

$$(2\alpha + 2N + 2)! = (2\alpha + 2N + 2)(2\alpha + 2N + 1)!$$

in the numerator, the expression for $R_{2N+1}(x)$ becomes identical with the Legendre polynomial $P_{2N+1}(x)$ as given by Equation (67). A similar analysis will establish Rodrigues' formula for n even.

EXERCISES

1. A set of functions $\phi_1(x)$, $\phi_2(x)$, $\phi_3(x)$, $\cdots$ is said to be *orthogonal* in the interval $[a, b]$ with respect to a *weighting function* $r(x) > 0$ if

$$\int_a^b r(x)\phi_n(x)\phi_m(x)dx \neq 0 \quad \text{if} \quad n = m$$
$$= 0 \quad \text{if} \quad n \neq m \quad .$$

Show that the Legendre polynomials are orthogonal in the interval $[-1, 1]$ with respect to the weighting function $r(x) \equiv 1$. That is, prove

$$\int_{-1}^{1} P_n(x)P_m(x)dx \neq 0 \quad \text{if} \quad n = m$$
$$= 0 \quad \text{if} \quad n \neq m \quad .$$

One can show, by an application of Rodrigues' formula, that

$$\int_{-1}^{1} P_n^2(x)dx = \frac{2}{2n+1} \quad \cdot\dagger$$

2. An identity involving only a finite number of functions from a set of functions is called a *recursion formula*. Show that the Legendre polynomials satisfy the following recursion formulas:

(i) $(n+1)P_{n+1}(x) = (2n+1)xP_n(x) - nP_{n-1}(x)$

(ii) $P'_{n+1}(x) - P'_{n-1}(x) = (2n+1)P_n(x)$.

3. Using Rodrigues' formula, establish the following integral relation:

$$\int_{-1}^{1} f(x)P_n(x)dx = \frac{(-1)^n}{2^n n!}\int_{-1}^{1}(x^2-1)^n \frac{d^n}{dx^n}f(x)dx \quad .$$

From this formula deduce the equations

$$\int_0^1 x^m P_0(x)dx = \frac{1}{m+1}$$

$$\int_0^1 x^m P_1(x)dx = \frac{1}{m+2}$$

$$\int_0^1 x^m P_n(x)dx = \frac{m(m-1)\cdots(m-n+2)}{(m+n+1)(m+n-1)\cdots(m-n+3)} \quad , \quad n \geqq 2 \quad .$$

4. Find the polynomial solutions of

$$(1-x^2)y'' - xy' + n^2 y = 0 \quad ,$$

where n is an integer. These polynomials, when suitably normalized (that is, multiplied by an appropriate constant), are called the *Tschebyscheff polynomials*, $T_n(x)$. They can also be represented by

$$T_n(x) = \frac{(-1)^n 2^n n!\sqrt{1-x^2}}{(2n)!}\frac{d^n}{dx^n}\frac{(1-x^2)^n}{\sqrt{1-x^2}} \quad ,$$

satisfy the *orthogonality conditions*,

$$\int_{-1}^{1}\frac{T_n(x)T_m(x)}{\sqrt{1-x^2}}dx = \frac{\pi}{2} \quad , \quad n=m \neq 0$$

$$= \pi \quad , \quad n=m=0$$

$$= 0 \quad , \quad n \neq m$$

---

† Compare also, Miller, *op. cit.*, p. 195.

and are related by the *recursion formula*

$$T_{n+1}(x) = 2xT_n(x) - T_{n-1}(x) \quad .$$

The first few Tschebyscheff polynomials are

$$T_0(x) = 1$$
$$T_1(x) = x$$
$$T_2(x) = 2x^2 - 1$$
$$T_3(x) = 4x^3 - 3x$$
$$T_4(x) = 8x^4 - 8x^2 + 1$$
$$T_5(x) = 16x^5 - 20x^3 + 5x \quad .$$

8. Hermite's Equation

In the last section we showed that the Legendre polynomials could be represented by Rodrigues' formula

$$P_n(x) = \frac{1}{2^n n!} \frac{d^n}{dx^n} (x^2 - 1)^n \quad .$$

One could also use the right-hand side of the above equation as the *definition* of the Legendre polynomials. It could then be shown that they satisfy Legendre's equation

$$(1 - x^2)P_n''(x) - 2xP_n'(x) + n(n + 1)P_n(x) = 0 \quad .$$

We shall use this alternate point of view in the present section. The *Hermite polynomials*, $H_n(x)$, which frequently occur in the theory of probability (cf. Chap. 7), can be defined by the expression

$$H_n(x) = e^{x^2/2} \frac{d^n}{dx^n} e^{-x^2/2} \quad , \quad n = 0, 1, 2, \cdots . \tag{71}$$

We shall show that they satisfy the differential equation

$$y'' - xy' + ny = 0 \quad , \tag{72}$$

where n is an integer.

To deduce Hermite's equation, Equation (72), we first establish the recursion formula

$$H_n'(x) = -nH_{n-1}(x) \quad ; \tag{73}$$

for, from Equation (71),

$$H_n'(x) = e^{x^2/2} \frac{d^{n+1}}{dx^{n+1}} e^{-x^2/2} + x e^{x^2/2} \frac{d^n}{dx^n} e^{-x^2/2}$$

$$= e^{x^2/2} \frac{d^n}{dx^n} [-xe^{-x^2/2}] + x H_n(x) \quad.$$

Now, applying the well-known differentiation formula

$$\frac{d^n}{dx^n} [f(x)g(x)] = \sum_{k=0}^{n} \binom{n}{k} \frac{d^k}{dx^k} f(x) \frac{d^{n-k}}{dx^{n-k}} g(x)$$

with $f(x) = x$ and

$$g(x) = e^{-x^2/2} \quad,$$

we obtain

$$H_n'(x) = -e^{x^2/2} \left[x \frac{d^n}{dx^n} e^{-x^2/2} + n \frac{d^{n-1}}{dx^{n-1}} e^{-x^2/2} \right] + x H_n(x)$$

or

$$H_n'(x) = -xH_n(x) - nH_{n-1}(x) + xH_n(x)$$
$$= -nH_{n-1}(x) \quad,$$

which proves Equation (73).

To derive Hermite's equation, differentiate Equation (73),

$$H_n''(x) = -nH_{n-1}'(x) = -n\frac{d}{dx} \left[e^{x^2/2} \frac{d^{n-1}}{dx^{n-1}} e^{-x^2/2} \right]$$

$$= -n[xH_{n-1}(x) + H_n(x)] \quad,$$

and again use Equation (73) to replace $nH_{n-1}(x)$ by $-H_n'(x)$, thus obtaining

$$H_n''(x) = xH_n'(x) - nH_n(x)$$

or

$$H_n''(x) - xH_n'(x) + nH_n(x) = 0 \quad. \tag{74}$$

Let us now consider Hermite's equation

$$y'' - xy' + vy = 0 \tag{75}$$

simply as a differential equation and attempt to solve it by the Frobenius method. First, we write it in the standard form,

$$x^2 y'' + x[-x^2]y' + [vx^2]y = 0 \quad; \tag{76}$$

note that the indicial equation $f_0(s)$ is

$$f_0(s) = s(s-1)$$

and that

$$f_1(s) = 0$$
$$f_2(s) = -s + \nu$$
$$f_r(s) = 0 \quad , \quad r \geq 3 \quad .$$

Hence by Equations (50)

$$a_0[s(s-1)] = 0$$
$$a_1[(s+1)s] = 0$$
$$a_2[(s+2)(s+1)] + a_0[\nu - s] = 0$$
$$a_3[(s+3)(s+2)] + a_1[\nu - s - 1] = 0$$
$$a_4[(s+4)(s+3)] + a_2[\nu - s - 2] = 0$$
$$a_5[(s+5)(s+4)] + a_3[\nu - s - 3] = 0$$
$$a_6[(s+6)(s+5)] + a_4[\nu - s - 4] = 0$$

· · · · · · · · · · · · · · · · · · ·

The above equations imply that all the a_n with n odd are zero, while the even coefficients are given by

$$a_2 = -a_0 \frac{(\nu - s)}{(s+2)(s+1)}$$

$$a_4 = a_0 \frac{(\nu - s - 2)(\nu - s)}{(s+4)(s+3)(s+2)(s+1)} \tag{77}$$

$$a_6 = -a_0 \frac{(\nu - s - 4)(\nu - s - 2)(\nu - s)}{(s+6)(s+5)(s+4)(s+3)(s+2)(s+1)}$$

· ·

Since the roots of the indicial equation are

$$s_1 = 1 \quad \text{and} \quad s_2 = 0 \quad ,$$

the function

$$y(x, s_1) = \sum_{n=0}^{\infty} a_n(s_1) x^{n+s_1} = \sum_{n=0}^{\infty} a_n(1) x^{n+1}$$

is a solution of Equation (76). From Equation (77) we conclude that

$$a_2(1) = - a_0 \frac{(\nu - 1)}{3!}$$

$$a_4(1) = a_0 \frac{(\nu - 1)(\nu - 3)}{5!}$$

$$a_6(1) = - a_0 \frac{(\nu - 1)(\nu - 3)(\nu - 5)}{7!}$$

. . . .

and

$$y(x, 1) = a_0(1) \left[x + \sum_{n=1}^{\infty} (- 1)^n \frac{(\nu - 1)(\nu - 3) \cdots (\nu - 2n + 1)}{(2n + 1)!} x^{2n+1} \right] \quad (78)$$

is a solution of Hermite's equation. It is easy to see that $y(x, 1)$ has an infinite radius of convergence.

Since $s_1 - s_2$ is equal to a nonzero integer and $s_2 = 0$, we must form

$$y^*(x, s) = sy(x, s) = \sum_{n=0}^{\infty} sa_n(s)x^{n+s}$$

in order to find the second distinct solution of Equation (76), which is

$$\left(\frac{\partial y^*}{\partial s} \right)_{s=0} = \sum_{n=0}^{\infty} a_n(0)x^{n+0} \quad .$$

As in the case of Legendre's equation, thé log term again disappears. The coefficients $a_n(0)$ are obtained from Equation (77) as

$$a_2(0) = - a_0 \frac{\nu}{2!}$$

$$a_4(0) = a_0 \frac{\nu(\nu - 2)}{4!}$$

$$a_6(0) = - a_0 \frac{\nu(\nu - 2)(\nu - 4)}{6!}$$

. . . . ,

and

$$\left(\frac{\partial y^*}{\partial s} \right)_{s=0} = a_0(0) \left[1 + \sum_{n=1}^{\infty} (- 1)^n \frac{\nu(\nu - 2) \cdots (\nu - 2n + 2)}{(2n)!} x^{2n} \right] \quad (79)$$

is the second distinct solution of Hermite's equation. It also has an infinite radius of convergence.

If ν is a positive integer, $y(x, 1)$ becomes a polynomial if ν is odd and $\frac{\partial}{\partial s} y^*(x, 0)$ becomes a polynomial if ν is even. Suppose, then, that $\nu = 2N + 1$ is an odd integer. Then from Equation (78),

$$
\begin{aligned}
y(x, 1) &= a_0(1) \left[x + \sum_{n=1}^{N} (-1)^n \frac{(2N)(2N - 2) \cdots (2N - 2n + 2)}{(2n + 1)!} x^{2n+1} \right] \\
&= a_0(1) \left[x + \sum_{n=1}^{N} (-1)^n \frac{2^n N(N - 1) \cdots (N - n + 1)}{(2n + 1)!} x^{2n+1} \right] \\
&= a_0(1) \sum_{n=0}^{N} \frac{(-1)^n 2^n N!}{(2n + 1)!(N - n)!} x^{2n+1} \quad .
\end{aligned}
\tag{80}
$$

On the other hand, if ν is an even integer, say $\nu = 2N$, then Equation (79) becomes

$$
\begin{aligned}
\frac{\partial}{\partial s} y^*(x, 0) &= a_0(0) \left[1 + \sum_{n=1}^{N} (-1)^n \frac{2N(2N - 2) \cdots (2N - 2n + 2)}{(2n)!} x^{2n} \right] \\
&= a_0(0) \left[1 + \sum_{n=1}^{N} \frac{(-1)^n 2^n N(N - 1) \cdots (N - n + 1)}{(2n)!} x^{2n} \right] \\
&= a_0(0) \sum_{n=0}^{N} \frac{(-1)^n 2^n N!}{(2n)!(N - n)!} x^{2n} \quad .
\end{aligned}
\tag{81}
$$

If $a_0(1)$ and $a_0(0)$ are assigned appropriate values, then Equations (80) and (81) become the Hermite polynomials. The correct choice is

$$
a_0(1) = (-1)^{N+1} \frac{(2N + 1)!}{N! 2^N}
$$

and

$$
a_0(0) = (-1)^N \frac{(2N)!}{N! 2^N} \quad .
$$

Then Equations (80) and (81) become the Hermite polynomials of odd and even order, respectively; namely,

$$
H_{2N+1}(x) = \sum_{n=0}^{N} \frac{(-1)^{N+1+n}(2N + 1)!}{(N - n)!(2n + 1)!} \frac{x^{2n+1}}{2^{N-n}} \quad ,
$$

$$
H_{2N}(x) = \sum_{n=0}^{N} \frac{(-1)^{N+n}(2N)!}{(N - n)!(2n)!} \frac{x^{2n}}{2^{N-n}} \quad .
$$

EXERCISES

1. Show that the Hermite polynomials satisfy the orthogonality conditions

$$\int_{-\infty}^{\infty} e^{-x^2/2} H_n(x) H_m(x) dx = n! \sqrt{2\pi} \quad , \quad n = m$$
$$= 0 \qquad , \quad n \neq m \quad .$$

HINT: Proceed by induction, using the fact that $\int_{-\infty}^{\infty} e^{-x^2/2} dx = \sqrt{2\pi}$ (cf. Chap. 2.)

2. Prove that

$$H_{n+1}(x) + xH_n(x) + nH_{n-1}(x) = 0 \quad .$$

3. Find the polynomial solutions of

$$xy'' + (1 - x)y' + ny = 0 \quad ,$$

where n is an integer. When suitably normalized, these solutions are called the *Laguerre polynomials*, $L_n(x)$. They can also be represented by

$$L_n(x) = \frac{e^x}{n!} \frac{d^n}{dx^n} (x^n e^{-x}) \quad ,$$

satisfy the orthogonality conditions

$$\int_0^{\infty} e^{-x} L_n(x) L_m(x) dx = 1 \quad , \quad n = m$$
$$= 0 \quad , \quad n \neq m \quad ,$$

and are related by the recursion formula

$$(n + 1)L_{n+1}(x) = (2n + 1 - x)L_n(x) - nL_{n-1}(x) \quad .$$

The first few Laguerre polynomials are

$$L_0(x) = 1$$
$$L_1(x) = 1 - x$$
$$L_2(x) = 1 - 2x + \frac{x^2}{2}$$
$$L_3(x) = 1 - 3x + \frac{3}{2}x^2 - \frac{x^3}{6}$$

$$L_4(x) = 1 - 4x + 3x^2 - \frac{2}{3}x^3 + \frac{x^4}{24}$$

$$L_5(x) = 1 - 5x + 5x^2 - \frac{5}{3}x^3 + \frac{5}{24}x^4 - \frac{x^5}{120} \quad .$$

9. Bessel's Equation with Purely Imaginary Argument

An integral that occurs in the mathematical theory of probability and stochastic processes (cf. Chap. 7) is

$$K(z) = \int_0^\infty e^{-z\cosh\theta}\, d\theta \quad , \quad z > 0 \quad .$$

This function is the solution of a differential equation which we shall now derive. If we differentiate $K(z)$ with respect to z, and then integrate by parts,

$$K'(z) = -\int_0^\infty \cosh\theta\, e^{-z\cosh\theta}\, d\theta$$

$$= -e^{-z\cosh\theta}\sinh\theta\,\Big|_0^\infty - z\int_0^\infty \sinh^2\theta\, e^{-z\cosh\theta}\, d\theta \quad .$$

Since z is assumed positive, $e^{-z\cosh\theta}\sinh\theta$ vanishes at $\theta = \infty$ as well as $\theta = 0$. The second derivative of $K(z)$ is

$$K''(z) = \int_0^\infty \cosh^2\theta\, e^{-z\cosh\theta}\, d\theta \quad ,$$

and

$$zK''(z) + K'(z) = z\int_0^\infty (\cosh^2\theta - \sinh^2\theta)e^{-z\cosh\theta} d\theta$$

$$= z\int_0^\infty e^{-z\cosh\theta} d\theta = zK(z) \quad .$$

Hence $K(z)$ satisfies the differential equation

$$zK''(z) + K'(z) - zK(z) = 0 \quad . \tag{82}$$

If we multiply by z, Equation (82) becomes

$$z^2K''(z) + zK'(z) - z^2K(z) = 0 \quad ,$$

which is the standard form of *Bessel's equation with purely imaginary argument of order zero*. The reason for calling this equation by the preceding imposing title is the following. Bessel's equation, which we shall study in the next section is

$$z^2 \frac{d^2u}{dz^2} + z \frac{du}{dz} + (z^2 - v^2)u = 0 \quad , \tag{83}$$

where v is a number, not necessarily an integer. For each value of v we have two distinct solutions of Equation (83) which, of course, depend on v. So Equation (83) is called *Bessel's equation of order v*. Now, if we make the substitution $z = jx$ and let $u(z) = y(x)$, then Equation (83) becomes

$$x^2 \frac{d^2y}{dx^2} + x \frac{dy}{dx} + (- x^2 - v^2)y = 0$$

or

$$x^2 y'' + xy' - (x^2 + v^2)y = 0 \quad , \tag{84}$$

which is called, for reasons which are now apparent, Bessel's equation with purely imaginary argument of order v. If, in particular, $v = 0$, Equation (84) reduces to

$$x^2 y'' + xy' - x^2 y = 0 \quad , \tag{85}$$

which is of order zero. This is our Equation (82).

To solve Equation (85) we proceed as usual by the method of Frobenius. The indicial equation is

$$f_0(s) = s(s - 1) + s = s^2 \quad ,$$

whose roots are $s_1 = s_2 = 0$, and

$$f_1(s) = 0$$
$$f_2(s) = - 1$$
$$f_r(s) = 0 \quad , \quad r \geq 3 \quad .$$

Assuming a solution of the form

$$y(x, s) = \sum_{n=0}^{\infty} a_n(s)x^{n+s} \quad , \tag{86}$$

we determine the $a_n(s)$ by Equations (50) to be

$$a_0 s^2 = 0$$
$$a_1(s + 1)^2 = 0$$
$$a_2(s + 2)^2 - a_0 = 0$$

$$a_3(s + 3)^2 - a_1 = 0$$

$$a_4(s + 4)^2 - a_2 = 0$$

$$a_5(s + 5)^2 - a_3 = 0$$

$$a_6(s + 6)^2 - a_4 = 0$$

$$\cdot \quad \cdot \quad \cdot \quad \cdot \quad \cdot \quad \cdot \quad \cdot \quad \cdot \quad .$$

All the a_n with n odd are zero, and the a_n with n even are given by

$$a_2 = \frac{a_0}{(s + 2)^2}$$

$$a_4 = \frac{a_0}{(s + 2)^2(s + 4)^2}$$

$$a_6 = \frac{a_0}{(s + 2)^2(s + 4)^2(s + 6)^2}$$

$$\cdot \quad \cdot \quad \cdot \quad \cdot \quad \cdot \quad \cdot \quad \cdot \quad \cdot \quad \cdot \quad \cdot \quad \cdot \quad .$$

If we substitute these expressions into Equation (86) with $s = 0$,

$$y(x, 0) = \sum_{n=0}^{\infty} a_n(0)x^{n+0} = a_0 \sum_{n=0}^{\infty} \frac{1}{2^2 \cdot 4^2 \cdots (2n)^2} x^{2n}$$

$$= a_0 \sum_{n=0}^{\infty} \frac{x^{2n}}{2^{2n}(n!)^2} \quad .$$

Now, if we let $a_0 = 1$, then the function $y(x, 0)$ is called the *Bessel function of the first kind of order zero* and is written

$$I_0(x) = \sum_{n=0}^{\infty} \frac{x^{2n}}{2^{2n}(n!)^2} \quad .$$

It is a tabulated function† and converges for all x.

The second distinct solution of Equation (86) is obtained from the expression

$$\frac{\partial}{\partial s} y(x, s) \Big|_{s=0} = y(x, 0) \log x + \sum_{n=0}^{\infty} \left(\frac{\partial a_n}{\partial s}\right)_{s=0} x^n$$

in accordance with the formula derived for the solution of differential equations in the case the roots of the indicial equation are repeated.

---

† Compare, for example, C.R.C., *Standard Mathematical Tables*, p. 303.

We see that

$$\frac{\partial}{\partial s}\, a_{2n+1} = 0 \quad ,$$

since all the a_p with p odd are zero, and

$$\left(\frac{\partial a_{2n}}{\partial s}\right)_{s=0} = \frac{-a_0}{2^{2n}(n!)^2}\left[1 + \frac{1}{2} + \frac{1}{3} + \cdots + \frac{1}{n}\right] \quad , \quad n = 1, 2, \cdots .$$

Hence the second solution of Bessel's equation with purely imaginary argument is

$$\frac{\partial}{\partial s}\, y(x, s)\bigg|_{s=0} = a_0 I_0(x) \log x - a_0 \sum_{n=1}^{\infty} \frac{x^{2n}}{2^{2n}(n!)^2}\left(1 + \frac{1}{2} + \frac{1}{3} + \cdots + \frac{1}{n}\right) \quad . \quad (87)$$

Since Equation (87) is a solution distinct from a multiple of $I_0(x)$, we can add $cI_0(x)$ (where c is any constant) to $\frac{\partial}{\partial s}\, y(x, s)\bigg|_{s=0}$ and still have a distinct solution. We shall use this device in order to define $K_0(x)$, which is a solution of Equation (85) distinct from $I_0(x)$. The function $K_0(x)$ is also a tabulated function† and is known as the *Bessel function of the second kind of order zero*.

If we define ψ by the equation

$$\psi(n + 1) = 1 + \frac{1}{2} + \cdots + \frac{1}{n} - \gamma \quad , \quad n \geq 1$$

$$\psi(1) = -\gamma \quad , \tag{88}$$

where γ is Euler's constant (cf. Chap. 2), then Equation (87) may be written as

$$\frac{\partial}{\partial s}\, y(x, 0) = a_0 I_0(x) \log x - a_0 \sum_{n=0}^{\infty} \frac{x^{2n}}{2^{2n}(n!)^2}\, [\psi(n + 1) + \gamma] \quad ,$$

or, on letting $a_0 = -1$, we obtain

$$\frac{\partial}{\partial s}\, y(x, 0) = -I_0(x) \log x + \gamma \sum_{n=0}^{\infty} \frac{x^{2n}}{2^{2n}(n!)^2} + \sum_{n=0}^{\infty} \frac{x^{2n}}{2^{2n}(n!)^2}\, \psi(n + 1)$$

$$= -I_0(x) \log x + \gamma I_0(x) + \sum_{n=0}^{\infty} \frac{x^{2n}}{2^{2n}(n!)^2}\, \psi(n + 1) \quad .$$

Now add $(\log 2 - \gamma)I_0(x)$ to the above expression. It is still a solution of Equation (86) distinct from $I_0(x)$. We shall call it $K_0(x)$.

$$K_0(x) = -I_0(x) \log x + I_0(x) \log 2 + \sum_{n=0}^{\infty} \frac{x^{2n}}{2^{2n}(n!)^2}\, \psi(n + 1) \quad ,$$

---

† See, for example, Watson, *A Treatise on the Theory of Bessel Functions*.

or

$$K_0(x) = -I_0(x)\log\frac{x}{2} + \sum_{n=0}^{\infty}\frac{\psi(n+1)}{(n!)^2}\left(\frac{x}{2}\right)^{2n} \quad . \tag{89}$$

The tabulated functions $I_0(x)$ and $K_0(x)$ are thus two distinct solutions of Bessel's equation with purely imaginary argument of order zero. Since the

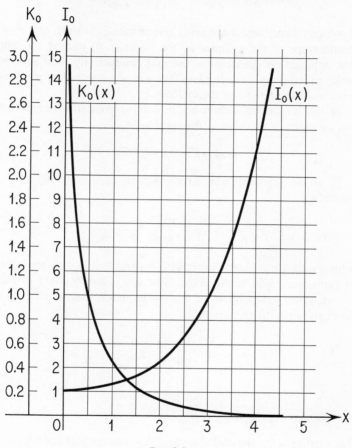

Fig. 3.3

original function $K(x)$, with which we started, satisfies Equation (85), it must be a linear combination of I_0 and K_0; that is,

$$K(x) = C_1 I_0(x) + C_2 K_0(x) \quad .$$

It can be shown that $C_1 = 0$ and $C_2 = 1$; that is,

$$K(x) \equiv K_0(x) \quad .$$

Graphs of $I_0(x)$ and $K_0(x)$ are shown in Figure 3.3.

10. Bessel's Equation

If the temperature distribution in a cylinder is given at time $t = 0$, then the temperature u at any time t satisfies the partial differential equation†

$$\frac{\partial^2 u}{\partial r^2} + \frac{1}{r}\frac{\partial u}{\partial r} + \frac{1}{r^2}\frac{\partial^2 u}{\partial \theta^2} = \frac{1}{k}\frac{\partial u}{\partial t} \ . \tag{90}$$

In the above equation r and θ are polar coordinates, t is time, and $u = u(r, \theta, t)$ is the temperature of the cylinder at the point (r, θ) and at the time t. The constant k depends on the density, thermal conductivity, and specific heat of the material making up the cylinder. (We are assuming that the temperature is independent of the height of the cylinder.)

One of the important techniques in solving partial differential equations consists in assuming a solution in the form

$$u(r, \theta, t) = R(r)\Theta(\theta)T(t)$$

(cf. Sec. 7). If we substitute this expression in Equation (90) and rearrange terms, we obtain

$$r^2\frac{R''}{R} + r\frac{R'}{R} - \frac{r^2}{k}\frac{T'}{T} = -\frac{\Theta''}{\Theta} \ ,$$

where primes indicate differentiation with respect to the only variable present. Since the right-hand side of the above equation is independent of t and r and the left-hand side is independent of θ, their common ratio must be a constant, say α^2. This gives rise to the equations

$$\Theta'' + \alpha^2\Theta = 0 \tag{91}$$

and

$$\frac{R''}{R} + \frac{1}{r}\frac{R'}{R} - \frac{\alpha^2}{r^2} = \frac{1}{k}\frac{T'}{T} \ .$$

Again this further separation of the variables implies that the above ratio is a constant, say $-\beta^2$. We then obtain the two additional ordinary differential equations

$$T' + k\beta^2 T = 0 \tag{92}$$

and

$$r^2 R'' + rR' + (\beta^2 r^2 - \alpha^2)R = 0 \ . \tag{93}$$

---

† Compare Miller, *op. cit.*

Hence the first step toward solving Equation (90) is to solve the three ordinary differential equations, Equations (91), (92), and (93). Equations (91) and (92) are trivial to solve. If we make the change of variables $s = \beta r$ in Equation (93), this equation becomes

$$s^2 \frac{d^2R}{ds^2} + s \frac{dR}{ds} + (s^2 - \alpha^2)R = 0 \quad . \tag{94}$$

Equation (94) is the standard form of *Bessel's equation of order* α.

Bessel equations arise in various other boundary value problems in the theory of partial differential equations. They also arise in certain problems in ordinary differential equations. For example, consider the problem of the buckling of a thin strut under its own weight. If we consider a thin vertical strut (cf. Fig. 3.4), then it is shown in Salvadori and Schwarz† that the equation of the deflection curve is

$$\frac{d^2u}{dz^2} + k^2 z u = 0 \quad , \tag{95}$$

where $u = y'$, $z = L - x$, and k^2 is a constant depending on the weight and flexural rigidity of the bar. Equation (95) is essentially a Bessel equation, although its form is not the standard one. To reduce Equation (95) to standard form, set

$$z = s^{\frac{2}{3}} \quad .$$

Then we obtain

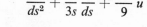

Fig. 3.4

$$\frac{d^2u}{ds^2} + \frac{1}{3s} \frac{du}{ds} + \frac{4k^2}{9} u = 0 \quad .$$

Making the further substitution

$$u(s) = s^{\frac{1}{3}} v(s)$$

reduces Equation (95) to

$$s^2 \frac{d^2v}{ds^2} + s \frac{dv}{ds} + \left(\frac{4k^2}{9} s^2 - \frac{1}{9} \right) v = 0 \quad .$$

---

† Salvadori and Schwarz, *op. cit.*, p. 271.

The final trivial transformation

$$t = \tfrac{2}{3} ks$$

yields the standard form of *Bessel's equation of order* $\tfrac{1}{3}$,

$$t^2 \frac{d^2v}{dt^2} + t \frac{dv}{dt} + \left[t^2 - \left(\frac{1}{3}\right)^2\right] v = 0 \quad . \tag{96}$$

Two linearly independent solutions of Bessel's equation of order ν,

$$x^2 y'' + x y' + (x^2 - \nu^2) y = 0 \quad , \tag{97}$$

can be found by the method of Frobenius. One of these is

$$J_\nu(x) = \sum_{k=0}^{\infty} \frac{(-1)^k}{k!\,\Gamma(\nu + k + 1)} \left(\frac{x}{2}\right)^{\nu+2k} \quad ; \tag{98}$$

it is called *Bessel's function of the first kind of order* ν. [$\Gamma(\nu + k + 1)$ is the Gamma function of Sec. 2, Chap. 2.]

If ν is *not* an integer it can also be shown that

$$J_{-\nu}(x)$$

is another solution of Bessel's equation linearly independent of $J_\nu(x)$. If ν is an integer, say n, then it is easily demonstrated that

$$J_n(x) = (-1)^n J_{-n}(x) \quad ; \tag{99}$$

hence J_n and J_{-n} are *not* linearly independent. In either case, however, we can find a second solution $Y_\nu(x)$ linearly independent of J_ν. When ν is an integer, n, the equation for $Y_n(x)$ becomes

$$Y_n(x) = -\frac{1}{\pi} \sum_{k=0}^{n-1} \frac{(n-k-1)!}{k!} \left(\frac{x}{2}\right)^{2k-n}$$

$$+ \frac{1}{\pi} \sum_{k=0}^{\infty} \frac{(-1)^k}{k!(n+k)!} \left(\frac{x}{2}\right)^{n+2k} \left[2 \log \frac{x}{2} - \psi(k+1) - \psi(n+k+1)\right] \quad , \tag{100}$$

which is a solution of Bessel's equation called *Bessel's function of the second kind of order* n. The function ψ which appears in Equation (100) has been defined in Equation (88).

The Bessel functions J_ν and Y_ν are well tabulated functions.† Probably the

---

† Compare, for example, Watson, *op. cit.*

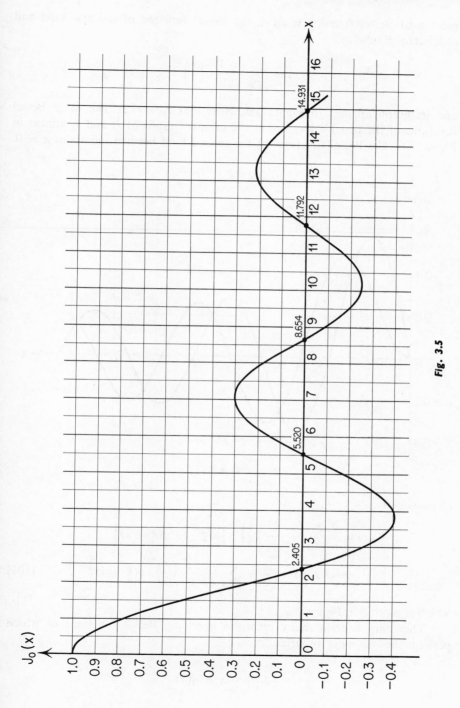

Fig. 3.5

most used Bessel function is $J_0(x)$, the Bessel function of the first kind and order zero. Explicitly,

$$J_0(x) = \sum_{k=0}^{\infty} \frac{(-1)^k}{(k!)^2} \left(\frac{x}{2}\right)^{2k} \quad ,$$

and its graph appears in Figure 3.5. Note that $J_0(0) = 1$. The other Bessel functions of the first kind vanish at the origin. Graphs of J_1 and J_2 appear in Figure 3.6. The Bessel functions of the second kind become infinite at $x = 0$.

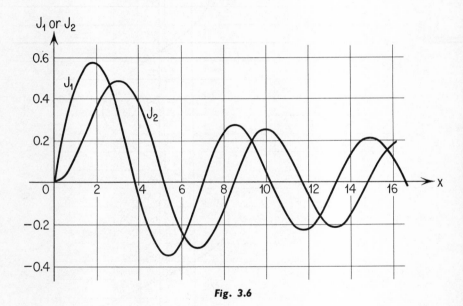

Fig. 3.6

In particular,

$$
\begin{aligned}
Y_0(x) &= \frac{2}{\pi} \sum_{k=0}^{\infty} \frac{(-1)^k}{(k!)^2} \left(\frac{x}{2}\right)^{2k} \left[\log \frac{x}{2} - \psi(k+1)\right] \\
&= \frac{2}{\pi} \left[J_0(x) \log \frac{x}{2} - \sum_{k=0}^{\infty} \frac{(-1)^k}{(k!)^2} \left(\frac{x}{2}\right)^{2k} \psi(k+1)\right] \quad ,
\end{aligned}
\tag{101}
$$

which is plotted in Figure 3.7.

There are a great many identities involving Bessel functions of which perhaps the two most important are

$$\frac{d}{dx} [x^n J_n(x)] = x^n J_{n-1}(x)$$

and

$$\frac{d}{dx}[x^{-n}J_n(x)] = -x^{-n}J_{n+1}(x) \quad .$$

These formulas can be deduced by a direct application of Equation (98). That is, multiply by x^{ν}, differentiate and algebraically manipulate the terms of the series. The identities necessary for future applications (cf., for example, Chap. 4)

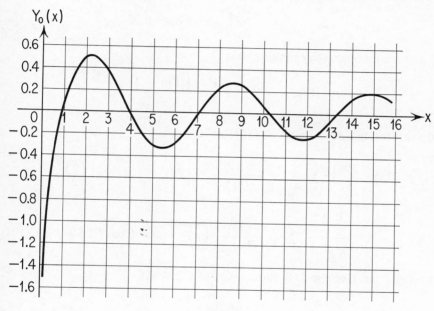

Fig. 3.7

will be derived as the need for them arises. A few of the common results are listed in the exercises.

A slightly more sophisticated formula involving Bessel functions is

$$J_\nu(x) = \frac{\left(\dfrac{x}{2}\right)^\nu}{\Gamma(\tfrac{1}{2})\Gamma(\nu + \tfrac{1}{2})} \int_0^\pi \cos(x \cos \theta) \sin^{2\nu} \theta \, d\theta \quad , \tag{102}$$

which is called a *Lommel integral*. Starting with Equation (98), we may write

$$J_\nu(x) = \left(\frac{x}{2}\right)^\nu \sum_{k=0}^\infty \frac{(-1)^k}{k!\,\Gamma(\nu + k + 1)} \left(\frac{x}{2}\right)^{2k} \quad . \tag{103}$$

From Chapter 2, Section 5, we recall the definition of the Beta function:

$$B(u, v) = 2 \int_0^{\pi/2} \sin^{2u-1} \theta \, \cos^{2v-1} \theta \, d\theta \quad ,$$

or

$$B(v + \tfrac{1}{2}, k + \tfrac{1}{2}) = 2 \int_0^{\pi/2} \sin^{2v} \theta \, \cos^{2k} \theta \, d\theta$$

$$= \int_0^{\pi} \sin^{2v} \theta \, \cos^{2k} \theta \, d\theta \quad ,$$

if k and v are nonnegative integers. But

$$B(v + \tfrac{1}{2}, k + \tfrac{1}{2}) = \frac{\Gamma(v + \tfrac{1}{2})\Gamma(k + \tfrac{1}{2})}{\Gamma(v + k + 1)} \quad ,$$

and substituting this in Equation (103) yields

$$J_v(x) = \left(\frac{x}{2}\right)^v \sum_{k=0}^{\infty} \frac{(-1)^k}{k!\,\Gamma(v + \tfrac{1}{2})\Gamma(k + \tfrac{1}{2})} B(v + \tfrac{1}{2}, k + \tfrac{1}{2}) \left(\frac{x}{2}\right)^{2k}$$

$$= \frac{\left(\dfrac{x}{2}\right)^v}{\Gamma(v + \tfrac{1}{2})} \sum_{k=0}^{\infty} \frac{(-1)^k}{k!\,\Gamma(k + \tfrac{1}{2})} \left(\frac{x}{2}\right)^{2k} \int_0^{\pi} \sin^{2v} \theta \, \cos^{2k} \theta \, d\theta \quad . \tag{104}$$

We recall from Exercise 2, Section 2, Chapter 2, that

$$\Gamma(k + \tfrac{1}{2}) = \frac{(2k)!}{k!\,2^{2k}} \sqrt{\pi} \quad .$$

Equation (104) then becomes

$$J_v(x) = \frac{\left(\dfrac{x}{2}\right)^v}{\sqrt{\pi}\,\Gamma(v + \tfrac{1}{2})} \int_0^{\pi} \sin^{2v} \theta \sum_{k=0}^{\infty} \frac{(-1)^k x^{2k}}{(2k)!} \cos^{2k} \theta \, d\theta \quad .$$

But

$$\sum_{k=0}^{\infty} \frac{(-1)^k}{(2k)!} (x \cos \theta)^{2k} = \cos (x \cos \theta) \quad ,$$

which establishes Equation (102).

In particular, if $v = 0$, Equation (102) becomes

$$J_0(x) = \frac{1}{\pi} \int_0^\pi \cos(x \cos \theta) d\theta \quad, \tag{105}$$

a result that will be used in Chapter 7.

EXERCISES

1. Solve completely Bessel's equation of orders zero and one.
2. Complete the solution of the problem of the buckling of a thin strut.
3. Prove that

$$J_{-n}(x) = (-1)^n J_n(x) \quad, \quad n = 0, 1, 2, \cdots \quad .$$

4. Prove that

$$\frac{d}{dx}[x^n J_n(x)] = x^n J_{n-1}(x)$$

and

$$\frac{d}{dx}[x^{-n} J_n(x)] = -x^{-n} J_{n+1}(x) \quad .$$

5. Establish the recursion formulas

$$J_{n-1}(x) + J_{n+1}(x) = \frac{2n}{x} J_n(x)$$

and

$$x J_n'(x) + n J_n(x) - x J_{n-1}(x) = 0 \quad .$$

6. Show that

$$J_{1/2}(x) = \sqrt{\frac{2}{\pi x}} \sin x \quad , \quad J_{-1/2}(x) = \sqrt{\frac{2}{\pi x}} \cos x \quad .$$

Solve the following differential equations by the method of Frobenius.

7. $x^2 y'' + x^2 y' - 2y = 0$.

8. $x(1 + 2x^2)y'' - \frac{1}{2}y' - 12xy = 0$.

9. $xy'' + \dfrac{2+x}{2} y' + \dfrac{x-1}{x} y = 0$.

10. $xy'' + 7y' + xy = 0$.

11. A particular case of *Mathieu's equation* is

$$y'' - (n^2 - \cosh 2x)y = 0 \quad .$$

Find one solution of this equation for the case $n = 2$.

12. An equation of great theoretical and practical importance is the *hypergeometric equation*

$$x(x - 1)y'' + [(\alpha + \beta + 1)x - \gamma]y' + \alpha\beta y = 0 \quad ,$$

where α, β, γ are constants. Under the assumption that γ is not an integer, find two distinct solutions of this equation.

Find the two linearly independent solutions of

13. $y'' + \dfrac{1}{x} y' + 4 \left(1 - \dfrac{1}{9x^2} \right) y = 0$.

14. $y'' - \dfrac{3}{x} y' + \left(\dfrac{4}{x^2} + 1 \right) y = 0$.

15. $xy'' + 2y' + \tfrac{1}{4} y = 0$.

16. $xy'' + 4y' + 9x^4 y = 0$.

17. An RLC circuit (cf. Fig. 3.2) has a resistance R which is varied as a linear function of the time. That is,

$$R = R_0 + \alpha t \quad .$$

The equation satisfied by the loop current $i(t)$ is

$$\frac{di}{dt} + \frac{R}{L} i + \frac{1}{LC} \int i \, dt = \frac{1}{L} E(t) \quad .$$

Assume that the impressed voltage $E(t)$ is zero, $L = 1\,h.$, $C = 1\,f.$, $R_0 = 10$ ohms, $\alpha = 1$ ohm/sec.; find the solutions of the current equation.

18. A bar is conducting heat along its length and is also radiating heat from its surface. If the temperature of the surroundings is T, and the radiation obeys Newton's law, it is not difficult to show that the temperature $u(x, t)$ satisfies the partial differential equation

$$\frac{k}{c\delta} \frac{\partial}{\partial x} \left(A \frac{\partial u}{\partial x} \right) = A\alpha(u - T) + A \frac{\partial u}{\partial t} \quad ,$$

where k = thermal conductivity, c = specific heat, δ = density, A = cross-sectional area, and t = time.† If the cross-sectional-area A varies linearly with the distance along the bar, that is, $A = A_0 + \beta x$, find the equation satisfied by the steady-state temperature distribution in the bar. Find one solution of the resulting equation if $c\delta/k = 2$, $\alpha = 1$, $A = 1 + \frac{1}{2}x$.

19. Show that

$$I_0(x) = J_0(jx) = \frac{1}{\pi} \int_0^\pi e^{x \cos \theta} \, d\theta \quad .$$

20. Prove that

$$\int_0^{2\pi} \int_0^{2\pi} e^{a \cos (u-v)} du dv = 4\pi^2 I_0(a) \quad .$$

REFERENCES

C.R.C., *Standard Mathematical Tables*, 10th ed. Cleveland, Ohio: Chemical Rubber Publishing Company, 1954.

Ince, E. L., *Ordinary Differential Equations*. New York: Dover Publications, 1944.

Miller, K. S., *Partial Differential Equations in Engineering Problems*. New York: Prentice-Hall, Inc., 1953.

Murray, F. J., and K. S. Miller, *Existence Theorems for Ordinary Differential Equations*. New York: New York University Press, 1954.

Salvadori, M. G., and K. S. Miller, *The Mathematical Solution of Engineering Problems*. New York: Columbia University Press, 1953.

Salvadori, M. G., and R. J. Schwarz, *Differential Equations in Engineering Problems*. New York: Prentice-Hall, Inc., 1954.

Watson, G. N., *A Treatise on the Theory of Bessel Functions*. New York: The Macmillan Company, 1944.

Woods, F. S., *Advanced Calculus*, rev. ed. Boston: Ginn & Co., 1934.

---

† Compare Miller, *op. cit.*, Chap. 1.

Chapter Four

FOURIER SERIES AND INTEGRALS

I. Introduction

Given an arbitrary function $f(x)$, there are many equivalent forms in which it can be written. For example, one can use the integral representation

$$f(x) = f(a) + \int_a^x f'(x)dx \quad .$$

Or, recalling that a function $g(x)$ is called *even* if $g(x) = g(-x)$ and *odd* if $g(x) = -g(-x)$, we may write $f(x)$ as the sum of an even function and an odd function, namely,

$$f(x) = \phi(x) + \psi(x) \quad ,$$

where

$$\phi(x) = \tfrac{1}{2}[f(x) + f(-x)]$$

is an even function and

$$\psi(x) = \tfrac{1}{2}[f(x) - f(-x)]$$

is an odd function.

Generally we write a given function in some equivalent form for the purpose of simplifying $f(x)$. Hence we frequently look for ways in which $f(x)$ can be expressed as a combination of functions less complicated than $f(x)$ itself. Perhaps the simplest functions we can imagine are the powers of x: $1, x, x^2, \cdots$. And we know that under suitable conditions we can express $f(x)$ in terms of these simple functions, namely, as a power series,

$$f(x) = a_0 + a_1 x + a_2 x^2 + \cdots \quad , \tag{1}$$

where

$$a_n = \frac{f^{(n)}(0)}{n!} \quad .$$

One important use of the power series representation has already been exploited in the previous chapter.

Now, in many practical problems in vibration theory, networks, oscillations —to mention a few—we must deal with *periodic phenomena*. For example, the solution to some vibration problem could be a *periodic function*† $f(x)$ of period T, and we might wish to express this function as a combination of simple periodic functions. Of course the most elementary functions are sines and cosines, and we might therefore attempt to write

$$f(x) = \frac{a_0}{2} + a_1 \cos \frac{2\pi x}{T} + a_2 \cos \frac{4\pi x}{T} + a_3 \cos \frac{6\pi x}{T} + \cdots$$

$$+ b_1 \sin \frac{2\pi x}{T} + b_2 \sin \frac{4\pi x}{T} + b_3 \sin \frac{6\pi x}{T} + \cdots \quad , \qquad (2)$$

since $\cos \frac{2n\pi}{T} x$ and $\sin \frac{2n\pi}{T} x$ all have period T.

Occasion also arises, for example, in some boundary value problems, in which it is convenient to express a function as a combination of Bessel functions or Legendre polynomials or other collections of functions. We shall see examples of such expansions later in this chapter. For the present, though, let us concentrate on the periodic expansion of Equation (2).

2. Fourier Series

The power series representation of Equation (1) would not be of much value unless there existed a convenient way of calculating the coefficients $a_0, a_1, \cdots$. Similarly, an expansion of a function $f(x)$ in sines and cosines would not be of practical value unless we could calculate the a_n and b_n in some simple and direct fashion. Fortunately, such a method exists. In the case of power series we *differentiated* to obtain the coefficients in Equation (1). However, a method that works for practically every type of expansion except power series

---

† We say that a function $f(x)$ is periodic of period T if $f(x + T) = f(x)$. It follows immediately that if $f(x)$ is known for x in the interval $\left[-\frac{T}{2}, \frac{T}{2} \right]$, then $f(x)$ is known for all x. For example, if x_0 is any value of x, we may write $x_0 = kT + x'$, where k is an integer and $-\frac{T}{2} < x' \leq \frac{T}{2}$. Then, using the periodicity of $f(x)$,

$$f(x_0) = f(kT + x') = f((k-1)T + x') = \cdots = f(T + x') = f(x') \quad .$$

is to *integrate* to determine the coefficients. The reason that integration is so fruitful in the case of sines and cosines is because of the following integral formulas derived in the calculus:

$$\int_{-T/2}^{T/2} \cos \frac{2m\pi}{T} x \cos \frac{2n\pi}{T} x \, dx = \frac{T}{2} \delta_{nm}$$

$$\int_{-T/2}^{T/2} \sin \frac{2m\pi}{T} x \sin \frac{2n\pi}{T} x \, dx = \frac{T}{2} \delta_{nm} \tag{3}$$

$$\int_{-T/2}^{T/2} \sin \frac{2m\pi}{T} x \cos \frac{2n\pi}{T} x \, dx = 0 \quad .$$

Equations (3) are known as *orthogonality conditions* and are valid for all non-negative integral values of m and n not both zero. δ_{nm} is the Kronecker delta ($\delta_{nm} = 1$ if $n = m$ and $\delta_{nm} = 0$ if $n \neq m$).

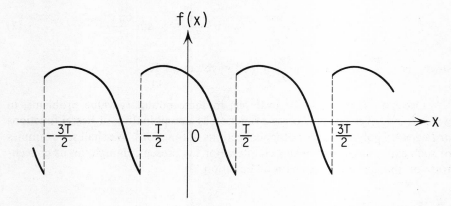

Fig. 4.1

Let us now suppose $f(x)$ is a periodic function of period T (cf. Fig. 4.1) and we wish to express it in the form of Equation (2), namely,

$$f(x) = \frac{a_0}{2} + \sum_{n=1}^{\infty} \left(a_n \cos \frac{2n\pi}{T} x + b_n \sin \frac{2n\pi}{T} x \right) \quad . \tag{4}$$

We shall see that the calculation of the coefficients a_n and b_n is an easy task if we use Equations (3). First, integrate Equation (4) from $-\frac{T}{2}$ to $\frac{T}{2}$:

$$\int_{-T/2}^{T/2} f(x)dx = \frac{a_0}{2} \int_{-T/2}^{T/2} dx + \sum_{n=1}^{\infty} \left(a_n \frac{T}{2} \delta_{0n} + b_n \frac{T}{2} \delta_{0n} \right)$$

$$= \frac{a_0 T}{2} \quad ,$$

and

$$a_0 = \frac{2}{T} \int_{-T/2}^{T/2} f(x)dx \quad .$$ (5)

If we multiply Equation (4) by $\cos \frac{2m\pi}{T} x$ with $m \neq 0$ and integrate, then

$$\int_{-T/2}^{T/2} f(x) \cos \frac{2m\pi}{T} x \, dx = 0 + \sum_{n=1}^{\infty}{}' \left(a_n \frac{T}{2} \delta_{nm} + 0 \right) = \frac{a_m T}{2} \quad ,$$

or

$$a_m = \frac{2}{T} \int_{-T/2}^{T/2} f(x) \cos \frac{2m\pi}{T} x \, dx \quad , \quad m = 1, 2, \cdots \quad ,$$ (6)

where we have again used Equations (3). Note that setting $m = 0$ in Equation (6) yields Equation (5). Hence Equation (6) is actually valid for $m = 0, 1, 2, \cdots$. This is the reason for using $a_0/2$ in the original expression, Equation (4), rather than a_0.

Finally, if we multiply Equation (4) by $\sin \frac{2m\pi}{T} x$ and integrate from $-\frac{T}{2}$ to $\frac{T}{2}$, we obtain

$$b_m = \frac{2}{T} \int_{-T/2}^{T/2} f(x) \sin \frac{2m\pi}{T} x \, dx \quad , \quad m = 1, 2, \cdots \quad .$$

In brief, then, we have shown the following: If $f(x)$ is periodic of period T, then $f(x)$ has the Fourier series expansion

$$f(x) = \frac{a_0}{2} + \sum_{n=1}^{\infty} \left(a_n \cos \frac{2n\pi}{T} x + b_n \sin \frac{2n\pi}{T} x \right) \quad ,$$ (7)

where

$$a_n = \frac{2}{T} \int_{-T/2}^{T/2} f(x) \cos \frac{2n\pi}{T} x \, dx \quad , \quad n = 0, 1, 2, \cdots$$ (8)

and

$$b_n = \frac{2}{T} \int_{-T/2}^{T/2} f(x) \sin \frac{2n\pi}{T} x \, dx \quad , \quad n = 1, 2, \cdots \quad .$$ (9)

Before going further into the properties of Fourier series, let us consider a practical problem. We recall that electrical networks are generally analyzed on the assumption that the applied voltages and currents are *sinusoidal*. (In Chap. 6 we shall elaborate on this subject.) Suppose, however, a sinusoidal voltage

$$E \sin \omega t$$

is passed through a half-wave rectifier which clips the negative portion of the wave at zero bias. Then the resulting function (cf. Fig. 4.2) is no longer sinu-

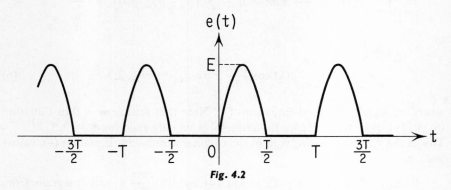

Fig. 4.2

soidal but, however, is still periodic. If we wanted to analyze further this voltage it would be convenient to express it as a sum of sinusoidal voltages, that is, as a Fourier series.

We see that the function of Figure 4.2 has period

$$T = \frac{2\pi}{\omega}$$

and that $e(t) = 0$ for $-\dfrac{T}{2} \leq t \leq 0$. Hence Equation (8) becomes

$$a_n = \frac{2}{T} \int_0^{T/2} E \sin \omega t \cos n\omega t \, dt$$

$$= \frac{2E}{T} \int_0^{T/2} \tfrac{1}{2}[\sin \omega(1 + n)t + \sin \omega(1 - n)t] dt$$

$$= \frac{E}{T}\left[-\frac{\cos \omega(1 + n)t}{\omega(1 + n)} - \frac{\cos \omega(1 - n)t}{\omega(1 - n)} \right]\Bigg|_0^{T/2} \quad , \quad n \neq 1$$

$$= \frac{E}{T}\left[-\frac{(-1)^{n+1}}{\omega(1+n)} + \frac{1}{\omega(1+n)} - \frac{(-1)^{n+1}}{\omega(1-n)} + \frac{1}{\omega(1-n)} \right] \quad , \quad n \neq 1$$

$$= 0 \quad \text{if } n \text{ is odd and unequal to one.}$$

If n is even,

$$a_n = \frac{2E}{T}\left[\frac{1}{\omega(1 + n)} + \frac{1}{\omega(1 - n)}\right] = \frac{4E}{\omega T}\left[\frac{1}{1 - n^2}\right] \; ,$$

and if $n = 1$,

$$a_1 = \frac{2}{T}\int_0^{T/2} E \sin \omega t \cos \omega t \, dt = \frac{E}{T}\int_0^{T/2} \sin 2\omega t \, dt = 0 \; .$$

Hence

$$a_n = \frac{2E}{\pi}\frac{1}{1 - n^2} \; , \quad n = 0, 2, 4, \cdots$$

$$a_n = 0 \qquad\qquad , \quad n = 1, 3, 5, \cdots \; .$$

The b_n coefficients are given by Equation (9) as

$$b_n = \frac{2}{T}\int_0^{T/2} E \sin \omega t \sin n\omega t \, dt$$

$$= \frac{2E}{T}\int_0^{T/2} \tfrac{1}{2}[\cos \omega(1 - n)t - \cos \omega(1 + n)t]dt$$

$$= \frac{E}{T}\left[\frac{\sin \omega(1 - n)t}{\omega(1 - n)} - \frac{\sin \omega(1 + n)t}{\omega(1 + n)}\right]\Big|_0^{T/2} \; , \quad n \neq 1$$

$$= 0 \quad \text{if } n \neq 1.$$

If n *does* equal one, then

$$b_1 = \frac{2}{T}\int_0^{T/2} E \sin^2 \omega t \, dt = \frac{2E}{T}\int_0^{T/2} \tfrac{1}{2}[1 - \cos 2\omega t]dt = \frac{E}{2} \; .$$

The Fourier series expansion of the half-wave rectified voltage is therefore

$$e(t) = \frac{E}{\pi} + \frac{E}{2} \sin \omega t + \frac{2E}{\pi}\sum_{n=2,4,6,\cdots}^{\infty} \frac{1}{1 - n^2} \cos n\omega t \; .$$

EXERCISES

1. Expand the function $f(x)$ defined by the equations:

$$f(x) = x \; , \quad 0 < x < 1$$

$$f(x) = 1 \; , \quad 1 < x < 2$$

$$f(x + 2) = f(x)$$

into a Fourier series.

2. A function $f(x)$ of period 4 is defined as

$$f(x) = x^3$$

for x between -2 and $+2$. Obtain its Fourier series expansion.

3. If in the example in the text the function $E \sin \omega t$ is passed through a *full*-wave rectifier, obtain the Fourier series expansion of the resulting function.

In general the sinusoidal components in a Fourier series expansion are called *harmonics*. For example, $\cos \dfrac{2n\pi}{T} t$ and $\sin \dfrac{2n\pi}{T} t$ are the nth harmonic. The size of the coefficients a_n and b_n indicates the *harmonic content* of the wave. In elementary physics it is shown that the *power ρ* dissipated by a DC current passing through a resistance of R ohms is

$$\rho = I^2 R \quad \text{watts} \quad .$$

If I is an AC current of period T, we write

$$\frac{1}{T} \int_0^T I^2 \, dt$$

in place of I^2. This means that a DC current with the numerical value

$$I = \sqrt{\frac{1}{T} \int_0^T I^2 \, dt}$$

will generate as much heat in the resistance R as the AC current I.

Suppose $x(t)$ is an arbitrary periodic function of period T. If we think of x as a current passing through a unit resistance, then the power ρ is

$$\rho = \frac{1}{T} \int_0^T x^2(t) dt \quad .$$

The power ρ is of course numerically the same as the *mean square value* of x and is an important parameter associated with $x(t)$ (cf., for example, Sec. 8 of this chapter and Chaps. 6 and 7). If we write the Fourier series expansion for $x(t)$,

$$x(t) = \frac{a_0}{2} + \sum_{n=1}^{\infty} \left(a_n \cos \frac{2n\pi}{T} t + b_n \sin \frac{2n\pi}{T} t \right) \quad ,$$

then

$$\rho = \frac{1}{T} \int_0^T \left[\frac{a_0^2}{4} + \sum_{n=1}^{\infty} \left(a_n^2 \cos^2 \frac{2n\pi}{T} t + b_n^2 \sin^2 \frac{2n\pi}{T} t \right) \right] dt \quad ,$$

since the integrals of all the cross products $\sin 2n\pi t/T \cos 2m\pi t/T$, as well as the products $\sin 2n\pi t/T \sin 2m\pi t/T$ and $\cos 2n\pi t/T \cos 2m\pi t/T$ with $n \neq m$, vanish by virtue of the orthogonality conditions of Equation (3). Thus, since

$$\int_0^T \cos^2 \frac{2n\pi}{T} t \, dt = \int_0^T \sin^2 \frac{2n\pi}{T} t \, dt = \frac{T}{2} \quad ,$$

we have

$$\rho = \frac{a_0^2}{4} + \frac{1}{2} \sum_{n=1}^{\infty} (a_n^2 + b_n^2) \quad , \tag{10}$$

and $\frac{1}{2}(a_n^2 + b_n^2)$ is the power content due to the nth harmonic.

Section 8 of this chapter will more closely investigate the notion of power content in both periodic and nonperiodic functions.

3. Some Properties of Fourier Series

Equations (7), (8), and (9) of the previous section can be simplified in certain instances. If, for example, $f(x)$ is an even function, that is, $f(x) = f(-x)$, then it can easily be seen that the b_n's are zero and that the expansion theorem becomes

If $f(x)$ is an even function of period T, then

$$f(x) = \frac{a_0}{2} + \sum_{n=1}^{\infty} a_n \cos \frac{2n\pi}{T} x \quad ,$$

where

$$a_n = \frac{4}{T} \int_0^{T/2} f(x) \cos \frac{2n\pi}{T} x \, dx \quad , \quad n = 0, 1, 2, \cdots \quad . \tag{11}$$

Similarly, if $f(x)$ is an odd function, $f(x) = -f(-x)$, then all the a_n's are zero and our expansion theorem becomes

If $f(x)$ is an odd function of period T, then

$$f(x) = \sum_{n=1}^{\infty} b_n \sin \frac{2n\pi}{T} x \quad ,$$

and

$$b_n = \frac{4}{T} \int_0^{T/2} f(x) \sin \frac{2n\pi}{T} x \, dx \quad , \quad n = 1, 2, \cdots \quad . \tag{12}$$

The function illustrated in Figure 4.3 is a *square wave* of amplitude h. We see that it is a periodic function of period $2a$ and an odd function. Hence, applying Equations (12) with $T = 2a$,

$$b_n = \frac{2}{a} \int_0^a (h) \sin \frac{n\pi x}{a} \, dx = \frac{2h}{n\pi} [1 - \cos n\pi] \quad .$$

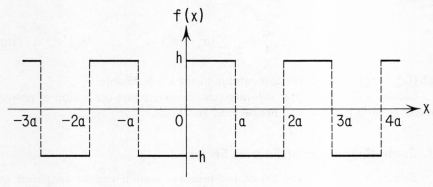

Fig. 4.3

Since $\cos n\pi = (-1)^n$,

$$b_n = \frac{4h}{n\pi} \quad \text{if} \quad n \text{ is odd}$$

$$b_n = 0 \quad \text{if} \quad n \text{ is even} \quad .$$

Thus the square wave of Figure 4.3 has the Fourier series representation

$$f(x) = \frac{4h}{\pi} \sum_{n=1,3,5,\cdots}^{\infty} \frac{1}{n} \sin \frac{n\pi x}{a} \quad .$$

The interval of periodicity, T, is called the *full Fourier interval*. Frequently we are given a function $f(x)$ defined only in the *half Fourier interval* $\left(0, \frac{T}{2}\right)$. If we wish to expand $f(x)$ into a Fourier series with period T, then we must prolong $f(x)$ into the interval $\left(-\frac{T}{2}, 0\right)$ and then repeat it periodically with period T. The prolongation into $\left(-\frac{T}{2}, 0\right)$ is, in general, arbitrary. Frequently it is convenient to use even or odd prolongations, since by Equations (11) and (12) the labor of calculating half the coefficients is avoided.

EXERCISES

1. Establish Equations (11) and (12).
2. Expand the function $f(x)$ defined in the full Fourier interval $-\pi < x < \pi$ by the equation

$$f(x) = \pi^2 - x^2$$

   into a Fourier series.
3. Expand the function given in Figure 4.4 below into a Fourier series.

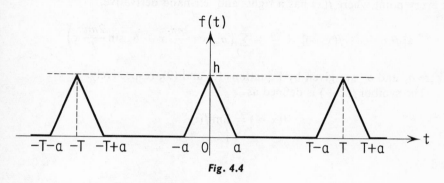

Fig. 4.4

4. Let $f(x)$ be defined as

$$f(x) = x \quad , \quad 0 < x < 1$$
$$f(x) = 1 \quad , \quad 1 < x < 2$$

   in the half Fourier interval $(0, 2)$. Extend this function as both an even and odd function in $(-2, 0)$, and obtain both Fourier series expansions.
5. Show that Equations (8) and (9) can be written

$$a_n = \frac{2}{T} \int_{\alpha}^{\alpha + T} f(x) \cos \frac{2n\pi}{T} x \, dx \quad , \quad n = 0, 1, 2, \cdots$$

   and

$$b_n = \frac{2}{T} \int_{\alpha}^{\alpha + T} f(x) \sin \frac{2n\pi}{T} x \, dx \quad , \quad n = 1, 2, \cdots \quad ,$$

   respectively, where α is any real number.

If $f(x)$ is an arbitrary function, it does not necessarily have a power series expansion. For example, the function

$$f(x) = |x|$$

does not have one, since to evaluate the coefficients of the power series we must compute the derivatives of $f(x)$ at $x = 0$; and in this case $f'(0)$ does not exist. Similarly, not every periodic function $f(x)$ has a Fourier series expansion. However, practically every function we are likely to encounter in practical problems *does* have a Fourier series expansion. The following theorem, whose proof will be found in Appendix 3 indicates what large class of functions are Fourier expandable.

THEOREM. Let $f(x)$ be periodic of period T and integrable on $[0, T]$. Then at every point where $f(x)$ has a right- and left-hand derivative,

$$\tfrac{1}{2}[f(x+) + f(x-)] = \frac{a_0}{2} + \sum_{n=1}^{\infty} \left(a_n \cos \frac{2n\pi}{T} x + b_n \sin \frac{2n\pi}{T} x \right) \ ,$$

where a_n and b_n are given by Equations (8) and (9), respectively.

The symbol $f(x+)$ is defined as

$$f(x+) = \lim_{\substack{t \to x \\ t > x}} f(t)$$

and

$$f(x-) = \lim_{\substack{t \to x \\ t < x}} f(t) \ .$$

If $f(x)$ happens to be continuous at $x = x$, then $f(x+) = f(x-) = f(x)$ and

$$\tfrac{1}{2}[f(x+) + f(x-)] = f(x) \ .$$

For example, if $f(x)$ is the square wave just considered, then $f(x)$ has a right- and left-hand derivative at $x = a$ (that is, the right-hand derivative is

$$\lim_{\substack{\delta \to 0 \\ \delta > 0}} \frac{f(a + \delta) - f(a+)}{\delta}$$

and the left-hand derivative is similarly defined). Also,

$$f(a+) = -h \ , \quad f(a-) = +h \ ,$$

and

$$\tfrac{1}{2}[f(a+) + f(a-)] = 0 \ .$$

In general, we can say that at a point of discontinuity the Fourier series converges to the average of the values of the function to the right and left of the discontinuity.

4. Applications to Differential Equations

Fourier series can be used in much the same way power series were to solve ordinary differential equations. We give a simple example of such an application. Consider a simply supported beam of length L loaded by a load $p(x)$,

$$p(x) = P_0 \frac{x}{L} \quad ,$$

as in Figure 4.5. Neglecting the weight of the beam itself we recall from elementary strength of materials† that the deflection $y(x)$ satisfies the differential equation

$$EIy^{(4)} = p(x) \quad , \tag{13}$$

where EI is the flexural rigidity of the beam.

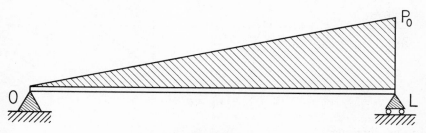

Fig. 4.5

The method of Fourier series consists in expanding $p(x)$ into a Fourier series (note that $p(x)$ is a known function), assuming that $y(x)$ can also be expanded in a Fourier series, and then equating coefficients. If we are to expand $p(x)$, we must first construct a periodic function which agrees with $p(x)$ from $x = 0$ to $x = L$. There is of course an infinite variety of such functions. However, we recall that a simply supported beam has zero deflection and zero moment at its ends; or, worded mathematically,

$$y(0) = y(L) = y''(0) = y''(L) = 0 \quad . \tag{14}$$

Now, if we choose a Fourier series expansion for $p(x)$ involving only sine terms of period $2L$, then, since the fourth derivative of $\sin x$ is again $\sin x$, we can assume that the Fourier series expansion for $y(x)$ contains only sine terms. In this way the boundary conditions of Equation (14) will be automatically

† Compare, for example, Salvadori and Schwarz, *Differential Equations in Engineering Problems*, p. 70.

satisfied. Hence if we prolong $p(x)$ as an odd function (cf. Fig. 4.6), its Fourier series expansion will contain only sine terms. If we apply Equations (12) with $T = 2L$ and $f(x) = p(x)$, the Fourier series expansion of $p(x)$ is readily determined to be

$$p(x) = \frac{2P_0}{\pi} \sum_{n=1}^{\infty} \frac{(-1)^{n+1}}{n} \sin \frac{n\pi x}{L} \ .$$

Now, assuming that $y(x)$ can be written in the form

$$y(x) = \sum_{n=1}^{\infty} B_n \sin \frac{n\pi x}{L} \ ,$$

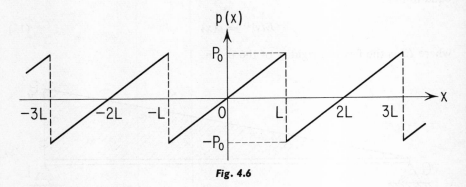

Fig. 4.6

we may compute

$$EIy^{(4)} = \frac{EI\pi^4}{L^4} \sum_{n=1}^{\infty} B_n n^4 \sin \frac{n\pi x}{L} \ .$$

Equating $EIy^{(4)}$ to $p(x)$ [cf. Equation (13)], we obtain

$$B_n = \frac{(-1)^{n+1}}{n^5} \frac{2P_0 L^4}{EI\pi^5}$$

or

$$y(x) = \frac{2P_0 L^4}{\pi^5 EI} \sum_{n=1}^{\infty} \frac{(-1)^{n+1}}{n^5} \sin \frac{n\pi x}{L} \ , \tag{15}$$

which is a very rapidly converging series because of the factor n^5 in the denominator. For example, when $x = L/2$, the deflection at the mid-point becomes

$$y\left(\frac{L}{2}\right) = \frac{P_0 L^4}{EI} \left[\frac{2}{\pi^5}\right] \sum_{n=1,3,5,\ldots}^{\infty} \frac{1}{n^5} (-1)^{\frac{n-1}{2}} \ .$$

(Note that this is not the point of maximum deflection.) By using *one* term of the expansion, we obtain

$$y\left(\frac{L}{2}\right) = 0.0065356A \quad,$$

where $A = P_0 L^4/EI$, while the exact value computed from the closed form†

$$y(x) = \frac{P_0 x}{360EIL}(3x^4 - 10L^2x^2 + 7L^4)$$

is

$$y\left(\frac{L}{2}\right) = 0.0065104A \quad,$$

which is an error of 0.387 %. Using two and three terms of the Fourier series expansion yields

$$y\left(\frac{L}{2}\right) = 0.0065087A \quad \text{(two terms)}$$

$$y\left(\frac{L}{2}\right) = 0.0065108A \quad \text{(three terms)}$$

with corresponding negligible errors of 0.026 % and 0.006 %, respectively.

This method of assuming a trial function Fourier series as a solution can also be advantageously used in the theory of partial differential equations.‡

EXERCISES

1. Find the deflection of a simply supported beam, uniformly loaded, by using the Fourier series method described above. Compare this result with the closed-form solution obtainable from the A.I.S.C., Steel Construction, or by a direct calculation.

2. The temperature $u(x, t)$ in a thin insulated wire satisfies the partial differential equation

$$\frac{\partial^2 u}{\partial x^2} = \frac{1}{c^2}\frac{\partial u}{\partial t} \quad .$$

If the wire is L units long and the ends are kept at zero temperature for all time t,

$$u(0, t) = 0$$

$$u(L, t) = 0 \quad ,$$

† Compare A.I.S.C., *Steel Construction*, p. 358.
‡ Compare Miller, *Partial Differential Equations in Engineering Problems*, Chap. 3.

find the temperature $u(x, t)$ in the wire at any time and place if initially

$$u(x, 0) = T \quad \text{(a constant)} \quad .$$

Assume a trial function solution of the form

$$u(x, t) = \sum f_n(t) \sin \frac{n\pi x}{L} \quad .$$

Another more practical application of Fourier series is to the systematic solution of partial differential equations by the powerful method of separation of variables. We illustrate this method with a problem in the steady flow of heat. If we have a plate, insulated on its plane surfaces, then the temperature $u(x, y)$ satisfies the two-dimensional Laplacian $\nabla^2 u = 0$,

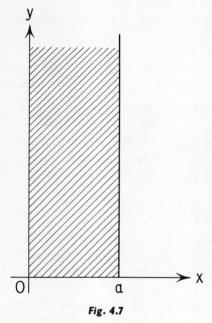

Fig. 4.7

$$\nabla^2 u \equiv \frac{\partial^2 u}{\partial x^2} + \frac{\partial^2 u}{\partial y^2} = 0 \quad , \qquad (16)$$

where x and y are cartesian coordinates.† Suppose that we have a semi-infinite plate as in Figure 4.7 whose edges $x = 0$ and $x = a$ are kept at zero temperature, and whose base $y = 0$ is kept at a constant temperature T. Then the problem becomes one of finding a function $u(x, y)$ which satisfies Equation (16) and the *boundary conditions*

$$u(0, y) = 0$$
$$u(a, y) = 0 \qquad (17)$$
$$u(x, 0) = T \quad .$$

From physical considerations we can also see that

$$\lim_{y \to \infty} u(x, y) = 0 \quad .$$

Now the method of separation of variables consists of assuming a solution to Equation (16) in the form

$$u(x, y) = X(x) Y(y) \quad . \qquad (18)$$

---

† Compare Miller, *op. cit.*, Chap. 1.

We have already introduced this technique in connection with Legendre's equation and Bessel's equation in the previous chapter. Substituting Equation (18) into Equation (16) and dividing by XY, we obtain

$$-\frac{X''}{X} = \frac{Y''}{Y} \ , \tag{19}$$

where primes indicate differentiation with respect to the only variable present. Since the right-hand side of the equation is independent of x and the left-hand side is independent of y, their common ratio must be a constant, say β^2. We thus obtain the two ordinary differential equations

$$X'' + \beta^2 X = 0$$

and

$$Y'' - \beta^2 Y = 0 \ ,$$

whose general solutions are

$$X(x) = A \cos \beta x + B \sin \beta x$$

and

$$Y(y) = Ce^{\beta y} + De^{-\beta y} \ ,$$

respectively. Thus for any value of β, and any constants A, B, C, D,

$$(A \cos \beta x + B \sin \beta x)(Ce^{\beta y} + De^{-\beta y})$$

is a solution of Equation (16). If the first boundary condition $u(0, y) = 0$ of Equation (17) is to be satisfied,

$$u(0, y) = X(0)Y(y) = 0 \ ,$$

which implies $X(0) = 0$ since $Y(y)$ is not identically zero. But

$$X(0) = A \ ;$$

hence $A = 0$. To satisfy $u(a, y) = X(a)Y(y) = 0$ we must have

$$X(a) = 0 \ . \tag{20}$$

But

$$X(a) = B \sin \beta a$$

and, since X is not identically zero, $B \neq 0$. Hence, to make Equation (20) true, we must have

$$\sin \beta a = 0 \quad \text{or} \quad \beta = \frac{n\pi}{a} \ , \quad n = 1, 2, \cdots \ .$$

Thus the function

$$\sum_{n=1}^{\infty} \sin \frac{n\pi x}{a} \left(a_n e^{\frac{n\pi y}{a}} + b_n e^{-\frac{n\pi y}{a}} \right)$$

satisfies Equation (16) and the first two boundary condition of Equation (17) no matter what the a_n and b_n may be.

The physical condition $u(x, \infty) = 0$ implies $a_n = 0$, since $e^{n\pi y/a}$ becomes arbitrarily large as y increases. We are thus left with the function

$$u(x, y) = \sum_{n=1}^{\infty} b_n \sin \frac{n\pi x}{a} e^{-\frac{n\pi y}{a}} \quad,$$

which satisfies the differential equation and the boundary conditions except for $u(x, 0) = T$. Since the b_n's are arbitrary, choose them so that

$$T = u(x, 0) = \sum_{n=1}^{\infty} b_n \sin \frac{n\pi x}{a} \quad ;$$

that is, choose them so that they are the sine Fourier coefficients

$$b_n = \frac{2}{a} \int_0^a T \sin \frac{n\pi x}{a} \, dx \quad .$$

Then

$$b_n = 0 \quad , \quad \text{if } n \text{ is even} \quad ,$$

$$b_n = \frac{4T}{n\pi} \quad , \quad \text{if } n \text{ is odd} \quad ,$$

and the solution to the boundary value problem is

$$u(x, y) = \frac{4T}{\pi} \sum_{n=1,3,5,\cdots}^{\infty} \frac{1}{n} \sin \frac{n\pi x}{a} e^{-\frac{n\pi y}{a}} \quad . \tag{21}$$

In this particular example we can write $u(x, y)$ in closed form. If we differentiate $u(x, y)$ with respect to x, then

$$\frac{\partial u}{\partial x} = \frac{4T}{a} \sum_{n=1,3,5,\cdots}^{\infty} \cos \frac{n\pi x}{a} e^{-\frac{n\pi y}{a}} \quad . \tag{22}$$

When we introduce the notation

$$\frac{\pi x}{a} = \alpha \quad \text{and} \quad \frac{\pi y}{a} = \beta \quad ,$$

for simplicity and replace cos $n\alpha$ by $\frac{1}{2}[e^{jn\alpha} + e^{-jn\alpha}]$, Equation (22) becomes

$$\frac{\partial u}{\partial x} = \frac{2T}{a} \sum_{n=1,3,5,\cdots}^{\infty} [e^{-n(\beta-j\alpha)} + e^{-n(\beta+j\alpha)}] \quad .$$

The sums are now geometric series with ratios $e^{-2(\beta-j\alpha)}$ and $e^{-2(\beta+j\alpha)}$, respectively. Hence

$$\frac{\partial u}{\partial x} = \frac{2T}{a} \left[\frac{e^{-(\beta-j\alpha)}}{1 - e^{-2(\beta-j\alpha)}} + \frac{e^{-(\beta+j\alpha)}}{1 - e^{-2(\beta+j\alpha)}} \right]$$

$$= \frac{2T}{a} \frac{(e^{j\alpha} + e^{-j\alpha})(e^{\beta} - e^{-\beta})}{(e^{2\beta} + e^{-2\beta}) - (e^{2j\alpha} + e^{-2j\alpha})}$$

$$= \frac{4T}{a} \frac{\cos \alpha \sinh \beta}{\cosh 2\beta - \cos 2\alpha}$$

$$= \frac{2T}{a} \frac{\cos \alpha \sinh \beta}{\sin^2 \alpha + \sinh^2 \beta} \quad .$$

If we now replace α and β by $\pi x/a$ and $\pi y/a$, respectively, and integrate with respect to x,

$$u(x, y) = \frac{2T}{a} \sinh \frac{\pi y}{a} \int \frac{\cos \dfrac{\pi x}{a} \, dx}{\sin^2 \dfrac{\pi x}{a} + \sinh^2 \dfrac{\pi y}{a}} + \phi(y) \quad ,$$

where ϕ is an arbitrary function of y, the "constant" of integration. Hence

$$u(x, y) = \frac{2T}{\pi} \arctan\left(\frac{\sin \dfrac{\pi x}{a}}{\sinh \dfrac{\pi y}{a}} \right) + \phi(y) \quad .$$

If $x = 0$, Equation (21) implies $u(0, y) = 0$ and

$$0 = u(0, y) = \frac{2T}{\pi} \arctan 0 + \phi(y) \quad .$$

Thus $\phi(y) \equiv 0$, and the solution of our boundary value problem in closed form becomes

$$u(x, y) = \frac{2T}{\pi} \arctan\left(\frac{\sin \pi x/a}{\sinh \pi y/a} \right) \quad . \tag{23}$$

EXERCISES

1. Solve the problem of the text if the boundary condition $u(a, y) = 0$ is replaced by the adiabatic condition $\dfrac{\partial}{\partial x} u(a, y) = 0$.

2. Solve the problem of two-dimensional heat flow for a square, a units on a side (instead of a semi-infinite strip) if the base $u(x, 0)$ is kept at a constant temperature T and the remaining three sides are kept at zero temperature.

3. The equation of motion of a vibrating string is

$$\frac{\partial^2 u}{\partial t^2} = a^2 \frac{\partial^2 u}{\partial x^2} \quad .$$

If the string is fixed at the end points $x = 0$ and $x = L$ and has an initial displacement $f(x)$ and zero initial velocity, find the displacement $u = u(x, t)$ of the string at any point x and any time t. Show that in this case the solution can also be put in the closed form

$$u(x, t) = \tfrac{1}{2}[f(x + at) + f(x - at)] \quad .$$

4. The voltage $e(x, t)$ in a transmission line satisfies the partial differential equation

$$\frac{\partial^2 e}{\partial x^2} = RC \frac{\partial e}{\partial t} \quad .$$

If the line is grounded at its ends $x = 0$ and $x = L$ and its initial voltage is

$$e(x, 0) = 0 \quad , \quad 0 < x < \frac{L}{2}$$

$$e(x, 0) = E \quad , \quad \frac{L}{2} < x < L \quad ,$$

find $e(x, t)$.

5. The Fourier Integral

We have just seen that Fourier series are a powerful tool in treating various problems in applied mathematics. However, Fourier series are restricted to periodic functions. Of course, many problems do not involve periodic functions. Is there then any way in which the methods of Fourier series can be generalized to include nonperiodic functions? The answer is yes, and such methods will be referred to as *Fourier analysis*.

Roughly speaking, if we start with a periodic function $f(x)$ of period T and let T approach infinity, then $f(x)$ is no longer periodic. For example, if we consider the function $f_T(x)$ defined as

$$f_T(x) = e^{-|x|} \quad , \quad -\frac{T}{2} < x < \frac{T}{2}$$

$$f_T(x + T) = f_T(x) \quad ,$$

then we have a periodic function as indicated in Figure 4.8 below. Now, if we let $T \to \infty$, the function $f_T(t)$ approaches the nonperiodic function $f(x) = e^{-|x|}$,

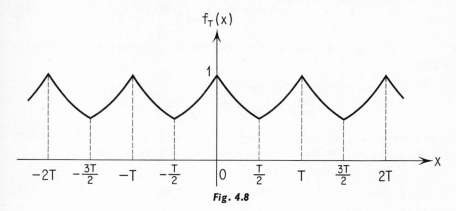

Fig. 4.8

$-\infty < x < \infty$. If we consider the Fourier series for $f_T(x)$ and let $T \to \infty$, then the resulting limiting form of the Fourier series will be the "Fourier series" for the nonperiodic function $f(x)$. Actually, instead of having an infinite series for $f(x)$, we shall have an infinite *integral*.

Suppose, then, that $f_T(x)$ is a periodic function of period T. Then its Fourier series expansion is given by Equation (7), where the a_n and b_n coefficients are given by Equations (8) and (9). Substituting Equations (8) and (9) into Equation (7), we may write

$$f_T(x) = \frac{1}{T} \int_{-T/2}^{T/2} f_T(\xi)d\xi + \frac{2}{T} \sum_{n=1}^{\infty} \left[\cos \frac{2n\pi}{T} x \int_{-T/2}^{T/2} f_T(\xi) \cos \frac{2n\pi}{T} \xi \, d\xi \right.$$

$$\left. + \sin \frac{2n\pi}{T} x \int_{-T/2}^{T/2} f_T(\xi) \sin \frac{2n\pi}{T} \xi \, d\xi \right] \quad . \quad (24)$$

Now we wish to consider the limit of the above expression as $T \to \infty$. Hence we introduce the notation

$$\frac{2n\pi}{T} = \omega_n$$

and define $\Delta\omega_n$ as

$$\Delta\omega_n = \omega_{n+1} - \omega_n = \frac{2(n+1)\pi}{T} - \frac{2n\pi}{T} = \frac{2\pi}{T} \quad .$$

Substituting this result in Equation (24), we have

$$f_T(x) = \frac{1}{T} \int_{-T/2}^{T/2} f_T(\xi)d\xi + \frac{1}{\pi} \sum_{\omega_n = \frac{2\pi}{T}}^{\infty} \left[\cos \omega_n x \, \Delta\omega_n \int_{-T/2}^{T/2} f_T(\xi) \cos \omega_n\xi \, d\xi \right.$$
$$\left. + \sin \omega_n x \, \Delta\omega_n \int_{-T/2}^{T/2} f_T(\xi) \sin \omega_n\xi \, d\xi \right] \quad . \tag{25}$$

If we let $T \to \infty$, then the discrete variable ω_n approaches a continuous variable ω,

$$\lim_{T\to\infty} \frac{1}{T} \int_{-T/2}^{T/2} f_T(\xi)d\xi = 0 \quad ,$$

the function $f_T(\xi)$ approaches the function $f(\xi)$, and the infinite sum becomes an integral from 0 to infinity. Equation (25) may thus be written

$$f(x) = \frac{1}{\pi} \int_0^{\infty} \left[\cos \omega x \, d\omega \int_{-\infty}^{\infty} f(\xi) \cos \omega\xi \, d\xi + \sin \omega x \, d\omega \int_{-\infty}^{\infty} f(\xi) \sin \omega\xi \, d\xi \right] \quad , \tag{26}$$

and letting

$$A(\omega) = \int_{-\infty}^{\infty} f(\xi) \cos \omega\xi \, d\xi$$
$$\tag{27}$$
$$B(\omega) = \int_{-\infty}^{\infty} f(\xi) \sin \omega\xi \, d\xi \quad ,$$

we may write Equation (26) as

$$f(x) = \frac{1}{\pi} \int_0^{\infty} [A(\omega) \cos \omega x + B(\omega) \sin \omega x]d\omega \quad . \tag{28}$$

Equation (26) is called a *Fourier integral*. The functions $A(\omega)$ and $B(\omega)$ are called the *Fourier cosine* and *sine transforms* of $f(x)$, respectively, or sometimes the *spectrum* of $f(x)$. Conversely, we refer to $f(x)$ as the *inverse Fourier transform* of $A(\omega)$ and $B(\omega)$.

Let us consider now some applications of the Fourier integral to ordinary and partial differential equations. As an illustration of its application to ordinary differential equations, we treat the following problem in mechanics. Suppose we wish to find the deflection y of an infinitely long beam resting on an elastic foundation with a concentrated load P at the origin (cf. Fig. 4.9). We shall assume that the foundation transmits no shear; that is, it can be considered as an infinite number of springs.

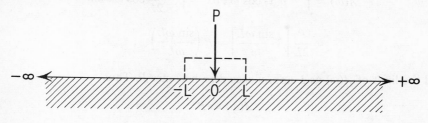

Fig. 4.9

In general, if a load of $p(x)$ lbs./ft. is placed on a beam resting on an elastic foundation, then the deflection $y(x)$ satisfies the differential equation

$$EIy^{(4)} = p(x) - Ky \quad , \tag{29}$$

where K is a constant called the *modulus of the foundation*.† Assuming that y can be expressed as a Fourier integral, we write

$$y(x) = \frac{1}{\pi} \int_0^\infty [a(\omega) \cos \omega x + b(\omega) \sin \omega x] d\omega \tag{30}$$

and

$$p(x) = \frac{1}{\pi} \int_0^\infty [A(\omega) \cos \omega x + B(\omega) \sin \omega x] d\omega \quad .$$

Note that $p(x)$ is the given function, and hence $A(\omega)$ and $B(\omega)$ are *known* functions,

$$A(\omega) = \int_{-\infty}^\infty p(x) \cos \omega x \, dx$$

$$B(\omega) = \int_{-\infty}^\infty p(x) \sin \omega x \, dx \quad .$$

The problem in hand requires a concentrated load P at the origin. For purposes of analysis it is convenient to assume

$$p(x) = \frac{P}{2L} \quad ,$$

---

† Compare Salvadori and Schwarz, *op. cit.*, p. 378.

that is, that the load is distributed over the finite distance $2L$ of the beam; find $A(\omega)$ and $B(\omega)$, and then let L approach zero. We obtain the result

$$A(\omega) = \int_{-\infty}^{\infty} p(x) \cos \omega x \, dx = \int_{-L}^{L} \frac{P}{2L} \cos \omega x \, dx$$

$$= \frac{P}{2L} \left[2 \frac{\sin \omega L}{\omega} \right] = P \left(\frac{\sin \omega L}{\omega L} \right) \quad,$$

and the limit of $A(\omega)$ as L approaches zero becomes P. Thus

$$A(\omega) = P$$

and

$$B(\omega) = \int_{-\infty}^{\infty} p(x) \sin \omega x \, dx = \int_{-L}^{L} \frac{P}{2L} \sin \omega x \, dx = 0 \quad.$$

Hence $p(x)$ has the Fourier integral representation

$$p(x) = \frac{1}{\pi} \int_{0}^{\infty} P \cos \omega x \, d\omega \quad. \tag{31}$$

Substituting Equations (30) and (31) into Equation (29), we have

$$\frac{EI}{\pi} \int_{0}^{\infty} [\omega^4 a(\omega) \cos \omega x + \omega^4 b(\omega) \sin \omega x] d\omega$$

$$= \frac{1}{\pi} \int_{0}^{\infty} P \cos \omega x \, d\omega - \frac{K}{\pi} \int_{0}^{\infty} [a(\omega) \cos \omega x + b(\omega) \sin \omega x] d\omega \quad,$$

and, collecting all terms under a single integral sign, the result is

$$\int_{0}^{\infty} \{[(EI\omega^4 + K)a(\omega) - P] \cos \omega x + [(EI\omega^4 + K)b(\omega)] \sin \omega x\} d\omega = 0 \quad.$$

Since the above equation must be identically true for all x,

$$(EI\omega^4 + K)a(\omega) - P = 0$$

$$(EI\omega^4 + K)b(\omega) \qquad = 0 \quad,$$

and we find

$$a(\omega) = \frac{P}{EI\omega^4 + K}$$

$$b(\omega) = 0 \quad.$$

Thus the deflection curve $y(x)$ of Equation (30) becomes

$$y(x) = \frac{P}{\pi} \int_0^\infty \frac{\cos \omega x}{EI\omega^4 + K} \, d\omega \quad . \tag{32}$$

As a numerical result, the deflection at the origin (where we have placed the concentrated load) is

$$y(0) = \frac{P}{\pi K} \int_0^\infty \frac{d\omega}{1 + \dfrac{EI}{K} \omega^4} \quad . \tag{33}$$

The above integral can be evaluated by using the Beta function. We recall that

$$B(u, v) = \int_0^1 x^{u-1}(1 - x)^{v-1} \, dx \quad .$$

Letting $x = \dfrac{y}{1 + y}$ yields

$$B(u, v) = \int_0^\infty \frac{y^{u-1}}{(1 + y)^{u+v}} \, dy \quad .$$

The substitution

$$y = z^4$$

yields

$$B(u, v) = \int_0^\infty \frac{4z^{4u-1}}{(1 + z^4)^{u+v}} \, dz$$

and

$$B(\tfrac{1}{4}, \tfrac{3}{4}) = 4 \int_0^\infty \frac{dz}{1 + z^4} \quad .$$

Making the substitution

$$z = \sqrt[4]{\frac{EI}{K}} \, \omega$$

in Equation (33) yields

$$y(0) = \frac{P}{\pi K} \sqrt[4]{\frac{K}{EI}} \int_0^\infty \frac{dz}{1 + z^4} = \frac{P}{4\pi K} \sqrt[4]{\frac{K}{EI}} \, \Gamma(\tfrac{1}{4}) \, \Gamma(\tfrac{3}{4}) \quad ,$$

and the Gamma function is a tabulated function. Actually in this case we can go one step further if we use the identity

$$\Gamma(u)\Gamma(1 - u) = \frac{\pi}{\sin \pi u} \quad u \neq 0, \pm 1, \pm 2, \cdots \quad ,$$

which can be deduced from the infinite product expansion for $\Gamma(u)$ (cf. Exercise 1, Sec. 7, Chap. 2). Then

$$\Gamma(\tfrac{1}{4})\Gamma(\tfrac{3}{4}) = \frac{2\pi}{\sqrt{2}} \quad ,$$

and

$$y(0) = \frac{P\sqrt{2}}{4K} \sqrt[4]{\frac{K}{EI}} \quad .$$

This is as far as we can proceed with our present methods. After we have introduced the delta function in Chapter 6 (cf. Exercise 2, Sec. 8, Chap. 6) we shall be in a position to complete the solution of the problem.

As a second application of the Fourier integral, let us consider the flow of electricity in an infinite cable. It is shown† that the voltage $e(x, t)$ in a transmission line satisfies the partial differential equation

$$RC \frac{\partial e}{\partial t} = \frac{\partial^2 e}{\partial x^2} \quad . \tag{34}$$

Let it be required to find $e(x, t)$ if the initial voltage in the line is $E(x)$, that is,

$$e(x, 0) = E(x) \quad . \tag{35}$$

The method of separation of variables used in Fourier series suggests that we first try a solution of the form

$$e(x, t) = X(x)T(t) \quad .$$

Substituting this into Equation (34) and dividing by XT gives

$$\frac{RC T'}{T} = \frac{X''}{X} \quad , \tag{36}$$

and noting that each side of the above equation is free of one variable, we see

---

† Cf. Miller, *op. cit.*, Chap. 1.

that the common ratio must be a constant, say $-\beta^2$. Equation (36) thus reduces to the two ordinary differential equations

$$T' + \frac{\beta^2}{RC} T = 0$$

and

$$X'' + \beta^2 X = 0 \quad .$$

Solving these two equations, we see that any function of the form

$$A_\beta e^{-\frac{\beta^2}{RC}t} \cos \beta x + B_\beta e^{-\frac{\beta^2}{RC}t} \sin \beta x$$

satisfies the partial differential equation of Equation (34) no matter what the β, A_β, and B_β. In this case we have a contribution from every real value of the separation constant β (instead of just integral values of β as in the case of Fourier series). Hence

$$e(x, t) = \frac{1}{\pi} \int_0^\infty [A(\beta)e^{-\frac{\beta^2}{RC}t} \cos \beta x + B(\beta)e^{-\frac{\beta^2}{RC}t} \sin \beta x]d\beta \tag{37}$$

is a candidate for a solution of Equation (34). Note that we have set $A_\beta = \frac{1}{\pi} A(\beta)$ and $B_\beta = \frac{1}{\pi} B(\beta)$. If $e(x, t)$ as given by Equation (37) is to satisfy the boundary condition of Equation (35), we must have

$$e(x, 0) = E(x) = \frac{1}{\pi} \int_0^\infty [A(\beta) \cos \beta x + B(\beta) \sin \beta x]d\beta \quad . \tag{38}$$

Thus, if we choose $A(\beta)$ and $B(\beta)$ as the Fourier cosine and sine transforms of $E(x)$, respectively, our problem will be solved.

Now $A(\beta)$ and $B(\beta)$ are given by Equation (27), and substituting these expressions into Equation (37), we have

$$e(x, t) = \frac{1}{\pi} \int_0^\infty \left\{ \left[\int_{-\infty}^\infty E(\zeta) \cos \beta\zeta \, d\zeta \right] e^{-\frac{\beta^2}{RC}t} \cos \beta x \right.$$
$$\left. + \left[\int_{-\infty}^\infty E(\zeta) \sin \beta\zeta \, d\zeta \right] e^{-\frac{\beta^2}{RC}t} \sin \beta x \right\} d\beta \quad ,$$

which upon rearrangement of terms and use of the trigonometric identity

$$\cos \beta\zeta \cos \beta x + \sin \beta\zeta \sin \beta x = \cos \beta(\zeta - x)$$

becomes

$$e(x, t) = \frac{1}{\pi} \int_{-\infty}^{\infty} E(\zeta) \left[\int_0^{\infty} e^{-\frac{\beta^2}{RC}t} \cos \beta(\zeta - x) d\beta \right] d\zeta \quad , \tag{39}$$

which is the desired result. However, we note that the integral with respect to β in Equation (39) involves only *known* functions, and by Exercise 2, Section 8, Chapter 2,

$$\int_0^{\infty} e^{-\frac{\beta^2}{RC}t} \cos \beta(\zeta - x) d\beta = \frac{\sqrt{\pi RC}}{2\sqrt{t}} e^{-\frac{RC(\zeta - x)^2}{4t}} \quad .$$

Thus the solution to the transmission line problem can be written in terms of a single quadrature as

$$e(x, t) = \frac{\sqrt{RC}}{2\sqrt{\pi t}} \int_{-\infty}^{\infty} E(\zeta) e^{-\frac{RC(\zeta - x)^2}{4t}} d\zeta \quad . \tag{40}$$

EXERCISES

1. If in the transmission line problem the initial voltage distribution was

$$E(x) = E_0 e^{-|x|} \quad ,$$

   show that

   $$e(x, t) = \tfrac{1}{2} E_0 e^{t/RC} \left[2 \cosh x - e^x \operatorname{erf}\left(\frac{RCx + 2t}{2\sqrt{RCt}}\right) + e^{-x} \operatorname{erf}\left(\frac{RCx - 2t}{2\sqrt{RCt}}\right) \right] \quad .$$

2. An infinite string has an initial displacement $u(x, 0) = f(x)$ and zero initial velocity. Recalling that the partial differential equation satisfied by the displacement $u(x, t)$ is

   $$\frac{\partial^2 u}{\partial x^2} = \frac{1}{a^2} \frac{\partial^2 u}{\partial t^2} \quad ,$$

   show that

   $$u(x, t) = \tfrac{1}{2}[f(x + at) + f(x - at)] \quad .$$

3. A semi-infinite thin bar has its end at $x = 0$ kept at zero temperature. If the rest of the bar is completely insulated and the initial temperature $u(x, 0)$ is a constant U_0, find the temperature distribution $u(x, t)$.

4. A semi-infinite string is fixed at the origin, is initially undisplaced but has an initial velocity $g(x)$. Find the transverse displacement $u(x, t)$ of the string.

5. The equation satisfied by the temperature $u(x, y, t)$ in a thin plate is

$$\frac{\partial^2 u}{\partial x^2} + \frac{\partial^2 u}{\partial y^2} = \frac{1}{c^2} \frac{\partial u}{\partial t}$$

where c is a constant depending on the density, thermal conductivity, and specific heat. If the plate is insulated on its plane surfaces, is infinite in extent, and has an initial temperature distribution $F(x, y)$, find the temperature $u(x, y, t)$.

6. The Fourier Transform

If in the Fourier series expansion of Equations (7), (8), and (9) we replace sines and cosines by complex exponentials according to the formulas

$$\cos \theta = \frac{e^{j\theta} + e^{-j\theta}}{2} \quad , \quad \sin \theta = \frac{e^{j\theta} - e^{-j\theta}}{2j} \quad ,$$

then we obtain the *complex form of the Fourier series*. Defining c_n as

$$c_n = a_n - jb_n \quad ,$$

then some trivial algebraic manipulations yield

$$f(x) = \tfrac{1}{2} \sum_{n=-\infty}^{\infty} c_n e^{j\omega_n x} \quad ,$$

$$c_n = \frac{2}{T} \int_{-T/2}^{T/2} f(x) e^{-j\omega_n x} dx \quad , \quad n = 0, \pm 1, \pm 2, \cdots \quad , \tag{41}$$

where

$$\omega_n = \frac{2n\pi}{T} \quad .$$

The complex Fourier series of Equations (41) is useful in certain network applications (cf. Chap. 6). Its form is also more compact than the sine-cosine Fourier series, since we do not have to make any distinction between sines and cosines, and all the coefficients c_n are given by the same formula. In the same manner in which the Fourier integral was derived from Equations (7), (8) and (9), we can deduce the complex form of the Fourier transform from Equations (41). To do this, suppose $f_T(t)$ is a periodic function of period T. Then, by virtue of Equations (41), we may write

$$f_T(t) = \frac{1}{T} \sum_{n=-\infty}^{\infty} F(j\omega_n) e^{j\omega_n t} \tag{42}$$

$$F(j\omega_n) = \int_{-T/2}^{T/2} f_T(t)e^{-j\omega_n t}dt \quad , \tag{43}$$

where we have made some slight changes in notation. If we let

$$\Delta\omega_n = \omega_{n+1} - \omega_n = \frac{2(n+1)\pi}{T} - \frac{2n\pi}{T} = \frac{2\pi}{T} \quad ,$$

Equation (42) becomes

$$f_T(t) = \frac{1}{2\pi} \sum_{n=-\infty}^{\infty} F(j\omega_n)e^{j\omega_n t}\,\Delta\omega_n \quad . \tag{44}$$

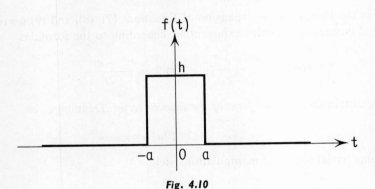

Fig. 4.10

Now, as $T \to \infty$, $f_T(t)$ approaches $f(t)$, the discrete variable ω_n becomes a continuous variable ω, the infinite sum of Equation (44) becomes an infinite integral,

$$f(t) = \frac{1}{2\pi} \int_{-\infty}^{\infty} F(j\omega)e^{j\omega t}d\omega \quad , \tag{45}$$

and Equation (43) becomes

$$F(j\omega) = \int_{-\infty}^{\infty} f(t)e^{-j\omega t}dt \quad . \tag{46}$$

Equation (46) is called the *Fourier transform* of $f(t)$ and is frequently written

$$F(j\omega) = \mathscr{F}[f(t)] \quad .$$

Similarly, we call $f(t)$ the *inverse transform* of $F(j\omega)$ and write symbolically

$$f(t) = \mathscr{F}^{-1}[F(j\omega)] \quad .$$

The dual relation of Equations (45) and (46) is apparent.

The functions $f(t)$ and $F(j\omega)$ are known as *Fourier transform pairs*. For example, if $f(t)$ is the finite pulse of Figure 4.10, then its Fourier transform $F(j\omega)$ is

$$F(j\omega) = \int_{-\infty}^{\infty} f(t)e^{-j\omega t}\, dt = \int_{-a}^{a} he^{-j\omega t} dt = 2ah \frac{\sin \omega a}{\omega a} \quad .$$

Similarly, if

$$f(t) = e^{-\alpha|t|} \quad , \quad \alpha > 0 \quad ,$$

then

$$F(j\omega) = \int_{-\infty}^{\infty} f(t)e^{-j\omega t}dt = \int_{-\infty}^{\infty} e^{-\alpha|t|}e^{-j\omega t}dt$$

$$= \int_{-\infty}^{0} e^{\alpha t}e^{-j\omega t}dt + \int_{0}^{\infty} e^{-\alpha t}e^{-j\omega t}dt$$

$$= \frac{1}{\alpha - j\omega} + \frac{1}{\alpha + j\omega} = \frac{2\alpha}{\alpha^2 + \omega^2} \quad .$$

Hence

$$e^{-\alpha|t|} \quad \text{and} \quad \frac{2\alpha}{\alpha^2 + \omega^2}$$

are *Fourier transform pairs*.

Again, if for $\alpha > 0$,

$$f(t) = e^{-\alpha t} \quad , \quad t > 0$$
$$f(t) = 0 \quad \quad , \quad t < 0 \quad ,$$

then

$$F(j\omega) = \int_{-\infty}^{\infty} f(t)e^{-j\omega t}dt = \int_{0}^{\infty} e^{-\alpha t}e^{-j\omega t}dt = \frac{1}{\alpha + j\omega} \quad ,$$

and the reader may construct other transform pairs.

As in the case of Fourier series, not every function has a Fourier transform. Precise mathematical conditions under which a function has a Fourier transform are set forth in the following theorem. A proof of this result will be found in Appendix 3.

THEOREM. Let $f(t)$ be integrable, and let $\int_{-\infty}^{\infty} |f(t)|dt < \infty$. Then

$$F(j\omega) = \int_{-\infty}^{\infty} f(t)e^{-j\omega t}dt$$

exists, and at every point where $f(t)$ has a right- and left-hand derivative

$$\tfrac{1}{2}[f(t+) + f(t-)] = \frac{1}{2\pi} \int_{-\infty}^{\infty} F(j\omega)e^{j\omega t}d\omega \quad .$$

Besides the "special" sets of Fourier transform pairs of which we have considered a few, we can also deduce various general formulas such as the following: If $F(j\omega)$ is the Fourier transform of $f(t)$, then the Fourier transform of $f(t - \tau)$ is $F(j\omega)e^{-j\omega\tau}$. This is easily shown, since

$$\mathscr{F}[f(t - \tau)] = \int_{-\infty}^{\infty} f(t - \tau)e^{-j\omega t}dt$$

by definition, and if we let $t - \tau = x$ in the above integral,

$$\mathscr{F}[f(t - \tau)] = e^{-j\omega\tau} \int_{-\infty}^{\infty} f(x)e^{-j\omega x}dx = e^{-j\omega\tau}F(j\omega) \quad .$$

Similarly, the Fourier transform of the *derivative* of $f(t)$ can be found in terms of $F(j\omega)$. By definition

$$\mathscr{F}[f'(t)] = \int_{-\infty}^{\infty} f'(t)e^{-j\omega t}dt \quad ,$$

which, upon integrating by parts becomes

$$\mathscr{F}[f'(t)] = f(t)e^{-j\omega t}\Big|_{-\infty}^{\infty} + (j\omega)\int_{-\infty}^{\infty} f(t)e^{-j\omega t}dt \quad .$$

But since $\int_{-\infty}^{\infty} |f(t)|dt < \infty$ if $f(t)$ has a Fourier transform, and if the limit of $f(t)$ exists as t approaches $\pm \infty$, then

$$\lim_{t \to \pm \infty} f(t) = 0 \quad ,$$

and the above formula becomes

$$\mathscr{F}[f'(t)] = (j\omega)F(j\omega) \quad . \tag{47}$$

Similarly, we can easily show that

$$\mathscr{F}[f''(t)] = (j\omega)^2 F(j\omega) = -\omega^2 F(j\omega)$$

and so forth for higher derivatives of $f(t)$.

EXERCISE

Show that if $f(t)$ is an even function then its transform $F(j\omega)$ is an even real valued function of ω.

7. Applications of the Fourier Transform

As a first example of the Fourier transform we shall consider an application to partial differential equations. The general idea is the following. If we transform a partial differential equation involving, say, x and t with respect to x, we get an ordinary differential equation on the variable t. Solving this equation for the transform of the unknown function, we can then find the inverse transform which is the desired solution. In the next chapter we shall consider the *Laplace transform*, which is an extension of the Fourier transform, as well as other transforms. Chapter 5, on the Laplace transform, will systematically exploit the technique we are now introducing.

For comparison, we shall solve the transmission line problem of Section 5 by the transform technique [cf. Equations (34) and (35)]. First, we transform Equation (34) with respect to x. Then, if $F(j\beta, t)$ is the Fourier transform of $e(x, t)$ with respect to x,

$$\mathscr{F}\left[\frac{\partial^2 e}{\partial x^2}\right] = (j\beta)^2 F(j\beta, t) = -\beta^2 F(j\beta, t) \quad ,$$

and

$$\mathscr{F}\left[\frac{\partial e}{\partial t}\right] = \int_{-\infty}^{\infty} \frac{\partial}{\partial t} e(x, t) e^{-j\beta x} dx = \frac{\partial}{\partial t} \int_{-\infty}^{\infty} e(x, t) e^{-j\beta x} dx$$

$$= \frac{\partial}{\partial t} F(j\beta, t) \quad .$$

Equation (34) then becomes the ordinary differential equation

$$RC \frac{d}{dt} F(j\beta, t) = -\beta^2 F(j\beta, t) \quad , \tag{48}$$

on the variable t. Considering β as a parameter, the solution of Equation (48) is

$$F(j\beta, t) = A(j\beta) e^{-\frac{\beta^2}{RC} t} \quad , \tag{49}$$

where $A(j\beta)$ is the "constant of integration." Letting $G(j\beta)$ be the Fourier transform of the boundary condition, $e(x, 0) = E(x)$,

$$G(j\beta) = \int_{-\infty}^{\infty} E(x) e^{-j\beta x} dx \quad , \tag{50}$$

and we see from Equations (49) and (50) that

$$F(j\beta, 0) = A(j\beta) = \mathscr{F}[e(x, 0)] = G(j\beta) \quad .$$

Hence

$$F(j\beta, t) = G(j\beta)e^{-\frac{\beta^2}{RC}t} \quad .$$

The solution to our boundary value problem, namely, $e(x, t)$ is therefore the inverse transform of $F(j\beta, t)$

$$\mathscr{F}^{-1}[F(j\beta, t)] = e(x, t) = \frac{1}{2\pi} \int_{-\infty}^{\infty} G(j\beta)e^{-\frac{\beta^2}{RC}t} e^{j\beta x} d\beta \quad . \tag{51}$$

This result can be further simplified by substituting $G(j\beta)$ as given by Equation (50) into Equation (51):

$$e(x, t) = \frac{1}{2\pi} \int_{-\infty}^{\infty} \int_{-\infty}^{\infty} E(\zeta)e^{-j\beta\zeta}e^{-\frac{\beta^2}{RC}t} e^{j\beta x} d\zeta \, d\beta$$

$$= \frac{1}{2\pi} \int_{-\infty}^{\infty} E(\zeta) \left[\int_{-\infty}^{\infty} e^{-j\beta\zeta + j\beta x - \frac{\beta^2}{RC}t} d\beta \right] d\zeta \quad . \tag{52}$$

The integral

$$I = \int_{-\infty}^{\infty} e^{-j\beta\zeta + j\beta x - \frac{\beta^2}{RC}t} d\beta \tag{53}$$

involves only known functions. If we complete the square to write

$$-j\beta\zeta + j\beta x - \frac{\beta^2}{RC}t = -\frac{t}{RC}\left[\beta + j\frac{RC(\zeta - x)}{2t}\right]^2 - \frac{RC(\zeta - x)^2}{4t} \quad ,$$

then from Equation (53)

$$I = e^{-\frac{RC(\zeta - x)^2}{4t}} \int_{-\infty}^{\infty} e^{-\frac{t}{RC}\alpha^2} d\alpha \quad ,$$

where $\alpha = \beta + j\dfrac{RC(\zeta - x)}{2t}$. If we use certain elementary properties of the error function, it is not hard to see that

$$I = \sqrt{\frac{RC\pi}{t}} \, e^{-\frac{RC(\zeta - x)^2}{4t}} \quad ,$$

and hence Equation (52) assumes the form

$$e(x, t) = \frac{\sqrt{RC}}{2\sqrt{\pi t}} \int_{-\infty}^{\infty} E(\zeta)e^{-\frac{RC(\zeta - x)^2}{4t}} d\zeta \quad ,$$

which is identical with Equation (40).

We now wish to consider applications of the Fourier transform to problems other than the solution of partial differential equations. Further applications will appear in the chapter on networks.

In information theory, as well as other branches of communication engineering, one often considers a function of time, $x(t)$, or, as we shall frequently say, a *signal*. The function $x(t)$ is generally thought of as extending from $-\infty$ to $+\infty$ or from 0 to ∞. Now the problem we wish to solve is the following. Suppose the continuous signal is *sampled*; that is, we give its ordinates at a sequence of equally spaced *discrete* points. Then how much information is lost? Or, in other words, from this set of discrete samples, how accurately can we reproduce the original function? A partial answer is given in the following theorem.

THEOREM. If a signal $x(t)$ extending from 0 to ∞ contains no frequencies above W cycles per second, then it is completely determined by giving its ordinates at a sequence of points spaced $1/2W$ seconds apart.

We are using electrical terminology when we say "signals." If a sine wave has a period of T seconds, then its *frequency f* is defined as $1/T$ cycles/second and its *angular frequency*, ω, equals $2\pi f$. If, for mathematical convenience, we extend the function $x(t)$ to negative values of time as an *even* function, then its Fourier transform, $X(j\omega)$, is a real valued function of ω. To emphasize the fact that $X(j\omega)$ takes on only real values, we write

$$g(\omega) \equiv X(j\omega) \quad .$$

Since $g(\omega) = \mathscr{F}[x(t)]$, $x(t)$ is given by the inverse Fourier transform of g,

$$x(t) = \frac{1}{2\pi} \int_{-\infty}^{\infty} g(\omega)e^{j\omega t}d\omega \quad . \tag{54}$$

But since by hypothesis, $g(\omega) = 0$ for $|\omega| > 2\pi W$, we may write this integral as

$$x(t) = \frac{1}{2\pi} \int_{-2\pi W}^{2\pi W} g(\omega)e^{j\omega t}d\omega \quad . \tag{55}$$

On the other hand, if we repeat $g(\omega)$ periodically with period $4\pi W$, we can write it as a complex Fourier series

$$g(\omega) = \sum_{n=-\infty}^{\infty} c_n e^{\frac{jn\omega}{2W}} \quad , \tag{56}$$

where

$$c_n = \frac{1}{4\pi W} \int_{-2\pi W}^{2\pi W} g(\omega)e^{-\frac{jn\omega}{2W}} d\omega \quad . \tag{57}$$

Therefore

$$x(t) = \frac{1}{2\pi} \int_{-2\pi W}^{2\pi W} \sum_{-\infty}^{\infty} c_n e^{j\frac{n\omega}{2W} + j\omega t} d\omega$$

$$= \frac{1}{2\pi} \sum_{-\infty}^{\infty} c_n \int_{-2\pi W}^{2\pi W} e^{j\omega \left(\frac{n}{2W} + t\right)} d\omega$$

$$= 2W \sum_{n=-\infty}^{\infty} c_n \frac{\sin \pi(2Wt + n)}{\pi(2Wt + n)} \quad . \tag{58}$$

Suppose, now, that the function $x(t)$ is sampled at the times

$$t = \cdots t_{-n}, t_{-n+1}, \cdots, t_{-1}, t_0, t_1, \cdots, t_n, \cdots \quad ,$$

where $t_k = k/2W$. Then

$$t_k - t_{k-1} = \frac{1}{2W} \quad , \quad k = 0, \pm 1, \pm 2, \cdots \quad .$$

We see from Equation (55) that

$$x(t_n) = \frac{1}{2\pi} \int_{-2\pi W}^{2\pi W} g(\omega) e^{j\frac{\omega n}{2W}} d\omega$$

and from Equation (57),

$$c_n = \frac{1}{2W} x(-t_n) = \frac{1}{2W} x\left(-\frac{n}{2W}\right) \quad .$$

Equation (58) then becomes

$$x(t) = \sum_{n=-\infty}^{\infty} x\left(\frac{n}{2W}\right) \frac{\sin \pi(2Wt - n)}{\pi(2Wt - n)} \quad . \tag{59}$$

Thus, recalling that $x(t)$ is an even function, if we know

$$x(0), x\left(\frac{1}{2W}\right), x\left(\frac{1}{W}\right), \cdots, x\left(\frac{n}{2W}\right), \cdots \quad ,$$

we know $x(t)$.

The last application of the Fourier integral that we shall consider in this section is to the evaluation of certain definite integrals. Suppose we consider a function $x(t)$ and find its Fourier transform $X(j\omega)$:

$$X(j\omega) = \int_{-\infty}^{\infty} x(t)e^{-j\omega t}dt \quad .$$

Then by the inverse transform

$$x(t) = \frac{1}{2\pi} \int_{-\infty}^{\infty} X(j\omega)e^{j\omega t}d\omega \quad ,$$

and, in particular,

$$2\pi x(0) = \int_{-\infty}^{\infty} X(j\omega)d\omega \quad .$$

Thus, if we can find $X(j\omega)$, we can also compute its integral from $-\infty$ to $+\infty$ by the above equation. Also, if $X(j\omega)$ happens to be a real even function of ω, then

$$2\pi x(t) = \int_{-\infty}^{\infty} X(j\omega) \cos \omega t \, d\omega = 2\int_{0}^{\infty} X(j\omega) \cos \omega t \, d\omega \quad .$$

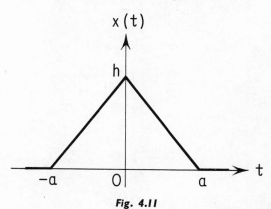

Fig. 4.11

Now, as an example, let $x(t)$ be the triangular function (cf. Fig. 4.11), which is defined analytically by the equations

$$x(t) = h\left(1 - \frac{t}{a}\right) \quad , \qquad a > t > 0$$

$$x(t) = h\left(1 + \frac{t}{a}\right) \quad , \quad -a < t < 0$$

$$x(t) = 0 \qquad\qquad\qquad |t| > a \quad .$$

The Fourier transform of this function is

$$X(j\omega) = \int_{-\infty}^{\infty} x(t)e^{-j\omega t}dt$$

$$= h \int_{-a}^{0} \left(1 + \frac{t}{a}\right) e^{-j\omega t} dt + h \int_{0}^{a} \left(1 - \frac{t}{a}\right) e^{-j\omega t} dt$$

$$= ah \left(\frac{\sin \dfrac{\omega a}{2}}{\dfrac{\omega a}{2}}\right)^{2} .$$

Therefore, from the inverse Fourier transform formula,

$$x(t) = \frac{1}{2\pi} \int_{-\infty}^{\infty} ah \left(\frac{\sin \omega a/2}{\omega a/2}\right)^{2} e^{j\omega t} \, d\omega \quad ,$$

and, in particular

$$x(0) = \frac{ah}{2\pi} \int_{-\infty}^{\infty} \left(\frac{\sin \omega a/2}{\omega a/2}\right)^{2} d\omega \quad .$$

But $x(0) = h$, and, making the change of variable $\omega a/2 = x$, we obtain

$$h = \frac{ah}{2\pi} \int_{-\infty}^{\infty} \left(\frac{\sin x}{x}\right)^{2} \frac{2}{a} \, dx$$

or

$$\int_{-\infty}^{\infty} \left(\frac{\sin x}{x}\right)^{2} dx = \pi \quad ,$$

which evaluates the infinite integral $\displaystyle\int_{-\infty}^{\infty} \left(\frac{\sin x}{x}\right)^{2} dx.$

EXERCISES

1. Solve Exercises 1 and 2 of Section 5 by the Fourier transform method.
2. Starting with the function $e^{-\alpha|t|}$, $\alpha > 0$, show that

$$\int_{-\infty}^{\infty} \frac{\cos \omega t}{\alpha^{2} + \omega^{2}} \, d\omega = \frac{\pi}{\alpha} e^{-\alpha|t|} \quad .$$

(Cf. Exercise 5, Sec. 8, Chap. 2.)

3. Prove that

$$\int_{0}^{\infty} \left(\frac{\sin x}{x}\right)^{3} dx = \frac{3\pi}{8} \quad .$$

The problem of finding the Fourier transform of a function $x(t)$ is frequently a straightforward process of integration. Invariably the problem of finding $x(t)$ when we know the Fourier transform $X(j\omega)$ is much more difficult. If the answer cannot be found in the tables,† one has to resort to integration in the complex plane. However, we shall give one example in which the inverse Fourier transform can be found by elementary methods.

Suppose

$$X(j\omega) = \frac{\sin \omega}{\omega}$$

and we wish to find $x(t) = \mathscr{F}^{-1}[X(j\omega)]$. By definition,

$$x(t) = \frac{1}{2\pi} \int_{-\infty}^{\infty} X(j\omega)e^{j\omega t}d\omega = \frac{1}{2\pi} \int_{-\infty}^{\infty} \frac{\sin \omega}{\omega} e^{j\omega t}d\omega$$

$$= \frac{1}{2\pi} \int_{-\infty}^{0} \frac{\sin \omega}{\omega} e^{j\omega t} d\omega + \frac{1}{2\pi} \int_{0}^{\infty} \frac{\sin \omega}{\omega} e^{j\omega t}d\omega \quad .$$

If we let $\omega = -\omega$ in the first integral, then we may write

$$x(t) = \frac{1}{\pi} \int_{0}^{\infty} \frac{\sin \omega \cos \omega t}{\omega} d\omega \quad .$$

By the use of the trigonometric identity

$$\tfrac{1}{2}[\sin \omega(1 + t) + \sin \omega(1 - t)] = \sin \omega \cos \omega t \quad ,$$

the above formula for $x(t)$ becomes

$$x(t) = \frac{1}{2\pi} \int_{0}^{\infty} \frac{\sin \omega(1 + t)}{\omega} d\omega + \frac{1}{2\pi} \int_{0}^{\infty} \frac{\sin \omega(1 - t)}{\omega} d\omega$$

$$= \frac{1}{2\pi} I \qquad\qquad + \frac{1}{2\pi} J \quad .$$

If $t = -1$, $I = 0$, and if $t = 1$, $J = 0$. Now let $1 + t \neq 0$. Then, if we make the substitution

$$u = \omega(1 + t)$$

in I,

$$I = \int_{0}^{\infty} \frac{\sin u}{u} du = \frac{\pi}{2} \quad \text{if} \quad 1 + t > 0 \quad ,$$

---

† Cf., for example, Campbell and Foster, *Fourier Integrals for Practical Applications.*

and

$$I = \int_0^{-\infty} \frac{\sin u}{u}\, du = -\frac{\pi}{2} \quad \text{if} \quad 1 + t < 0 \quad .$$

Similarly, if $1 - t \neq 0$, we make the substitution

$$v = \omega(1 - t)$$

in J,

$$J = \int_0^{\infty} \frac{\sin v}{v}\, dv = \frac{\pi}{2} \quad \text{if} \quad 1 - t > 0 \quad ,$$

and

$$J = \int_0^{-\infty} \frac{\sin v}{v}\, dv = -\frac{\pi}{2} \quad \text{if} \quad 1 - t < 0 \quad .$$

Thus we may write

$$x(t) = \frac{1}{2\pi} [I + J]$$

$$= \frac{1}{2\pi}\left[-\frac{\pi}{2} + \frac{\pi}{2} \right] = 0 \quad , \qquad t < -1$$

$$= \frac{1}{2\pi}\left[0 + \frac{\pi}{2} \right] \quad = \frac{1}{4} \quad , \qquad t = -1$$

$$= \frac{1}{2\pi}\left[\frac{\pi}{2} + \frac{\pi}{2} \right] \quad = \frac{1}{2} \quad , \quad -1 < t < 1$$

$$= \frac{1}{2\pi}\left[\frac{\pi}{2} + 0 \right] \quad = \frac{1}{4} \quad , \qquad 1 = t$$

$$= \frac{1}{2\pi}\left[\frac{\pi}{2} - \frac{\pi}{2} \right] \quad = 0 \quad , \qquad 1 < t \quad .$$

Comparing this with the theorem of Section 6, we see the exact agreement, including the fact that the Fourier transform yields the average values of $x(t)$ at the points of discontinuity $t = \pm 1$.

8. The Power Spectrum

In all physical, mechanical, and electrical systems unwanted phenomena variously called noise, jitter, random errors, or spurious disturbances always occur. One has an intuitive idea of noise; for example, the current flowing in a resistor due to thermal agitation of the electrons or the fading record of a radar signal. Good design can generally minimize these random errors; nevertheless, they are always present. A precise formulation of the concept of "noise" and "random process" will be made in Chapter 7. Roughly speaking, we consider functions of time, say $x(t)$ (cf. Fig. 4.12), which extend from $-\infty$ to $+\infty$.

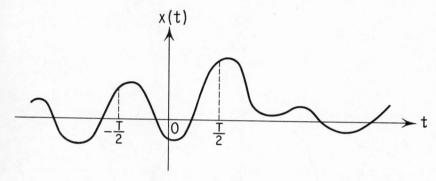

Fig. 4.12

Such functions have many interesting properties, for example, their frequency content and amplitude distribution. For an analysis of amplitude distributions, a certain amount of probability theory is prerequisite, and this study will be deferred to Chapter 7. Certain fundamental results regarding harmonic content, however, are extensions of the method of Fourier analysis, which we have just considered, and will now be presented.

One of the important characteristics of the noise is its total power. The smaller the power of the unwanted disturbance in the system, the less effect it will have on the accurate functioning of the device. However, it is not sufficient just to know the *total* power. We must know how it is distributed among the various frequencies present. We saw in Section 2 that if

$$\frac{a_0}{2} + \sum_{n=1}^{\infty} \left(a_n \cos \frac{2n\pi}{T} t + b_n \sin \frac{2n\pi}{T} t \right)$$

were the Fourier series expansion of a periodic function of period T, then the power content due to the nth harmonic was $\frac{1}{2}(a_n^2 + b_n^2)$, or the energy per cycle, (that is, watts per c.p.s.), $w(f_n)$, is

$$w(f_n) = T[\tfrac{1}{2}(a_n^2 + b_n^2)] \quad .$$

Our immediate interest will be to extend the notion of power content to *non-periodic* functions.

In our future work we shall sometimes consider a signal $x(t)$ of finite duration T and let T approach infinity as a limiting case. We shall indicate now two methods of finding the Fourier transform of such a function, and we shall demonstrate by methods which are heuristic, rather than rigorous, that the limit exists in both cases and is the Fourier transform.

Consider then a function $x(t)$ extending from $-\infty$ to $+\infty$ (cf. Fig. 4.12). We define a new function $x^T(t)$ as follows (cf. Fig. 4.13),

$$x^T(t) = x(t) \quad , \quad -\frac{T}{2} < t \leq \frac{T}{2}$$

$$x^T(t + T) = x^T(t) \quad .$$

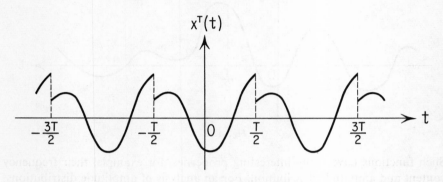

Fig. 4.13

The function $x^T(t)$ is a periodic function of period T and by Equations (42) and (43), with a slight change of notation

$$x^T(t) = \frac{1}{T} \sum_{n=-\infty}^{\infty} X(j\omega_n)e^{j\omega_n t} \quad ,$$

and its frequency spectrum is

$$X(j\omega_n) = \int_{-T/2}^{T/2} x^T(t)e^{-j\omega_n t}dt \quad , \tag{60}$$

where

$$\omega_n = \frac{2n\pi}{T} \quad .$$

It is plausible that

$$\lim_{T \to \infty} X(j\omega_n) = X(j\omega) \quad ,$$

where $X(j\omega)$ is the Fourier transform of $x(t)$.

We could also define a function $x_T(t)$ as follows (cf. Fig. 4.14):

$$x_T(t) = x(t) \quad , \quad -\frac{T}{2} < t \leq \frac{T}{2}$$

$$x_T(t) = 0 \quad , \quad \text{otherwise.}$$

Then the Fourier transform of $x_T(t)$ is [cf. Equation (46)],

$$X_T(j\omega) = \int_{-T/2}^{T/2} x_T(t)e^{-j\omega t}dt$$

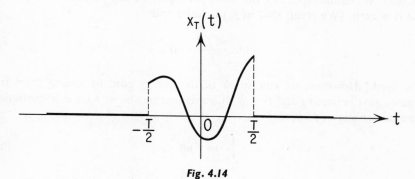

Fig. 4.14

{since $x_T(t)$ is zero outside the interval $(-T/2, T/2]$.} From physical considerations (cf. Figs. 4.12 and 4.14),

$$\lim_{T\to\infty} X_T(j\omega) = X(j\omega) \quad .$$

Hence we conclude

$$\lim_{T\to\infty} X(j\omega_n) = \lim_{T\to\infty} X_T(j\omega) = \int_{-\infty}^{\infty} x(t)e^{-j\omega t}\, dt \quad . \tag{61}$$

Suppose, now, that $x(t)$ is a periodic function of period T. Then we may write $x(t)$ as a Fourier series, that is, as a sum of sinusoidal components of frequencies $0, f, 2f, \cdots$, where $f = 1/T$. If we think of $x(t)$ as a current flowing through a unit resistance, it will dissipate a certain average amount of power, say ρ watts. If the frequency component $f_n \, (= nf)$ yields $w(f_n)$ watts per c.p.s., then the contribution to ρ from the frequency f_n is $w(f_n)/T$ watts. Hence

$$\rho = \sum_{n=0}^{\infty} w(f_n)\frac{1}{T} \quad . \tag{62}$$

The function $w(f_n)$ has the dimensions of energy and is called the *power spectrum* of $x(t)$. If we let

$$\Delta f_n = f_{n+1} - f_n = \frac{n+1}{T} - \frac{n}{T} \quad,$$

then Equation (62) may be written as

$$\rho = \sum_{n=0}^{\infty} w(f_n)\Delta f_n \quad.$$

Now, if we let $T \to \infty$, the discrete frequencies f_n tend toward a continuous variable f. We cannot speak of the watts per c.p.s. for any *particular* frequency, since it is zero. [We recall that $w(f_n)$ is finite and

$$\lim_{T \to \infty} \frac{w(f_n)}{T} = 0$$

for n fixed.] However, we can speak of the energy content arising from frequencies, say, between f and $f + df$. If we denote this by $w(f)$, the contribution to the power ρ is $w(f)df$, and

$$\rho = \int_0^{\infty} w(f)df \quad. \tag{63}$$

In the above formula we think of $x(t)$ as a time function extending from $-\infty$ to $+\infty$, and $w(f)$ is called the *power spectrum* of $x(t)$. From elementary considerations we also know that the average power may be expressed as

$$\rho = \lim_{T \to \infty} \frac{1}{T} \int_{-T/2}^{T/2} x^2(t)dt \quad.$$

We shall show later that this expression is indeed the same as Equation (63).

Notice that we have restricted ourselves to nonnegative frequencies only. If we put aside for the moment our physical picture of a current flowing through a resistance, and allow the energy content to be distributed over frequencies from $-\infty$ to $+\infty$ with the same energy content in $-(f+df)$ to $-f$ as in f to $f + df$, then Equation (63) assumes the form

$$\rho = \int_{-\infty}^{\infty} S(\omega)df \quad,$$

where $S(\omega)$ is called the *spectral density* of $x(t)$. From our definition of $S(\omega)$ we have

$$S(\omega) = S(-\omega) = \frac{w(f)}{2} \quad, \quad f \geqq 0 \quad.$$

(Cf. Fig. 4.15 on the page opposite.)

We shall now try to find an expression for $w(f)$, or equivalently, $S(\omega)$, in terms of the frequency spectrum of $x(t)$. Since $x(t)$ is a time function extending from $-\infty$ to $+\infty$, let us define a periodic function $x^T(t)$ by the equations

$$x^T(t) = x(t) \quad , \quad -\frac{T}{2} < t \leqq \frac{T}{2}$$
$$x^T(t + T) = x^T(t) \quad .$$

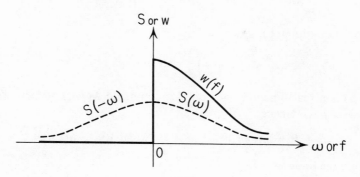

Fig. 4.15

We shall compute $w(f_n)$ for this function and then let $T \to \infty$. If we expand $x^T(t)$ in a Fourier series,

$$x^T(t) = \frac{a_0}{T} + \frac{2}{T} \sum_{n=1}^{\infty} (a_n \cos \omega_n t + b_n \sin \omega_n t) \quad ,$$

where

$$a_n = \int_{-T/2}^{T/2} x(t) \cos \omega_n t \, dt$$

and

$$b_n = \int_{-T/2}^{T/2} x(t) \sin \omega_n t \, dt \quad .$$

The energy content (watts per c.p.s.) is

$$w(f_n) = \int_{-T/2}^{T/2} \left(\frac{2}{T} a_n \cos \omega_n t + \frac{2}{T} b_n \sin \omega_n t \right)^2 dt$$

$$= \frac{2}{T} (a_n^2 + b_n^2) \quad , \quad n > 0$$

and

$$w(f_0) = \int_{-T/2}^{T/2} \left(\frac{a_0}{T} \right)^2 dt = \frac{a_0^2}{T} \quad .$$

Now

$$a_n^2 + b_n^2 = (a_n + jb_n)(a_n - jb_n)$$

$$= \left[\int_{-T/2}^{T/2} x(t)(\cos \omega_n t + j \sin \omega_n t)dt \right] \left[\int_{-T/2}^{T/2} x(t)(\cos \omega_n t - j \sin \omega_n t)dt \right]$$

$$= \left[\int_{-T/2}^{T/2} x(t)e^{j\omega_n t}dt \right] \left[\int_{-T/2}^{T/2} x(t)e^{-j\omega_n t}dt \right] \quad ,$$

and, from Equation (60),

$$X(j\omega_n) = \int_{-T/2}^{T/2} x(t)e^{-j\omega_n t}dt \quad .$$

Since $x(t)$ is a real function, the complex conjugate $X(j\omega_n)$, namely $\overline{X(j\omega_n)}$, is simply $X(-j\omega_n)$. Hence

$$a_n^2 + b_n^2 = X(j\omega_n)X(-j\omega_n) = |X(j\omega_n)|^2 \quad , \quad n > 0 \quad .$$

If we take the limit as $T \to \infty$,

$$\lim_{T \to \infty} w(f_n) = w(f)$$

and

$$w(f) = \lim_{T \to \infty} \frac{2}{T} |X(j\omega_n)|^2 \quad , \quad n \geq 0 \quad .$$

By virtue of Equations (61) we may write

$$w(f) = \lim_{T \to \infty} \frac{2}{T} |X_T(j\omega)|^2 = \lim_{T \to \infty} \frac{2}{T} \left| \int_{-T/2}^{T/2} x(t)e^{-j\omega t}dt \right|^2 \quad , \tag{64}$$

for $f \geq 0$.

The above demonstration is, of course, not mathematically rigorous, although it does make Equation (64) seem plausible. We shall therefore take Equation (64) as the *definition* of $w(f)$ in our future mathematical investigations. If in Equation (64) we allow f (or ω) to range over both positive and negative frequencies, we may write Equation (64) in terms of the spectral density; namely,

$$S(\omega) = \lim_{T \to \infty} \frac{1}{T} |X_T(j\omega)|^2 \quad .$$

We noted earlier that the average power ρ could also be expressed as

$$\rho = \lim_{T \to \infty} \frac{1}{T} \int_{-T/2}^{T/2} x^2(t)dt \quad .$$

This is readily verified, for

$$\rho = \int_{-\infty}^{\infty} S(\omega)df = \lim_{T\to\infty} \frac{1}{T} \int_{-\infty}^{\infty} |X_T(j\omega)|^2 \, df$$

$$= \lim_{T\to\infty} \frac{1}{T} \int_{-\infty}^{\infty} X_T(j\omega) X_T(-j\omega) df$$

$$= \lim_{T\to\infty} \frac{1}{T} \int_{-\infty}^{\infty} X_T(-j\omega) df \int_{-T/2}^{T/2} x(t)e^{-j\omega t} dt$$

$$= \lim_{T\to\infty} \frac{1}{T} \int_{-T/2}^{T/2} x(t) dt \int_{-\infty}^{\infty} X_T(-j\omega)e^{-j\omega t} df$$

$$= \lim_{T\to\infty} \frac{1}{T} \int_{-T/2}^{T/2} x(t) x_T(t) dt$$

$$= \lim_{T\to\infty} \frac{1}{T} \int_{-T/2}^{T/2} x^2(t) dt \quad ,$$

as we wished to prove.

9. Correlation Functions

One of the main reasons for introducing the autocorrelation function $\psi(\tau)$ of a time function $x(t)$ is that it enables us to compute the power spectrum of $x(t)$ in a practical fashion. We shall show that the power spectrum $w(f)$ and the autocorrelation function $\psi(\tau)$ are Fourier transform pairs. This is the famed Wiener-Khintchine relation. Since the autocorrelation function is fairly easy to compute, the task of finding the power spectrum is reduced to a problem in integration.

We start with a more general definition. Let $x(t)$ and $y(t)$ be two time functions extending from $-\infty$ to $+\infty$. Then the *correlation function* $R(\tau)$ of $x(t)$ and $y(t)$ is defined as

$$R(\tau) = \lim_{T\to\infty} \frac{1}{T} \int_{-T/2}^{T/2} x(t)y(t + \tau) dt \quad .$$

It is a measure of the "correlation" between x and y. If in particular we let $y(t) = x(t)$, then we have the *auto*correlation function

$$\psi(\tau) = \lim_{T\to\infty} \frac{1}{T} \int_{-T/2}^{T/2} x(t)x(t + \tau) dt \quad .$$

To show the relation between $\psi(\tau)$ and the power spectrum $w(f)$ of $x(t)$ we proceed as follows. Define a function $x^T(t)$ by the equations

$$x^T(t) = x(t) \quad , \quad -\frac{T}{2} < t \leq \frac{T}{2}$$

$$x^T(t + T) = x^T(t) \quad .$$

Then $x^T(t)$ is a periodic function of period T and we may expand it in a Fourier series

$$x^T(t) = \frac{a_0}{T} + \frac{2}{T} \sum_{n=1}^{\infty} (a_n \cos \omega_n t + b_n \sin \omega_n t) \quad ,$$

where

$$a_n = \int_{-T/2}^{T/2} x^T(t) \cos \omega_n t \, dt$$

and

$$b_n = \int_{-T/2}^{T/2} x^T(t) \sin \omega_n t \, dt \quad .$$

Also, we may write

$$x^T(t + \tau) = \frac{a_0}{T} + \frac{2}{T} \sum_{n=1}^{\infty} [a_n \cos \omega_n(t + \tau) + b_n \sin \omega_n(t + \tau)] \quad .$$

Now the functions $x^T(t)$ and $x^T(t + \tau)$ are defined on the common interval $-T/2 \leq t < T/2 - \tau$, if τ is positive or $-T/2 - \tau < t \leq T/2$ if τ is negative. Hence

$$\int_{-T/2}^{T/2} x(t)x(t + \tau)dt = \frac{a_0^2}{T} + \frac{4}{T^2} \sum_{n=1}^{\infty} \frac{T}{2} (a_n^2 + b_n^2) \cos \omega_n \tau + \varepsilon \quad . \tag{65}$$

The integration of Equation (65) is carried out by the use of well-known integral formulas, and the term ε is an error term owing to the fact that the intervals of definition of $x^T(t)$ and $x^T(t + \tau)$ do not coincide.

We recall from the previous section that

$$w(f_n) = \frac{2}{T} (a_n^2 + b_n^2) \quad , \quad n > 0$$

$$w(f_0) = w(0) = \frac{a_0^2}{T} \quad .$$

Hence

$$\frac{1}{T} \int_{-T/2}^{T/2} x(t)x(t+\tau)dt = \frac{w(f_0)}{T} + \frac{1}{T} \sum_{n=1}^{\infty} w(f_n) \cos \omega_n \tau + \frac{\varepsilon}{T} \quad .$$

If, as in earlier developments, we let

$$\Delta f_n = f_{n+1} - f_n = \frac{n+1}{T} - \frac{n}{T} = \frac{1}{T} \quad ,$$

then

$$\frac{1}{T} \int_{-T/2}^{T/2} x(t)x(t+\tau)dt = \sum_{n=0}^{\infty} w(f_n) \cos \omega_n \tau \, \Delta f_n + \frac{\varepsilon}{T} \quad .$$

Therefore

$$\psi(\tau) = \lim_{T \to \infty} \frac{1}{T} \int_{-T/2}^{T/2} x(t)x(t+\tau)dt$$

$$= \lim_{T \to \infty} \sum_{n=0}^{\infty} w(f_n) \cos \omega_n \tau \, \Delta f_n + \lim_{T \to \infty} \frac{\varepsilon}{T} \quad ,$$

and we have

$$\psi(\tau) = \int_0^{\infty} w(f) \cos \omega \tau \, df \quad . \tag{66}$$

The function $\psi(\tau)$ is an even function, since

$$\psi(-\tau) = \int_0^{\infty} w(f) \cos \omega(-\tau)df = \int_0^{\infty} w(f) \cos \omega \tau \, df = \psi(\tau) \quad .$$

If we replace the power spectrum $w(f)$ by the spectral density $S(\omega)$, we have

$$\psi(\tau) = \int_{-\infty}^{\infty} S(\omega) \cos \omega \tau \, df \quad .$$

Now $S(\omega)$ is an even function of ω, and, since

$$\int_{-\infty}^{\infty} S(\omega) \sin \omega \tau \, df = 0 \quad ,$$

we may alternatively write

$$\psi(\tau) = \int_{-\infty}^{\infty} S(\omega)[\cos \omega \tau + j \sin \omega \tau]df = \frac{1}{2\pi} \int_{-\infty}^{\infty} S(\omega)e^{j\omega \tau}d\omega \quad .$$

Thus $S(\omega)$ is the Fourier transform of $\psi(\tau)$ and, conversely, using the inverse transform,

$$S(\omega) = \int_{-\infty}^{\infty} \psi(\tau)e^{-j\omega\tau}d\tau \quad .$$

But, if we recall that $\psi(\tau)$ is an even function of τ, we know that

$$
\begin{aligned}
S(\omega) &= \int_{-\infty}^{\infty} \psi(\tau) \cos \omega\tau \, d\tau - j \int_{-\infty}^{\infty} \psi(\tau) \sin \omega\tau \, d\tau \\
&= \int_{-\infty}^{\infty} \psi(\tau) \cos \omega\tau \, d\tau + 0 \\
&= 2 \int_{0}^{\infty} \psi(\tau) \cos \omega\tau \, d\tau \quad .
\end{aligned}
$$

Replacing $S(\omega)$ by the power spectrum $w(f)/2$, we obtain the result that

$$w(f) = 4 \int_{0}^{\infty} \psi(\tau) \cos \omega\tau \, d\tau \quad , \quad \omega \geqq 0 \quad . \tag{67}$$

Equations (66) and (67) are the Wiener-Khintchine relations and show that the power spectrum and the autocorrelation function are Fourier transform pairs.

The autocorrelation function has some interesting properties. We have already seen that it is an even function of τ; that is, $\psi(\tau) = \psi(-\tau)$. It also has the property that

$$\rho = \psi(0) \quad ,$$

for

$$\psi(0) = \int_{0}^{\infty} w(f) \cos 0\omega \, df = \int_{0}^{\infty} w(f)df = \rho \quad .$$

Another elementary property of $\psi(\tau)$ is that it assumes its maximum value at $\tau = 0$. That is,

$$\psi(0) \geqq |\psi(\tau)| \quad .$$

To prove this, we write

$$
\begin{aligned}
|\psi(\tau)| &= \left| \int_{0}^{\infty} w(f) \cos \omega\tau \, df \right| \leqq \int_{0}^{\infty} |w(f)||\cos \omega\tau| \, df \\
&\leqq \int_{0}^{\infty} |w(f)|df = \int_{0}^{\infty} w(f)df = \psi(0) \quad .
\end{aligned}
$$

Finally, it can also be shown that if $\psi(\tau) = 0$ for $\tau \geqq T$, then

$$\psi\left(\frac{T}{n}\right) \leq \psi(0) \cos \frac{\pi}{n+1} \quad ,$$

where n is an integer.

If we are given a time function $x(t)$, we can calculate its autocorrelation function in a practical fashion; hence, as remarked earlier, we are then in a position to calculate its spectral density by means of the Wiener-Khintchine relations.

To carry out this calculation, we assume a large value of T. Then

$$\psi(\tau) = \lim_{T \to \infty} \frac{1}{T} \int_{-T/2}^{T/2} x(t)x(t+\tau)dt \doteq \frac{1}{T} \int_{-T/2}^{T/2} x(t)x(t+\tau)dt \quad .$$

We can now replace this integral by an approximating sum. To do this, we divide the interval $(-T/2, T/2)$ into a large number, say $2n + 1$ of equal pieces and let $\Delta t = T/(2n + 1)$. Let t_α be the midpoint of the αth interval. Then it is readily seen that

$$\psi(\tau_k) = \frac{1}{2n+1-k} \sum_{\alpha=-n}^{n-k} x(t_\alpha)x(t_\alpha + k\Delta t) \quad , \quad k = 0, 1, \cdots \quad .$$

This calculation may be conveniently carried out with the aid of a desk calculator.

Finally, we should like to give an example of the Wiener-Khintchine formulas. Let us therefore consider a *Markoffian spectrum* which is one of the most common power spectra that occur in practice. Its equation is of the form

$$\frac{1}{\omega^2 + a^2} \quad ,$$

and it is sketched in Figure 4.16 below. The half-power point occurs at $\omega = a$. If we assume

$$w(f) = \frac{4a}{\omega^2 + a^2} \quad , \quad \omega \geqq 0$$

(the $4a$ in the numerator is simply a normalizing factor), the autocorrelation function associated with this $w(f)$ can be obtained from the Wiener-Khintchine relations, namely,

$$\psi(\tau) = \int_0^\infty w(f) \cos \omega\tau \, df = 4a \int_0^\infty \frac{\cos \omega\tau}{\omega^2 + a^2} df \quad . \tag{68}$$

In Exercise 2 of Section 7 we showed that this integral had the value

$$\psi(\tau) = e^{-a|\tau|} \quad . \tag{69}$$

Of course, if we were given $\psi(\tau)$ (as would be the case in a practical problem), $w(f)$ could also be found by Equation (67),

$$w(f) = 4 \int_0^\infty \psi(\tau) \cos \omega\tau \, d\tau = 4 \int_0^\infty e^{-a|\tau|} \cos \omega\tau \, d\tau$$

$$= 4 \int_0^\infty e^{-a\tau} \cos \omega\tau \, d\tau \quad , \quad \tau \gtreqless 0$$

$$= \frac{4a}{\omega^2 + a^2} \quad . \tag{70}$$

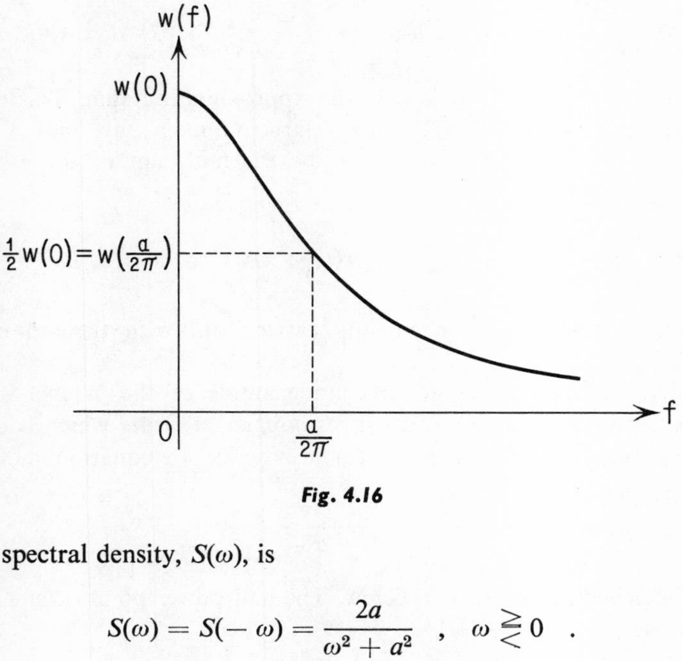

Fig. 4.16

The spectral density, $S(\omega)$, is

$$S(\omega) = S(-\omega) = \frac{2a}{\omega^2 + a^2} \quad , \quad \omega \gtreqless 0 \quad .$$

The average power dissipated, namely, ρ, is

$$\rho = \psi(0) = 1 \quad . \tag{71}$$

It can also be computed by the formula

$$\rho = \int_0^\infty w(f) df = \int_0^\infty \frac{4a}{\omega^2 + a^2} \, df = \frac{2a}{\pi} \int_0^\infty \frac{d\omega}{\omega^2 + a^2}$$

$$= \frac{2}{\pi} \arctan \frac{\omega}{a} \Big|_0^\infty = 1 \quad .$$

Verification that the half-power point occurs at $\omega = a$ is given by

$$\int_0^{a/2\pi} w(f)\,df = \frac{2}{\pi}\arctan\frac{\omega}{a}\Big|_0^a = \frac{1}{2} \ .$$

EXERCISES

1. An autocorrelation function which frequently arises in practical problems is

$$\Psi(\tau) = \frac{\psi(\tau)}{\psi(0)} = e^{-\alpha|\tau|}\cos\beta\tau \ ,$$

where we have normalized by dividing by $\psi(0)$.

(i) Calculate the power spectrum $w(f)$ and the spectral density $S(\omega)$ for this autocorrelation function.

(ii) For what value of ω does $w(f)$ assume its maximum value?

(iii) Show that $w(f)$ has a maximum at a frequency unequal to zero only if $\alpha < \sqrt{3}\,\beta$.

(iv) Compute the maximum value of the power spectrum $w(f)$.

(v) Find the power $\rho(\Omega)$,

$$\rho(\Omega) = \int_0^\Omega w(f)\,df$$

contained in the frequency band $(0, \Omega)$.

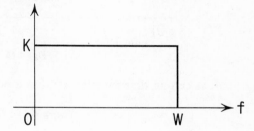

Fig. 4.17

(vi) Show that the half-power point occurs at $\Omega = \gamma$ (where $\gamma^2 = \alpha^2 + \beta^2$) and is always to the right of the peak value.

(vii) Show that the quarter and three-quarter power points are

$$\Omega = \sqrt{\alpha^2 + \gamma^2} - \alpha \quad \text{and} \quad \Omega = \sqrt{\alpha^2 + \gamma^2} + \alpha \ ,$$

respectively.

(viii) Typical values for α and β might be

$$\alpha = 1.0$$
$$\beta = 2.0 \ .$$

Using these values for α and β, plot $\Psi(\tau)$ versus τ and $w(f)$ versus f. [Use semilog paper for $w(f)$.]

2. A signal $x(t)$ has a power spectrum as indicated in Figure 4.17 on previous page.
   (i) Define and sketch the spectral density $S(\omega)$.
   (ii) What is the autocorrelation function?
   (iii) What is the power ρ?
3. Prove that the autocorrelation function of the power spectrum shown in Figure 4.18 is

$$\frac{Ww(0)}{2} \left(\frac{\sin \pi W\tau}{\pi W\tau}\right)^2 .$$

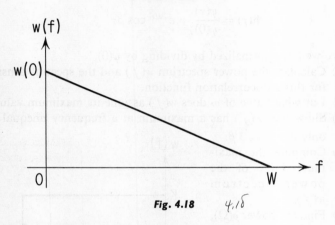

Fig. 4.18 4.18

4. A certain time function $x(t)$ has a power spectrum

$$w(f) = 1 + \omega^2 , \quad 0 \leq \omega \leq 1$$
$$w(f) = 0 , \quad \omega > 1 .$$

What is the autocorrelation function, power, and spectral density of $x(t)$?
5. Utilizing the nonnegative character of $[x(t) \pm x(t + \tau)]^2$, prove the result that $\psi(0) \geq |\psi(\tau)|$.

10. Orthogonal Functions

Parenthetically (cf. the exercises at the end of Sec. 7, Chap. 3) we have defined orthogonal functions. We repeat the definition here. A set of functions

$$\phi_1(x), \phi_2(x), \cdots, \phi_n(x), \cdots$$

is said to be *orthogonal* in the interval $[a, b]$ with respect to the *weighting function* $r(x) > 0$ if

$$\int_a^b r(x)\phi_n(x)\phi_m(x)dx = A_n \neq 0 \quad \text{if} \quad n = m$$
$$= 0 \qquad \text{if} \quad n \neq m \quad. \tag{72}$$

The sines and cosines of Fourier series form an orthogonal set of functions in the interval $[-\pi, \pi]$, with respect to the weighting function $r(x) \equiv 1$. It is particularly simple to expand an arbitrary function $f(x)$ in terms of an orthogonal set, since the coefficients are easy to evaluate. Suppose, for example, we wish to express $f(x)$ in terms of the ϕ_i's mentioned above. That is, we wish to write

$$f(x) = a_1\phi_1(x) + a_2\phi_2(x) + \cdots + a_n\phi_n(x) + \cdots . \tag{73}$$

If we multiply both sides of Equation (73) by $r(x)\phi_m(x)$ and integrate from a to b,

$$\int_a^b f(x)r(x)\phi_m(x)dx = \int_a^b r(x)\phi_m(x) \sum_{n=1}^{\infty} a_n\phi_n(x)dx$$
$$= \sum_{n=1}^{\infty} a_n \int_a^b r(x)\phi_n(x)\phi_m(x)dx$$
$$= \sum_{n=1}^{\infty} a_n A_n \delta_{nm} = a_m A_m \quad,$$

and

$$a_m = \frac{1}{A_m} \int_a^b f(x)r(x)\phi_m(x)dx \quad,$$

which evaluates the coefficients of the series of Equation (73).

Besides Fourier series there are innumerable other sets of orthogonal functions, for example, the functions associated with the names of Legendre, Bessel, Hermite, Laguerre, and Tschebyscheff, to mention a few. These functions appear in a number of places in mathematical physics, for example, in the solution of certain boundary value problems. We recall that Fourier series arose when we attempted to solve partial differential equations in cartesian coordinates. Later in this section we shall see that the Legendre polynomials will appear when the partial differential equation is expressed in spherical coordinates and that Bessel functions will appear when the equation is expressed in cylindrical coordinates.

To begin with, let us first show that the Legendre polynomials $P_0(x)$, $P_1(x)$, $P_2(x)$, $\cdots$ are orthogonal in the interval $[-1, 1]$ with respect to the weighting function $r(x) = 1$ and then consider an application of these functions to partial differential equations. To do this, we recall that $P_n(x)$ satisfies Legendre's equation

$$\frac{d}{dx}\left[(1 - x^2)\frac{d}{dx}P_n\right] + n(n + 1)P_n = 0 \quad,$$

and $P_m(x)$ satisfies

$$\frac{d}{dx}\left[(1 - x^2)\frac{d}{dx}P_m\right] + m(m + 1)P_m = 0 \quad .$$

If we multiply the first of these equations by P_m, the second by P_n and subtract,

$$P_n\frac{d}{dx}[(1 - x^2)P_m'] - P_m\frac{d}{dx}[(1 - x^2)P_n'] + [m(m + 1) - n(n + 1)]P_nP_m = 0 \quad .$$

Integrating the first two terms on the left by parts, we obtain

$$-\int_{-1}^{1}(1 - x^2)P_m'P_n'\,dx + \int_{-1}^{1}(1 - x^2)P_n'P_m'\,dx$$

$$+ [m(m + 1) - n(n + 1)]\int_{-1}^{1}P_nP_m\,dx = 0$$

or

$$(m^2 + m - n^2 - n)\int_{-1}^{1}P_n(x)P_m(x)dx = 0 \quad .$$

If $m \neq n$, we can cancel $m^2 + m - n^2 - n$ and obtain

$$\int_{-1}^{1}P_n(x)P_m(x)dx = 0 \quad , \quad n \neq m \quad .$$

Thus one-half our orthogonality conditions are proved.

To prove the remaining portion, namely,

$$\int_{-1}^{1}P_n^2(x)dx = \frac{2}{2n + 1} \quad ,$$

we use Rodrigues' formula to write

$$\int_{-1}^{1}P_n^2(x)dx = \frac{1}{2^{2n}(n!)^2}\int_{-1}^{1}\frac{d^n}{dx^n}(x^2 - 1)^n\frac{d^n}{dx^n}(x^2 - 1)^n dx \quad ,$$

which, upon integration by parts n times, becomes

$$\int_{-1}^{1}P_n^2(x)dx = \frac{(-1)^n}{2^{2n}(n!)^2}\int_{-1}^{1}(x^2 - 1)^n\frac{d^{2n}}{dx^{2n}}(x^2 - 1)^n dx$$

$$= \frac{(-1)^n}{2^{2n}(n!)^2}\int_{-1}^{1}(x^2 - 1)^n(2n)!\,dx$$

$$= \frac{(2n)!}{2^{2n}(n!)^2}\int_{-1}^{1}(1 - x^2)^n\,dx \quad .$$

Making the substitution $x = \sin \theta$ results in

$$\int_{-1}^{1} P_n^2(x)dx = \frac{(2n)!}{2^{2n}(n!)^2} \int_{-\pi/2}^{\pi/2} \cos^{2n+1} \theta \, d\theta \quad .$$

But, if we use the Beta function,

$$B(\tfrac{1}{2}, n+1) = 2\int_0^{\pi/2} \cos^{2n+1} \theta \, d\theta = \frac{\Gamma(\tfrac{1}{2})\Gamma(n+1)}{\Gamma(n+1+\tfrac{1}{2})}$$

$$= \frac{2^{2n+1}(n!)^2}{(2n+1)!} \quad ,$$

and, since

$$2\int_0^{\pi/2} \cos^{2n+1} \theta \, d\theta = \int_{-\pi/2}^{\pi/2} \cos^{2n+1} \theta \, d\theta \quad ,$$

we may write

$$\int_{-1}^{1} P_n^2(x)dx = \frac{(2n)!}{2^{2n}(n!)^2} \frac{2^{2n+1}(n!)^2}{(2n+1)!} = \frac{2}{2n+1} \quad .$$

Thus the Legendre polynomials satisfy the orthogonality conditions

$$\int_{-1}^{1} P_n(x)P_m(x)dx = \frac{2\delta_{nm}}{2n+1} \quad . \tag{74}$$

Now, as an example of the use of this orthogonality property, consider the problem posed at the beginning of Section 7 of Chapter 3, where Legendre polynomials were first introduced. To be specific, suppose we wish to find the electrostatic potential u inside a sphere S of unit radius if the potential on the surface of S is a given function of θ, say,

$$u(1, \theta) = f(\cos \theta) \quad . \tag{75}$$

Then we have seen [cf. Equation (57) of Chap. 3] that the potential satisfies the partial differential equation

$$\sin \theta \frac{\partial}{\partial r} \left(r^2 \frac{\partial u}{\partial r} \right) + \frac{\partial}{\partial \theta} \left(\sin \theta \frac{\partial u}{\partial \theta} \right) = 0 \quad . \tag{76}$$

Separating the variables leads to the two ordinary differential equations

$$\frac{d}{dr} (r^2 R') - \nu(\nu + 1)R = 0$$

and

$$\frac{1}{\sin \theta} \frac{d}{d\theta} (\Theta' \sin \theta) + \nu(\nu + 1)\Theta = 0 \tag{77}$$

[cf. Equations (59) and (60) of Chap. 3]. The first is a Cauchy equation whose general solution is

$$C_1 r^\nu + C_2 r^{-(\nu+1)} \quad , \tag{78}$$

and the second is Legendre's equation.

Now, introducing the change of variable

$$z = \cos \theta$$

reduces Equation (77) to

$$\frac{d}{dz} \left[(1 - z^2) \frac{d\Theta}{dz} \right] + \nu(\nu + 1)\Theta = 0 \quad .$$

The only solutions of Legendre's equation which remains finite when $z = 1$ (that is when $|\cos \theta| = 1$ or $\theta = 0, \pi$) are the Legendre polynomials. Hence the solution to the partial differential equation can be expressed as a combination of terms of the form

$$[C_1 r^n + C_2 r^{-(n+1)}] P_n(z) \quad . \tag{79}$$

But as $r \to 0$, the potential is finite, and since

$$\lim_{r \to 0} r^{-(n+1)} = \infty \quad ,$$

we conclude $C_2 = 0$. Recalling that $z = \cos \theta$, we may write the general solution of the partial differential equation as a linear combination of terms such as

$$a_n r^n P_n (\cos \theta) \quad .$$

Thus the function

$$u(r, \theta) = \sum_{n=0}^{\infty} a_n r^n P_n (\cos \theta)$$

satisfies the partial differential equation of Equation (76) and remains finite at the origin and on the surface of the sphere. To satisfy the boundary conditions of Equation (75) we must have

$$u(1, \theta) = f(\cos \theta) = \sum_{n=0}^{\infty} a_n P_n (\cos \theta) \quad . \tag{80}$$

That is, *we must expand f in terms of the Legendre polynomials.* Here, then, is where we use the orthogonality conditions of Equation (74). Multiplying Equation (80) by $P_m(\cos \theta)$ and writing $z = \cos \theta$, we have, on integrating from -1 to 1,

$$\int_{-1}^{1} f(z)P_m(z)dz = \sum_{n=0}^{\infty} a_n \int_{-1}^{1} P_n(z)P_m(z)dz = \sum_{n=0}^{\infty} a_n \frac{2\delta_{nm}}{2n+1}$$

$$= \frac{2a_m}{2m+1}$$

and

$$a_m = \frac{2m+1}{2} \int_{-1}^{1} f(z)P_m(z)dz \quad .$$

The solution of the original boundary value problem is therefore

$$u(r, \theta) = \frac{1}{2} \sum_{n=0}^{\infty} \left[(2n+1) \int_{-1}^{1} f(z)P_n(z)dz \right] r^n P_n(\cos \theta) \quad . \tag{81}$$

Bessel functions are also orthogonal functions. The reader may first be tempted to prove that $J_0(x), J_1(x), J_2(x), \cdots$ are orthogonal functions over some interval with respect to some weighting function $r(x)$. This, however, is not the case. It turns out that for every value of $n \geq 0$ the functions

$$J_n\left(\lambda_{1n}\frac{x}{c}\right) \quad , \quad J_n\left(\lambda_{2n}\frac{x}{c}\right) \quad , \quad J_n\left(\lambda_{3n}\frac{x}{c}\right) \quad , \quad \cdots$$

are orthogonal in the interval $[0, c]$ with respect to the weighting function $r(x) = x$, where the λ_{mn}, $m = 1, 2, \cdots$ are the positive roots of the equation

$$J_n(x) = 0 \quad .$$

Hence every Bessel function J_n generates an orthogonal set of functions. We shall show that the functions

$$J_n\left(\omega_{1n}\frac{x}{c}\right) \quad , \quad J_n\left(\omega_{2n}\frac{x}{c}\right) \quad , \quad J_n\left(\omega_{3n}\frac{x}{c}\right) \quad , \quad \cdots$$

also form an orthogonal set where the ω_{mn}, $m = 1, 2, \cdots$ are the non-negative roots of the derivative equation

$$J_n'(x) = 0 \quad .$$

From Section 10 of Chapter 3 we may write Bessel's equation of order n in the form

$$\frac{d}{dx}[xJ_n'(x)] + \left(x - \frac{n^2}{x}\right)J_n(x) = 0 \quad . \tag{82}$$

Making the change of variable

$$x = \alpha z \quad ,$$

we may write Equation (82) as

$$\alpha \frac{d}{dz} [z J_n'(\alpha z)] + \left(\alpha^2 z - \frac{n^2}{z}\right) J_n(\alpha z) = 0 \quad , \tag{83}$$

which is the equation satisfied by $J_n(\alpha z)$. Similarly,

$$\beta \frac{d}{dz} [z J_n'(\beta z)] + \left(\beta^2 z - \frac{n^2}{z}\right) J_n(\beta z) = 0 \tag{84}$$

is the equation satisfied by $J_n(\beta z)$. [The primes on J_n in Equations (83) and (84) refer to differentiation with respect to the total argument present.] We may now proceed as in the case of the Legendre functions to multiply Equation (83) by $J_n(\beta z)$, Equation (84) by $J_n(\alpha z)$ and subtract

$$\alpha J_n(\beta z) \frac{d}{dz} [z J_n'(\alpha z)] - \beta J_n(\alpha z) \frac{d}{dz} [z J_n'(\beta z)] + (\alpha^2 z - \beta^2 z) J_n(\alpha z) J_n(\beta z) = 0 \quad .$$

Integrating the first two terms on the left by parts, we obtain

$$(\alpha^2 - \beta^2) \int_0^c z J_n(\alpha z) J_n(\beta z) dz = c[\beta J_n(\alpha c) J_n'(\beta c) - \alpha J_n(\beta c) J_n'(\alpha c)] \quad . \tag{85}$$

Now, if $\alpha = \lambda/c$ and $\beta = \mu/c$ where λ and μ are two distinct positive roots of

$$J_n(z) = 0 \quad ,$$

then

$$J_n(\alpha c) = J_n(\lambda) = 0 \quad , \quad J_n(\beta c) = J_n(\mu) = 0 \quad ,$$

and

$$\alpha^2 - \beta^2 \neq 0 \quad .$$

Equation (85) thus becomes, on canceling $(\alpha^2 - \beta^2)$,

$$\int_0^c z J_n\left(\frac{\lambda}{c} z\right) J_n\left(\frac{\mu}{c} z\right) dz = 0 \quad , \tag{86}$$

which is one-half our orthogonality conditions. Similarly, if $\alpha = \omega/c$ and $\beta = \zeta/c$, where ω and ζ are two distinct non-negative roots of

$$J_n'(z) = 0 \quad ,$$

then

$$J_n'(\alpha c) = J_n'(\omega) = 0 \quad , \quad J_n'(\beta c) = J_n'(\zeta) = 0$$

and

$$\int_0^c z J_n\left(\frac{\omega}{c}z\right) J_n\left(\frac{\zeta}{c}z\right) dz = 0 \quad . \tag{87}$$

It remains now but to determine the constants

$$\int_0^c z J_n^2\left(\frac{\lambda}{c}z\right) dz = A_\lambda$$

$$\int_0^c z J_n^2\left(\frac{\omega}{c}z\right) dz = B_\omega \quad ,$$

where λ and ω are as defined above. These are evaluated by first differentiating Equation (85) with respect to αc and then letting $\alpha = \beta$. We have, on differentiating,

$$\frac{2\alpha}{c}\int_0^c z J_n(\alpha z) J_n(\beta z) dz + (\alpha^2 - \beta^2)\frac{d}{d(\alpha c)}\left[\int_0^c z J_n(\alpha z) J_n(\beta z) dz\right]$$

$$= c\left[\beta J_n'(\alpha c) J_n'(\beta c) - \alpha J_n(\beta c) J_n''(\alpha c) - \frac{1}{c} J_n(\beta c) J_n'(\alpha c)\right] \quad . \tag{88}$$

From Bessel's equation itself,

$$J_n''(\alpha c) = -\frac{1}{\alpha c} J_n'(\alpha c) - \frac{(\alpha^2 c^2 - n^2)}{\alpha^2 c^2} J_n(\alpha c) \quad .$$

Substituting this result in Equation (88) and letting $\alpha = \beta$, we have

$$\frac{2\alpha}{c}\int_0^c z J_n^2(\alpha z) dz = \alpha c[J_n'(\alpha c)]^2 + \frac{(\alpha^2 c^2 - n^2)}{\alpha c} J_n^2(\alpha c) \quad . \tag{89}$$

Now, if $\alpha = \lambda/c$ where λ is a positive root of $J_n(z) = 0$,

$$2\frac{\lambda}{c^2}\int_0^c z J_n^2\left(\frac{\lambda}{c}z\right) dz = \lambda[J_n'(\lambda)]^2 \quad . \tag{90}$$

But from both parts of Exercise 5, Section 10, Chapter 3,

$$J_n'(\alpha c) = \frac{n}{\alpha c} J_n(\alpha c) - J_{n+1}(\alpha c) \quad ,$$

or

$$J_n'(\lambda) = -J_{n+1}(\lambda)$$

and Equation (90) becomes

$$\int_0^c zJ_n^2\left(\frac{\lambda}{c}z\right) dz = \frac{c^2}{2}[J_{n+1}(\lambda)]^2 \quad, \tag{91}$$

which is the other half of the orthogonality conditions. If, however, ω is a root of $J_n'(z) = 0$, then, if we let $\alpha = \omega/c$ in Equation (89),

$$\int_0^c zJ_n^2\left(\frac{\omega}{c}z\right) dz = \frac{c^2(\omega^2 - n^2)}{2\omega^2}J_n^2(\omega) \quad, \tag{92}$$

which is the other half of the orthogonality conditions when ω is a root of $J_n'(z) = 0$. The only exceptional case to note is when $n = 0$, for in this case $\omega = 0$ is a root of $J_0'(z) = 0$. But if $n = 0$, Equation (92) becomes

$$\int_0^c zJ_0^2\left(\frac{\omega}{c}z\right) dz = \frac{c^2}{2}J_0^2(\omega)$$

and if $\omega = 0$, we see that the above formula is still valid.

We now wish to consider a few applications of the orthogonality properties of the Bessel functions to partial differential equations. As a first problem we shall solve the equation of the longitudinal vibrations of a tapered bar of length L whose linear density is uniform along the length of the beam. The equation of motion† is

$$x\frac{\partial^2 u}{\partial x^2} + \frac{\partial u}{\partial x} = a^2\frac{\partial^2 u}{\partial t^2} \quad, \tag{93}$$

where x is distance measured along the length of the bar and t is time. We shall assume that the end $x = L$ is fixed, that the initial displacement is a given function, $f(x)$, and that the bar has zero initial velocity. In formulas, then, the boundary conditions become

$$u(x, 0) = f(x)$$

$$\frac{\partial}{\partial t}u(x, 0) = 0 \tag{94}$$

$$u(L, t) = 0 \quad.$$

Assuming a solution of Equation (93) of the form

$$u(x, t) = X(x)T(t) \quad,$$

---

† Cf. Miller, *op. cit.*, Chap. 1.

we can separate the variables, as we have done in similar problems, to obtain the two ordinary differential equations

$$xX'' + X' + \beta^2 X = 0 \tag{95}$$

and

$$T'' + \frac{\beta^2}{a^2} T = 0 \quad , \tag{96}$$

where β is the separation constant. The equation on T is trivial to solve, and if we make the substitution

$$z = 2\beta\sqrt{x}$$

in the equation on X, we obtain

$$\frac{d^2 X}{dz^2} + \frac{1}{z}\frac{dX}{dz} + X = 0 \quad , \tag{97}$$

which is a Bessel equation of order zero in standard form whose general solution is

$$AJ_0(z) + BY_0(z) \quad .$$

If we return to the variable x, the solution of Equation (95) may be written

$$X(x) = AJ_0(2\beta\sqrt{x}) + BY_0(2\beta\sqrt{x}) \quad .$$

Since Y_0 becomes infinite at $x = 0$, we discard this solution. The last boundary condition of Equations (94) implies $X(L)T(t) = 0$ or $X(L) = 0$, since $T(t)$ is not identically zero. But $X(L) = 0$ implies

$$J_0(2\beta\sqrt{L}) = 0$$

or

$$2\beta\sqrt{L} = \lambda_n \quad , \quad n = 1, 2, \cdots \quad ,$$

where the λ_n are the positive roots of $J_0(x) = 0$.

Also the solution of Equation (96) is

$$T(t) = C \cos\frac{\beta}{a}t + D \sin\frac{\beta}{a}t \quad ,$$

and from the boundary condition

$$\frac{\partial}{\partial t} u(x, 0) = X(x)T'(0) = 0$$

we conclude that $D = 0$, since

$$T'(t) = -\frac{\beta}{a} C \sin \frac{\beta}{a} t + \frac{\beta}{a} D \cos \frac{\beta}{a} t$$

and

$$T'(0) = \frac{\beta}{a} D = 0 \quad .$$

Thus any linear combination such as

$$u(x, t) = \sum_{n=1}^{\infty} a_n J_0\left(\lambda_n \sqrt{\frac{x}{L}}\right) \cos \frac{\lambda_n}{2a\sqrt{L}} t \tag{98}$$

satisfies the differential equation of Equation (93) and the last two boundary conditions. If we choose the a_n such that

$$u(x, 0) = f(x) = \sum_{n=1}^{\infty} a_n J_0\left(\lambda_n \sqrt{\frac{x}{L}}\right) \quad , \tag{99}$$

then our problem will be solved. But Equation (99) is just an *expansion of f(x) in terms of a set of Bessel functions.* Hence, multiplying Equation (99) by

$$\sqrt{\frac{x}{L}} J_0\left(\lambda_m \sqrt{\frac{x}{L}}\right)$$

and integrating with respect to $\sqrt{x/L}$, (x ranging from 0 to L), we have

$$\int_0^1 \sqrt{\frac{x}{L}} f(x) J_0\left(\lambda_m \sqrt{\frac{x}{L}}\right) d\sqrt{\frac{x}{L}} = \sum_{n=1}^{\infty} a_n \int_0^1 \sqrt{\frac{x}{L}} J_0\left(\lambda_m \sqrt{\frac{x}{L}}\right) J_0\left(\lambda_n \sqrt{\frac{x}{L}}\right) d\sqrt{\frac{x}{L}} \quad ,$$

and, using Equation (91) with $n = 0$,

$$\frac{1}{2L} \int_0^L f(x) J_0\left(\lambda_m \sqrt{\frac{x}{L}}\right) dx = \frac{a_m}{2} [J_1(\lambda_m)]^2 \quad ,$$

or

$$a_m = \frac{1}{L J_1^2(\lambda_m)} \int_0^L f(x) J_0\left(\lambda_m \sqrt{\frac{x}{L}}\right) dx \quad .$$

Thus Equation (98) is the solution to our boundary value problem where the a_n are given by the above equation.

Note that we have only used positive values of the separation constant β. If we let $\beta = 0$, then Equations (95) and (96) become

$$xX'' + X' = 0$$

and

$$T'' = 0 \quad ,$$

respectively. Solving these equations, we see that a function of the form

$$(A \log x + B)(Ct + D)$$

also satisfies Equation (93). But physical considerations imply $A = 0$, the second boundary condition implies $BC = 0$, and the third boundary condition implies $BD = 0$.

As a second example, consider the problem of finding the temperature $u(r, t)$ in a thin circular disk whose bases and edge are insulated, and whose initial temperature $u(r, 0) = f(r)$ is independent of the angle θ. The equation satisfied by the temperature is

$$\frac{\partial^2 u}{\partial r^2} + \frac{1}{r} \frac{\partial u}{\partial r} - \frac{1}{k^2} \frac{\partial u}{\partial t} = 0 \quad , \tag{100}$$

where r is the distance from the center of the disk to any point. The adiabatic condition on the rim of the disk implies

$$\frac{\partial}{\partial r} u(a, t) = 0 \quad , \tag{101}$$

where a is the radius of the disk. Thus we must solve Equation (100) subject to the boundary condition of Equation (101) and (102),

$$u(r, 0) = f(r) \quad . \tag{102}$$

If we assume a solution of the form $R(r)T(t)$ Equation (100) reduces to a Bessel equation of order zero on R,

$$R'' + \frac{1}{r} R' + \beta^2 R = 0 \quad ,$$

and a linear equation with constant coefficients,

$$T' + k^2 \beta^2 T = 0$$

on T, where β is the separation constant. The solution $Y_0(\beta r)$ can be discarded on physical grounds, and thus any function of the form

$$b_\beta e^{-k^2 \beta^2 t} J_0(r\beta)$$

satisfies the partial differential equation and remains finite at $r = 0$. The above equation is based on the assumption $\beta \neq 0$. If $\beta = 0$,

$$R'' + \frac{1}{r} R' = 0 \quad ,$$

$$T' = 0 \quad ,$$

and

$$a_0 \log r + b_0$$

is a candidate for a solution of Equation (100). Since $\log r$ becomes infinite at $r = 0$, we conclude $a_0 = 0$.

Now, if the boundary condition of Equation (101) is to be satisfied, we must have

$$\frac{\partial}{\partial r} u(a, t) = R'(a)T(t) = 0$$

or $R'(a) = 0$. That is,

$$J_0'(a\beta) = 0 \quad ,$$

or

$$a\beta = \omega_n \quad , \quad n = 1, 2, \cdots \quad ,$$

where the ω_n are the non-negative roots of $J_0'(z) = 0$. Thus any function of the form

$$u(r, t) = \sum_{n=1}^{\infty} b_n J_0 \left(\frac{r}{a} \omega_n \right) e^{-(k\omega_n/a)^2 t} \tag{103}$$

satisfies the partial differential equation of Equation (100) and the boundary condition of Equation (101). Note that since $\omega_1 = 0$ and $J_0(0) = 1$ we can include b_0 with the constant b_1. In order that $u(r, t)$ satisfy Equation (102) we must choose the b_n's such that

$$u(r, 0) = f(r) = \sum_{n=1}^{\infty} b_n J_0 \left(\frac{r}{a} \omega_n \right) \quad . \tag{104}$$

Thus we must expand $f(r)$ in a series of Bessel functions. Multiplying by $r J_0 \left(\frac{r}{a} \omega_m \right)$ and integrating from 0 to a, we obtain

$$\int_0^a r f(r) J_0 \left(\frac{r}{a} \omega_m \right) dr = \sum_{n=1}^{\infty} b_n \int_0^a r J_0 \left(\frac{r}{a} \omega_m \right) J_0 \left(\frac{r}{a} \omega_n \right) dr \quad .$$

By Equations (87) and (92) with $n = 0$, we may write

$$\int_0^a rf(r)J_0\left(\frac{r}{a}\omega_m\right) dr = b_m \frac{a^2}{2} J_0^2(\omega_m) \quad , \tag{105}$$

or

$$b_m = \frac{2}{a^2 J_0^2(\omega_m)} \int_0^a rf(r)J_0\left(\frac{r}{a}\omega_m\right) dr \quad . \tag{106}$$

Thus the solution to the boundary value problem is given by the equation

$$u(r, t) = \frac{2}{a^2} \sum_{n=1}^{\infty} \frac{1}{J_0^2(\omega_n)} \left[\int_0^a sf(s)J_0\left(\frac{s}{a}\omega_n\right) ds\right] J_0\left(\frac{r}{a}\omega_n\right) e^{-(k\omega_n/a)^2 t} \quad . \tag{107}$$

In analogy with Fourier series, an expansion of an arbitrary function in terms of Bessel functions, such as Equations (99) and (104), is called a *Fourier-Bessel* series expansion.

EXERCISES

1. A sphere of unit radius has its lower hemisphere kept at a constant temperature T and its upper half kept at zero temperature. Find the temperature distribution $u(r, \theta)$ outside the sphere.

2. Solve the following differential system

$$\frac{\partial^2 u}{\partial r^2} + \frac{1}{r}\frac{\partial u}{\partial r} - \frac{1}{k}\frac{\partial u}{\partial t} = 0$$

$$u(a, t) = 0$$

$$u(r, 0) = f(r)$$

which might represent the temperature u in a thin disk of radius a insulated on its plane surfaces whose circumference is held at zero temperature and whose initial temperature is $f(r)$.

3. Solve the partial differential equation which was used to introduce Bessel functions (cf. Sec. 10, Chap. 3) if the curved surface of the infinite cylinder is kept at zero temperature and the initial temperature $f(r, \theta)$ is independent of z.

4. A circular membrane of radius a clamped on its boundary has an initial displacement $u(r, 0) = f(r)$ and zero initial velocity. If the equation of motion of the membrane is

$$\frac{\partial^2 u}{\partial r^2} + \frac{1}{r}\frac{\partial u}{\partial r} = \frac{1}{k^2}\frac{\partial^2 u}{\partial t^2} \quad ,$$

find $u(r, t)$.

5. A semi-infinite right circular cylinder has its base and curved surfaces insulated. Find the temperature $u(r, t)$ if the initial temperature distribution is $f(r)$.

6. Find the temperature $u(r, \theta, t)$ in a completely insulated thin circular disk if initially the temperature distribution is $f(r, \theta)$.

7. If $\beta_1, \beta_2, \cdots$ are the positive roots of the transcendental equation

$$\tan \beta a = -\beta \quad ,$$

prove that $\{\sin \beta_n x\}$ are orthogonal in the interval $[0, a]$. That is, prove

$$\int_0^a \sin \beta_n x \sin \beta_m x \, dx = \frac{\delta_{nm}}{2} [a + \cos^2 a \beta_n] \quad .$$

8. Consider the flow of heat in a one-dimensional rod of length L insulated on its lateral surface. The end of the rod at $x = 0$ is kept at zero temperature while the end $x = L$ is exposed to the ambient room temperature T. Find the temperature $u(x, t)$ if the rod is initially at zero temperature. [HINT: Use the results of Exercise 7 and note that the boundary condition at $x = L$ can be expressed as

$$\frac{\partial}{\partial x} u(L, t) = \alpha[T - u(L, t)] \quad ,$$

where α is a constant of proportionality.]

The set of sine functions

$$\sin x, \sin 2x, \cdots, \sin nx, \cdots$$

is an orthogonal set of functions in the interval $[-\pi, \pi]$ with respect to the weighting function $r(x) = 1$, since

$$\int_{-\pi}^{\pi} \sin nx \sin mx \, dx = \pi \delta_{nm} \quad .$$

Yet, if we attempt to write

$$\cos x = \sum_{n=1}^{\infty} b_n \sin nx \quad ,$$

we arrive at the conclusion that $b_n = 0$, $n = 1, 2, \cdots$ and hence

$$\cos x \equiv 0 \quad ,$$

which is absurd.

In general, if $\phi_1(x)$, $\phi_2(x)$, $\cdots$ is an orthogonal set of functions in the interval $[a, b]$ with respect to the weighting function $r(x) > 0$ and if $f(x)$ is an arbitrary function, then we have written

$$f(x) = \sum_{n=1}^{\infty} a_n \phi_n(x) \quad, \tag{108}$$

where, if

$$N_n = \int_a^b r(x) \phi_n^2(x) dx \quad,$$

then the coefficients a_n of Equation (108) are given by the formula

$$a_n = \frac{1}{N_n} \int_a^b f(x) r(x) \phi_n(x) dx \quad. \tag{109}$$

However, from the example of the sine function in the previous paragraph, we see that if Equation (108) is actually to represent $f(x)$ we must impose additional conditions on the orthogonal set $\phi_1(x)$, $\phi_2(x)$, $\cdots$, $\phi_n(x)$, $\cdots$.

Let, then, $\{\phi_n(x)\}$ be an orthogonal set of functions as above. If

$$\int_a^b f(x) r(x) \phi_i(x) dx = 0 \quad, \quad i = 1, 2, \cdots \quad,$$

then the function $f(x)$ is said to be *orthogonal* to the orthogonal set $\{\phi_n(x)\}$. If the above condition implies $f(x) \equiv 0$, for all functions $f(x)$ belonging to a certain class, then we say $\{\phi_n(x)\}$ is a *complete orthogonal set*.

We are generally interested in how good an approximation

$$S_N(x) = \sum_{n=1}^{N} a_n \phi_n(x) \tag{110}$$

is to $f(x)$ for large N, where $f(x)$ is an arbitrary function and

$$a_n = \frac{1}{N_n} \int_a^b f(x) r(x) \phi_n(x) dx \quad.$$

If there exists a function $g(x)$ such that $|S_N(x) - g(x)|$ can be made arbitrarily small for N sufficiently large and for all x in $[a, b]$, then, if $\{\phi_n(x)\}$ is complete, we can show that

$$g(x) \equiv f(x) \quad.$$

Consider the function

$$h(x) = g(x) - f(x) \quad.$$

Since $h(x)$ is orthogonal to the complete orthogonal set $\{\phi_n(x)\}$, we must have $h(x) \equiv 0$, and, hence, $g(x) \equiv f(x)$.

A less severe criterion is to require that

$$\lim_{N \to \infty} \int_a^b [f(x) - S_N(x)]^2 dx = 0 \quad . \tag{111}$$

If Equation (111) is true, then we say $S_N(x)$ *converges in the mean* to $f(x)$ and write

$$\underset{N \to \infty}{\text{l.i.m.}} \, S_N(x) = f(x) \quad .$$

The symbol "l.i.m." is read "limit in the mean." If $S_N(x)$ can be made arbitrarily close to $f(x)$ in absolute value for large N and all x in $[a, b]$, then clearly it converges in the mean to $f(x)$. In symbols

$$\lim_{N \to \infty} S_N(x) = f(x)$$

implies

$$\underset{N \to \infty}{\text{l.i.m.}} \, S_N(x) = f(x) \quad .$$

The converse is not necessarily true. If $S_N(x)$ converges in the mean, it may fail to converge at a given x in $[a, b]$.

If

$$\underset{N \to \infty}{\text{l.i.m.}} \, S_N(x) = f(x)$$

for all functions $f(x)$ belonging to a certain class, then we say the orthogonal set $\{\phi_n(x)\}$ is *closed* with respect to this class. If a set is closed, it is complete. For suppose the set $\{\phi_n(x)\}$ is closed but not complete. Since it is not complete, there exists a function $\psi(x)$ not identically zero such that

$$\int_a^b r(x)\phi_j(x)\psi(x)dx = 0 \quad , \quad j = 1, 2, \cdots \quad . \tag{112}$$

Let

$$A = \int_a^b r(x)\psi^2(x)dx \quad . \tag{113}$$

Since $\psi(x) \not\equiv 0$ and $r(x) > 0$, we have $A > 0$. Now choose N so large that for all $n \geq N$,

$$\int_a^b r(x)[\psi(x) - S_n(x)]^2 \, dx < \frac{A}{2} \quad . \tag{114}$$

This is possible, since $S_n(x)$ converges in the mean to $\psi(x)$.

But

$$S_n(x) = \sum_{j=1}^{n} a_j \phi_j(x)$$

and by Equation (112) all the $a_j = 0$. Thus Equation (114) implies

$$\int_a^b r(x)\psi^2(x)dx < \frac{A}{2}$$

which contradicts Equation (113).

Hence the orthogonal set $\{\phi_n(x)\}$ is complete.

Clearly, if any of the expansions involving Fourier series, Legendre, or Bessel functions are to be meaningful, the sets of functions involved must be complete. The proof of completeness is beyond the scope of this book, but the sines and cosines, Legendre polynomials, and Bessel functions do actually form complete sets of orthogonal functions.

REFERENCES

A.I.S.C., *Steel Construction*. New York: American Institute of Steel Construction, 1941.

Campbell, G. A., and R. M. Foster, *Fourier Integrals for Practical Applications*. New York: D. Van Nostrand Company, Inc., 1948.

Churchill, R. V., *Fourier Series and Boundary Value Problems*. New York: McGraw-Hill Book Co., Inc., 1941.

Lawson, J. L., and G. E. Uhlenbeck, *Threshold Signals*. New York: McGraw-Hill Book Co., Inc., 1950.

Miller, K. S., *Partial Differential Equations in Engineering Problems*. New York: Prentice-Hall, Inc., 1953.

Rice, S. O., "Mathematical Analysis of Random Noise," *Bell System Technical Journal*, 23, No. 3, 282–332 (1944); 24, No. 1, 46–156 (1945).

Salvadori, M. G., and R. J. Schwarz, *Differential Equations in Engineering Problems*. New York: Prentice-Hall, Inc., 1954.

Sneddon, I. N., *Fourier Transforms*. New York: McGraw-Hill Book Co., Inc., 1951.

| # LAPLACE TRANSFORM

1. Introduction

In the last chapter we considered the Fourier transform $X(i\omega)$ of a function $x(t)$,

$$\mathscr{F}[x(t)] = X(j\omega) = \int_{-\infty}^{\infty} x(t)e^{-j\omega t}dt \tag{1}$$

and its inverse transform

$$\mathscr{F}^{-1}[X(j\omega)] = x(t) = \frac{1}{2\pi}\int_{-\infty}^{\infty} X(j\omega)e^{j\omega t}d\omega \quad . \tag{2}$$

The numerous applications we made of the Fourier transform showed that these relations were of great value in certain applied problems. We also noted that not every function *has* a Fourier transform. For example, such a simple function as the *unit step* function $u(t)$ defined by the equations

$$u(t) = 0 \quad , \quad t < 0$$
$$u(t) = 1 \quad , \quad t > 0$$

does *not* have a Fourier transform. For if we write

$$U(j\omega) = \mathscr{F}[u(t)] = \int_{-\infty}^{\infty} u(t)e^{-j\omega t}dt = \int_{0}^{\infty} e^{-j\omega t}dt$$
$$= -\frac{e^{-j\omega t}}{j\omega}\Big|_0^{\infty} \quad , \tag{3}$$

then $e^{-j\omega t}\big|_{t=\infty}$ does not exist, since $e^{-j\omega t} = \cos\omega t - j\sin\omega t$ oscillates indefinitely as t approaches infinity. However, let us consider the following artifice:

Let the function $x(t)$ be defined as

$$x(t) = 0 \quad , \quad t < 0$$
$$x(t) = e^{-\alpha t} \quad , \quad t > 0 \quad , \quad \alpha > 0 \quad .$$

Then

$$\lim_{\alpha \to 0} x(t) = u(t) \quad ,$$

and the Fourier transform of $x(t)$ is

$$X(j\omega) = \int_{-\infty}^{\infty} x(t) e^{-j\omega t} dt = \int_{0}^{\infty} e^{-\alpha t} e^{-j\omega t} dt$$
$$= \frac{e^{-\alpha t - j\omega t}}{-(\alpha + j\omega)} \bigg|_{0}^{\infty} \quad . \tag{4}$$

Since

$$\left| e^{-\alpha t} e^{-j\omega t} \right| = e^{-\alpha t}$$

approaches zero as $t \to \infty$, since $\alpha > 0$, we conclude

$$X(j\omega) = \frac{1}{\alpha + j\omega}$$

—as we have already seen in Section 6 of Chapter 4. Now, if we allow the interchange of the operations "lim" and "$\mathscr{F}$," we may write
$$\alpha \to 0$$

$$U(j\omega) = \mathscr{F}[u(t)] = \mathscr{F}[\lim_{\alpha \to 0} x(t)] = \lim_{\alpha \to 0} \mathscr{F}[x(t)] = \lim_{\alpha \to 0} \frac{1}{\alpha + j\omega} = \frac{1}{j\omega}$$

and call $1/j\omega$ the Fourier transform of the unit step function $u(t)$.

However, there is no guarantee that the above change of limits is valid. The Laplace transform can be considered as a generalization of the Fourier transform which surmounts this mathematical difficulty. Returning to Equation (3), we see that if we had $e^{-(\sigma + j\omega)t}$ with $\sigma > 0$ in place of $e^{-j\omega t}$, then the integral would exist. That is, $e^{-\sigma t}$ is a *convergence factor*.

Let us systematically exploit this point of view. Suppose we wish to find the transform of the function $f(t)$. Now, from the theorem of Section 6 of the previous chapter, $f(t)$ must be absolutely integrable; that is, $\int_{-\infty}^{\infty} |f(t)| dt < \infty$ if the Fourier transform is to exist. As we have seen, the function $u(t)$ does not satisfy this requirement, and the common functions such as $t, t^2, \cdots, \sin t, \cos t$ are also not absolutely integrable. However, if we define a function $x(t)$ as

$$x(t) = 0 \quad , \quad t < 0$$
$$x(t) = f(t) e^{-\sigma t} \quad , \quad t > 0 \quad , \tag{5}$$

then it may be that $x(t)$ *does* have a Fourier transform. In fact, if $f(t)$ is a power of t or a trigonometric function, then $x(t)$ will have a Fourier transform if $\sigma > 0$. Suppose, then, that $x(t)$ as given by Equation (5) *does* have a Fourier transform. Therefore, we may write

$$X(j\omega) = \int_{-\infty}^{\infty} x(t)e^{-j\omega t}dt = \int_{0}^{\infty} f(t)e^{-\sigma t}e^{-j\omega t}dt \quad,$$

and, introducing the change of variable

$$s = \sigma + j\omega \quad,$$

we have

$$X(j\omega) = \int_{0}^{\infty} f(t)e^{-st}dt \quad. \tag{6}$$

Now, conversely, if we use the inverse Fourier transform,

$$x(t) = \frac{1}{2\pi} \int_{-\infty}^{\infty} X(j\omega)e^{j\omega t}d\omega \quad,$$

and multiply both sides of this equation by $e^{\sigma t}$, the result is

$$x(t)e^{\sigma t} = f(t) = \frac{1}{2\pi} \int_{-\infty}^{\infty} X(j\omega)e^{(\sigma + j\omega)t}d\omega \quad.$$

Then, making the change of variable

$$\sigma + j\omega = s \quad,$$

we obtain

$$f(t) = \frac{1}{2\pi j} \int_{\sigma - j\infty}^{\sigma + j\infty} X(j\omega)e^{st}ds \quad. \tag{7}$$

Now, in both Equations (6) and (7), $X(j\omega)$ depends on $\sigma + j\omega$. Let us therefore write

$$F(s) \equiv X(j\omega) \quad.$$

Equations (6) and (7) then become

$$F(s) = \int_{0}^{\infty} f(t)e^{-st}dt \quad, \tag{8}$$

and

$$f(t) = \frac{1}{2\pi j} \int_{\sigma - j\infty}^{\sigma + j\infty} F(s)e^{st}ds \quad, \tag{9}$$

respectively. Equation (8) is known as the *Laplace transform* of $f(t)$ and is frequently written

$$F(s) = \mathscr{L}[f(t)] \quad ,$$

whereas Equation (9) is called the *inverse Laplace transform* of $F(s)$ and is written symbolically as

$$f(t) = \mathscr{L}^{-1}[F(s)] \quad .$$

Note that s is now a complex variable with real part σ, written $\mathfrak{R}(s) = \sigma$, and imaginary part ω, written $\mathfrak{I}(s) = \omega$. If $\sigma = 0$, we are back to the Fourier transform.

The Laplace transform is defined for piecewise continuous functions $f(t)$ which have the properties:

(i) $f(t)$ is zero for negative values of t.

(ii) $|f(t)| \leq Me^{\sigma t}$ for some constants σ and M and for all t.

Condition (i) is not too stringent a restriction, since in most physical problems involving $t = $ time as the independent variable, all phenomena start at $t = 0$ or later. A function $f(t)$ having the property (ii) is said to be of *exponential order* and σ is called an *abscissa of convergence* [because of its appearance in Equation (9)]. If σ is the smallest number† satisfying (ii), then we say σ is the *exponential order* of $f(t)$. Thus, if $f(t)$ is of exponential order σ and $\beta > \sigma$, then

$$e^{-\beta t}|f(t)| \leq Me^{-(\beta-\sigma)t} \quad ,$$

and, since $\beta - \sigma > 0$,

$$\int_0^\infty e^{-\beta t} f(t)\, dt \leq \int_0^\infty |f(t)| e^{-\beta t} dt \leq \int_0^\infty Me^{-(\beta-\sigma)t} dt = \frac{M}{\beta - \sigma} < \infty \quad .$$

We infer, therefore, that the Laplace transform of $f(t)$ exists. The above conditions, however, are sufficient rather than necessary.‡

---

† Actually, there may be no smallest number. For example,

$$|t| \leq e^{\sigma t}$$

for any positive number σ no matter how small but is not true for $\sigma = 0$. Now, to be precise, consider the set Σ of all σ's which satisfy the above inequality. Then the exponential order of $f(t) = t$ is defined as the greatest lower bound of Σ. In this case, it is zero. An abscissa of convergence is then defined as any number greater than the exponential order.

‡ For example, $f(t)$ may be Laplace transformable even it becomes infinite at $t = 0$ as long as $|t^\alpha f(t)|$ with $\alpha < 1$ remains bounded at the origin. The function $f(t) = t^{-\frac{1}{2}}$ belongs to this category. Hence

$$\mathscr{L}[t^{-\frac{1}{2}}] = \int_0^\infty t^{-\frac{1}{2}} e^{-st} dt = \frac{1}{\sqrt{s}} \int_0^\infty x^{-\frac{1}{2}} e^{-x}\, dx$$

$$= \frac{1}{\sqrt{s}} \Gamma\left(\frac{1}{2}\right) = \sqrt{\frac{\pi}{s}}$$

exists.

The functions t^n, $n > 0$, sin at, cos at are all of exponential order zero. Not every function is of exponential order. For example, the function e^{t^2} is *not* of exponential order; hence its Laplace transform does not exist.

2. Some Elementary Transforms

Unless the contrary is explicitly stated, any function $f(t)$ whose Laplace transform we wish to consider will be defined as zero for negative values of t. We sometimes emphasize this by writing

$$u(t)f(t)$$

in place of $f(t)$, where $u(t)$ is the unit step function defined above as $u(t) = 0$ for $t < 0$ and $u(t) = 1$ for $t > 0$.

The Laplace transform, $\mathscr{L}$, is a *linear operator*; that is, if $f(t)$ and $g(t)$ are two functions of t, then

$$\mathscr{L}[af(t) + bg(t)] = a\mathscr{L}[f(t)] + b\mathscr{L}[g(t)] \quad,$$

where a and b are any constants. This result may be verified by a direct application of Equation (8).

Before considering various applications of the Laplace transform let us calculate the transforms of a number of elementary functions. We have already seen that $\mathscr{L}[u(t)] = 1/s$. The Laplace transform of e^{-at} is $1/(s + a)$. To find $\mathscr{L}[\sin at]$ we write, by definition,

$$\mathscr{L}[\sin at] = \int_0^\infty \sin at\, e^{-st} dt$$

$$= \frac{e^{-st}}{s^2 + a^2}[-s \sin at - a \cos at]\Big|_0^\infty \quad,$$

and, as long as $\Re(s) > 0$, that is, as long as the abscissa of convergence is positive, e^{-st} approaches zero as $t \to \infty$. Thus

$$\mathscr{L}[\sin at] = \frac{a}{s^2 + a^2} \quad.$$

Similarly, we can compute

$$\mathscr{L}[\cos at] = \frac{s}{s^2 + a^2} \quad.$$

The Laplace transform of t^n, $n > -1$, is by definition

$$\mathscr{L}[t^n] = \int_0^\infty t^n e^{-st} dt \quad,$$

which, upon making the change of variable $\zeta = st$, becomes the Gamma function

$$\mathscr{L}[t^n] = \frac{1}{s^{n+1}} \int_0^\infty \zeta^n e^{-\zeta} d\zeta = \frac{\Gamma(n+1)}{s^{n+1}} \quad .$$

In particular,

$$\mathscr{L}[t] = \frac{1}{s^2} \quad ,$$

and

$$\mathscr{L}[t^n] = \frac{n!}{s^{n+1}} \quad , \quad n \text{ a non-negative integer} \quad .$$

One can quickly see by glancing at a list of transforms† that many of the functions we have previously studied, such as Bessel functions, Hermite polynomials, Laguerre polynomials, error function, sine-integral function appear in the table.

In addition to the "special formulas" illustrated above, we can prove "general formulas" regarding the transforms of derivatives, integrals, translated functions, and derivatives and integrals of the transform itself. First let us find the transform of $f'(t)$. If $F(s)$ is the Laplace transform of $f(t)$, then

$$\mathscr{L}[f'(t)] = \int_0^\infty f'(t)e^{-st}dt = f(t)e^{-st}\Big|_0^\infty + s\int_0^\infty f(t)e^{-st}dt$$

$$= -f(0) + sF(s) \quad ,$$

and

$$\mathscr{L}[f'(t)] = sF(s) - f(0) \quad . \tag{10}$$

Also,

$$\mathscr{L}[f''(t)] = s\mathscr{L}[f'(t)] - f'(0)$$

$$= s[sF(s) - f(0)] - f'(0)$$

$$= s^2 F(s) - sf(0) - f'(0) \quad ,$$

and so forth, for higher derivatives.

Earlier we computed $\mathscr{L}[\sin at]$. Without bothering to integrate by parts, we can compute $\mathscr{L}[\cos at]$ by using Equation (10), since

$$\frac{d}{dt}\sin at = a\cos at \quad .$$

---

† A rather extensive list of transform pairs can be found in the C.R.C., *Standard Mathematical Tables*, pp. 307–315.

Thus

$$\mathcal{L}[a\cos at] = \mathcal{L}\left[\frac{d}{dt}\sin at\right] = s\mathcal{L}[\sin at] - \sin 0 = s\frac{a}{s^2 + a^2} \quad,$$

and canceling the a,

$$\mathcal{L}[\cos at] = \frac{s}{s^2 + a^2} \quad.$$

Having found the transform of the *derivative* of $f(t)$ in terms of the Laplace transform $F(s)$ of $f(t)$, let us now calculate the transform of the *integral* of $f(t)$. By definition,

$$\mathcal{L}\left[\int_a^t f(t)dt\right] = \int_0^\infty \left[\int_a^t f(x)dx\right]e^{-st}dt \quad,$$

and, integrating by parts, we obtain

$$\mathcal{L}\left[\int_a^t f(t)dt\right] = \left[\int_a^t f(x)dx\right]\left[\frac{e^{-st}}{-s}\right]\Big|_0^\infty + \frac{1}{s}\int_0^\infty e^{-st}f(t)dt$$

$$= \frac{1}{s}\int_a^0 f(x)dx + \frac{1}{s}F(s) \quad.$$

Another important formula is the *translation* equation. Suppose we consider a function $f(t)$ (cf. Fig. 5.1), which is shifted to the right by a units (cf. Fig. 5.2). Then, if we call this translated function $g(t)$, we may write

$$g(t) = f(t - a)u(t - a) \quad,$$

since the unit step function $u(t - a)$ is zero if $t - a < 0$, that is, if $t < a$. Now,

$$G(s) = \mathcal{L}[g(t)] = \mathcal{L}[f(t - a)u(t - a)]$$

$$= \int_0^\infty f(t - a)u(t - a)e^{-st}dt = \int_a^\infty f(t - a)e^{-st}dt \quad.$$

With the change of variable,

$$t - a = x \quad,$$

$G(s)$ becomes

$$G(s) = \int_0^\infty f(x)e^{-s(x+a)}dx = e^{-as}\mathcal{L}[f(t)] \quad.$$

Thus, if $F(s)$ is the Laplace transform of $f(t)$,

$$\mathscr{L}[f(t-a)u(t-a)] = e^{-as}F(s) \quad .$$

Conversely, we can easily find the Laplace transform of $e^{-at}f(t)$ as a translation of the s variable. For

$$\mathscr{L}[e^{-at}f(t)] = \int_0^\infty e^{-at}f(t)e^{-st}dt = \int_0^\infty e^{-(a+s)t}f(t)dt \quad .$$

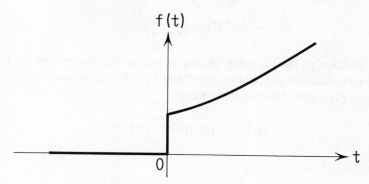

Fig. 5.1

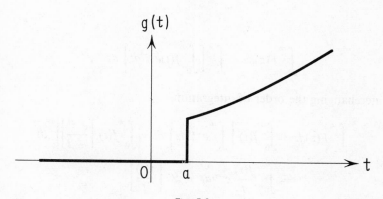

Fig. 5.2

Now, letting $a + s = y$, the above integral becomes

$$\mathscr{L}[e^{-at}f(t)] = \int_0^\infty e^{-yt}f(t)dt = F(y) = F(s+a) \quad ,$$

where $F(s)$ is the Laplace transform of $f(t)$. Hence

$$\mathscr{L}[e^{-at}f(t)] = F(s+a) \quad .$$

This formula can be used, for example, to compute the transform of $e^{-at} \sin bt$,

$$\mathscr{L}[e^{-at} \sin bt] = \frac{b}{(s+a)^2 + b^2} \quad ,$$

where we have simply replaced s by $s + a$ in the formula for the transform of $\sin bt$. One can also immediately write

$$\mathscr{L}[e^{-at}t^n] = \frac{\Gamma(n+1)}{(s+a)^{n+1}} \quad .$$

In addition to the formulas for the derivative and integral of the function $f(t)$ we can consider the results involving the derivative and integral of its *transform*, $F(s)$. For example, if we write

$$F(s) = \mathscr{L}[f(t)] = \int_0^\infty f(t)e^{-st}dt$$

and differentiate with respect to s,

$$F'(s) = \int_0^\infty -tf(t)e^{-st}dt = -\mathscr{L}[tf(t)] \quad .$$

Also

$$\int_s^\infty F(z)dz = \int_s^\infty \left[\int_0^\infty f(t)e^{-zt}dt \right] dz \quad ,$$

and, interchanging the order of integration,

$$\int_s^\infty F(z)dz = \int_0^\infty f(t) \left[\int_s^\infty e^{-zt}dz \right] dt = \int_0^\infty f(t) \left[\frac{e^{-zt}}{-t} \right]\Big|_s^\infty dt$$

$$= \int_0^\infty \frac{f(t)}{t} e^{-st}dt = \mathscr{L}\left[\frac{f(t)}{t} \right] \quad .$$

For convenient reference, a brief table of transforms summarizing the formulas we have derived to date is given in the table on page 205.

As a final manipulation of transforms, before we turn to differential equations, let us consider the problem of finding the inverse Laplace transform of the rather complicated function

$$F(s) = \frac{1}{s} \arctan s \quad . \tag{11}$$

$f(t) = \mathscr{L}^{-1}[F(s)]$	$F(s) = \mathscr{L}[f(t)]$
$\dfrac{1}{2\pi j}\displaystyle\int_{\sigma-j\infty}^{\sigma+j\infty} F(s)e^{st}\,ds$	$\displaystyle\int_0^\infty f(t)e^{-st}\,dt$
$af(t) + bg(t)$	$aF(s) + bG(s)$
$f'(t)$	$sF(s) - f(0)$
$f''(t)$	$s^2F(s) - sf(0) - f'(0)$
$\displaystyle\int_a^t f(t)\,dt$	$\dfrac{1}{s}F(s) - \dfrac{1}{s}\displaystyle\int_0^a f(t)\,dt$
$tf(t)$	$-F'(s)$
$\dfrac{f(t)}{t}$	$\displaystyle\int_s^\infty F(z)\,dz$
$f(t-a)u(t-a)$	$e^{-as}F(s) \quad,\quad a \geqq 0$
$e^{-at}f(t)$	$F(s+a)$
$u(t)$	$\dfrac{1}{s}$
$u(t-a)$	$\dfrac{e^{-as}}{s}$
t	$\dfrac{1}{s^2}$
t^n	$\dfrac{\Gamma(n+1)}{s^{n+1}} \quad,\quad n > -1$
e^{-at}	$\dfrac{1}{s+a}$
$e^{-at}t^n$	$\dfrac{\Gamma(n+1)}{(s+a)^{n+1}} \quad,\quad n > -1$
$\sin bt$	$\dfrac{b}{s^2+b^2}$
$\cos bt$	$\dfrac{s}{s^2+b^2}$
$e^{-at}\sin bt$	$\dfrac{b}{(s+a)^2+b^2}$
$e^{-at}\cos bt$	$\dfrac{s+a}{(s+a)^2+b^2}$

The evaluation of the function $f(t)$ with the property that

$$\mathscr{L}[f(t)] = F(s)$$

will make use of a number of the formulas already derived. Looking at Equation (11), we see that if we multiply by s and then differentiate, the result will be $1/(1 + s^2)$, a function whose inverse transform is known. Now,

$$\mathscr{L}[f'(t)] = sF(s) - f(0) = \arctan s - f(0)   .$$

Calling this function $G(s)$, that is,

$$G(s) = \arctan s - f(0)   ,$$

we have

$$G'(s) = \frac{1}{1 + s^2}   ,$$

and, since

$$G(s) = \mathscr{L}[f'(t)]   ,$$

it follows that

$$- tf'(t) = \mathscr{L}^{-1}[G'(s)] = \sin t   .$$

Thus

$$f'(t) = - \frac{\sin t}{t}   ,$$

and

$$f(t) = C - \int_0^t \frac{\sin t}{t}\, dt   ,$$

where C is a constant of integration. To evaluate C we note that

$$F(s) = \mathscr{L}[f(t)] = \frac{C}{s} - \frac{1}{s}\mathscr{L}\left[\frac{\sin t}{t}\right] = \frac{C}{s} - \frac{1}{s}\int_s^\infty \frac{ds}{1 + s^2}$$

$$= \frac{C}{s} + \frac{1}{s}\left[\arctan s - \frac{\pi}{2}\right]   .$$

But $F(s)$ is given by Equation (11) as $\dfrac{1}{s}\arctan s$. Hence

$$\frac{1}{s}\arctan s = \frac{C}{s} + \frac{1}{s}\arctan s - \frac{\pi}{2s}   ,$$

and

$$C = \frac{\pi}{2} \ .$$

Thus

$$f(t) = \frac{\pi}{2} - \text{Si}\,(t)$$

is the function whose Laplace transform is given by Equation (11).

3. Applications to Ordinary Differential Equations

As a first example of the use of the Laplace transform, let us solve the differential equation

$$\ddot{x} + 4\dot{x} + 4x = 4e^{2t} \tag{12}$$

with the boundary conditions

$$x(0) = 1 \quad , \quad \dot{x}(0) = -4 \ . \tag{13}$$

The method we shall employ consists in finding the transform of Equation (12). This will result in an *algebraic* equation on the Laplace transform $X(s)$ of $x(t)$ which we can solve for $X(s)$. Finding the inverse transform of $X(s)$ will then complete the solution of the problem. We recall that this technique was briefly considered when applications of the Fourier transform were treated (cf. Sec. 7 of Chap. 4).

If we let $X(s)$ be the Laplace transform of $x(t)$,

$$\mathscr{L}[\dot{x}(t)] = sX(s) - x(0) = sX(s) - 1 \ ,$$

since $x(0) = 1$, and

$$\mathscr{L}[\ddot{x}(t)] = s^2X(s) - sx(0) - \dot{x}(0) = s^2X(s) - s + 4 \ ,$$

since $\dot{x}(0) = -4$ by Equation (13). Transforming Equation (12) thus leads to

$$[s^2X(s) - s + 4] + 4[sX(s) - 1] + 4X(s) = \frac{4}{s - 2} \ , \tag{14}$$

since $1/(s - 2)$ is the Laplace transform of e^{2t}. Now Equation (14) is a linear algebraic equation on $X(s)$ which may be solved for $X(s)$,

$$X(s) = \frac{s^2 - 2s + 4}{(s - 2)(s + 2)^2} \ .$$

In order to find the inverse transform of $X(s)$, we write it as the sum of *partial fractions* (cf. the next section), namely,

$$X(s) = \frac{s^2 - 2s + 4}{(s - 2)(s + 2)^2} = \frac{1}{4}\frac{1}{s - 2} - \frac{3}{(s + 2)^2} + \frac{3}{4}\frac{1}{s + 2} \quad,$$

and from the table on page 205,

$$x(t) = \tfrac{1}{4}e^{2t} - 3te^{-2t} + \tfrac{3}{4}e^{-2t} \quad, \tag{15}$$

which is the solution of the differential equation of Equation (12) with the boundary conditions of Equation (13).

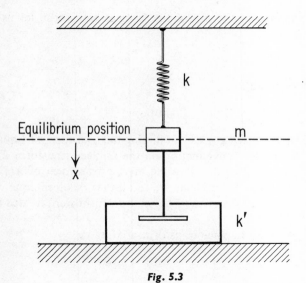

Fig. 5.3

Of course we could have solved this differential equation by standard methods (cf. Chap. 3). However, the Laplace transform presents a somewhat different philosophy in the theory of solving differential equations. Sometimes such a different point of view aids in the visualization of the problem in hand. Such, for example, is the situation in the case of electrical networks to be considered in the next chapter.

As a second example of the Laplace transform, suppose we consider the equation of motion of a mass m attached to a spring with spring constant k and braked by a dashpot with frictional constant k' (cf. Fig. 5.3). The equation of motion is

$$m\ddot{x} = -kx - k'\dot{x} + f(t) \quad,$$

where $f(t)$ represents an external forcing function applied in the positive direction of the x-axis. To obtain numerical results, let us suppose $m = k = k' = 1$. The equation of motion is then

$$\ddot{x} + \dot{x} + x = f(t) \quad . \tag{16}$$

Now we shall assume that at $t = 0$ the mass is in its equilibrium position and that it has zero initial velocity; that is,

$$x(0) = 0$$
$$\dot{x}(0) = 0 \quad . \tag{17}$$

If at time $t = 0$ a constant force F is suddenly applied, then mathematically

$$f(t) = F \cdot u(t) \quad ,$$

where $u(t)$ is the unit step function. Thus the equation we must solve is

$$\ddot{x} + \dot{x} + x = F \cdot u(t) \quad , \tag{18}$$

subject to the boundary conditions of Equation (17). Taking the Laplace transform of both sides of Equation (18), we arrive at

$$s^2 X(s) + s X(s) + X(s) = F/s \quad ,$$

where $X(s)$ is the Laplace transform of $x(t)$. Solving this equation for $X(s)$, we obtain

$$X(s) = \frac{F}{s(s^2 + s + 1)} \quad ,$$

which becomes

$$X(s) = \frac{F}{s} - \frac{F(s + 1)}{(s + \frac{1}{2})^2 + \frac{3}{4}}$$

$$= \frac{F}{s} - \frac{F(s + \frac{1}{2})}{(s + \frac{1}{2})^2 + \frac{3}{4}} - \frac{\frac{1}{2}F}{(s + \frac{1}{2})^2 + \frac{3}{4}}$$

in terms of partial fractions. The inverse transform of $X(s)$ is therefore given by

$$x(t) = F \cdot u(t) - F \cdot e^{-\frac{1}{2}t} \cos \frac{\sqrt{3}}{2} t - F \cdot \frac{\sqrt{3}}{3} e^{-\frac{1}{2}t} \sin \frac{\sqrt{3}}{2} t \quad .$$

EXERCISES

Find the Laplace transform of the following functions:

1. $\sinh at$

2. $\dfrac{\sin at}{t}$

3. $te^{-t} \cos t$

4. e^{-t^2}

Find the functions whose transforms are

5. $\dfrac{2b(s + a)}{[(s + a)^2 + b^2]^2}$

6. $\dfrac{1}{\sqrt{s^2 + 1}}$

7. $\log \dfrac{s^2 - 1}{s^2}$

Solve the following differential systems by the Laplace transform method:

8. $y''' + 2y'' - y' - 2y = 0$; $y(0) = y'(0) = 0$, $y''(0) = 6$

9. $y'' - y = t^2 + t$; $y(0) = y'(0) = 0$

10. $y'' - 2y' - y = 3 \sin t$; $y(0) = 2$, $y'(0) = 0$

11. $y'' + 2y + 3 \displaystyle\int_0^t y \, dt = t$; $y(0) = 1$, $y'(0) = 0$

12. $y''' - 3y' + 2y = (18t + 6)e^t + 9e^{-2t}$; $y(0) = y'(0) = y''(0) = 0$.

13. $\ddot{x} + 4\dot{x} + 13x = 2e^{-t}$; $x(0) = -1$, $\dot{x}(0) = 4$.

14. A body of mass 1.2 slugs hangs from a spring with spring constant 1.2 lbs./ft., and is braked by a dashpot with frictional constant 1.2 slugs/sec. If initially the mass is in its equilibrium position and has zero initial velocity, determine the vertical displacement x, as a function of time if the mass is acted on by a force $F = 12 \cos \left(3t + \dfrac{\pi}{6}\right)$ lbs. applied at $t = 0$.

4. Partial Fractions

In both the examples considered in the previous section, one of the most difficult parts of the problem was to decompose the rational function $X(s)$ into partial fractions. Many other practical problems involving the Laplace transform also give rise to rational functions of s. It will therefore be profitable for us to investigate in some detail the problem of expressing a rational function in terms of partial fractions. We know that if we have a rational function of s, say,

$$F(s) = \frac{N(s)}{M(s)} = \frac{a_0 s^n + a_1 s^{n-1} + \cdots + a_n}{b_0 s^m + b_1 s^{m-1} + \cdots + b_m} ,$$

where $N(s)$ and $M(s)$ are polynomials of degree n and m, respectively, with $m > n$, then we may write $F(s)$ in the form

$$F(s) = \frac{A_1}{s - s_1} + \frac{A_2}{s - s_2} + \cdots + \frac{A_m}{s - s_m} , \tag{19}$$

where $s_1, s_2, \cdots, s_m$ are the roots of the algebraic equation

$$M(s) = 0$$

and the A_i's are constants. In this section we wish to consider a systematic procedure for calculating the A_i's. Suppose for the moment that we have obtained the expression indicated by Equation (19) above. Then the inverse Laplace transform of $F(s)$ can be immediately written as

$$\mathscr{L}^{-1}[F(s)] = A_1 e^{s_1 t} + A_2 e^{s_2 t} + \cdots + A_m e^{s_m t} . \tag{20}$$

Thus, given a rational function of s, if we can break it up into partial fractions we can easily find its inverse transform. We see, then, the value of being able to reduce a given transform into partial fractions, namely, that the inverse transform of each fraction may readily be found.

In writing Equation (19) we have tacitly assumed that the roots $s_1, s_2, \cdots, s_m$ were *distinct*. Suppose this is not the case and that s_1 is a root of multiplicity r_1, that s_2 is a root of multiplicity $r_2, \cdots$, that s_β is a root of multiplicity r_β, where $\beta \leq m$ and $r_1 + r_2 + \cdots + r_\beta = m$. Then the expression comparable to Equation (19) becomes

$$
\begin{aligned}
F(s) = {} & \frac{A_{11}}{s - s_1} + \frac{A_{12}}{(s - s_1)^2} + \cdots + \frac{A_{1r_1}}{(s - s_1)^{r_1}} \\[2mm]
& + \frac{A_{21}}{s - s_2} + \frac{A_{22}}{(s - s_2)^2} + \cdots + \frac{A_{2r_2}}{(s - s_2)^{r_2}} \\[2mm]
& + \cdots \cdots \cdots \cdots \cdots \cdots \\[2mm]
& + \frac{A_{\beta 1}}{s - s_\beta} + \frac{A_{\beta 2}}{(s - s_\beta)^2} + \cdots + \frac{A_{\beta r_\beta}}{(s - s_\beta)^{r_\beta}} .
\end{aligned}
\tag{21}
$$

The inverse transform of a term such as

$$\frac{A}{(s-a)^n}$$

is still easy to find. From the table on page 205 we have

$$\mathscr{L}^{-1}\left[\frac{A}{(s-a)^n}\right] = \frac{Ae^{at}t^{n-1}}{(n-1)!} \quad .$$

We wish to make one more remark concerning Equation (19) before proving our expansion theorem. Some of the roots of $M(s) = 0$ may be complex. If, for example, $a = \alpha + j\beta$ is a complex root of $M(s) = 0$, then Equation (19) will contain a pair of terms

$$\frac{A}{s-a} + \frac{\bar{A}}{s-\bar{a}} \tag{22}$$

corresponding to a and its complex conjugate $\bar{a} = \alpha - j\beta$. The inverse transform of Equation (22) is still

$$\phi(t) = Ae^{at} + \bar{A}e^{\bar{a}t} \quad , \tag{23}$$

but now the a and A are complex numbers. However, if we let

$$A = C + jD \quad ,$$

then $\bar{A} = C - jD$, and $\phi(t)$ may be written

$$\begin{aligned}
\phi(t) &= (C+jD)e^{\alpha t}(\cos \beta t + j\sin \beta t) + (C - jD)e^{\alpha t}(\cos \beta t - j\sin \beta t) \\
&= 2e^{\alpha t}[C\cos \beta t - D\sin \beta t] \quad ,
\end{aligned}$$

in which no complex constants appear. Thus, although our partial fraction expansion may contain complex numbers, we can always reduce the inverse transform to a function of t involving only real constants. Alternatively, instead of using the partial fraction expansion given in Equation (22), we can use the *quadratic term*

$$\begin{aligned}
\frac{(A+\bar{A})s - (\bar{A}a + A\bar{a})}{s^2 - (a+\bar{a})s + a\bar{a}} &\equiv \frac{2Cs - 2(\alpha C + \beta D)}{s^2 - 2\alpha s + (\alpha^2 + \beta^2)} \\
&= 2C\left[\frac{s-\alpha}{(s-\alpha)^2 + \beta^2}\right] - 2D\left[\frac{\beta}{(s-\alpha)^2 + \beta^2}\right] \quad ,
\end{aligned}$$

as we did in the second example of the previous section. This quadratic form involves only real constants, and its inverse is readily found in terms of the trigonometric functions.

We now turn to the problem of expanding a rational function into partial fractions. Such a decomposition is sometimes called a *Heaviside Expansion Theorem*. Suppose, then, that $N(s)$ and $M(s)$ are polynomials in s with the degree of N less than that of M. Then

$$F(s) = \frac{N(s)}{M(s)} \tag{24}$$

is a rational function of s. Let the roots of $M(s)$ be distinct, say $s_1, s_2, \cdots, s_m$. We can assume without loss of generality that $N(s)$ and $M(s)$ have no common factors, for if they did, we could cancel them before starting our reduction. If we write

$$\frac{N(s)}{M(s)} = \frac{A_1}{s - s_1} + \frac{A_2}{s - s_2} + \cdots + \frac{A_m}{s - s_m}$$

and multiply both sides of this equation by $(s - s_1)$, then

$$\frac{N(s)(s - s_1)}{M(s)} = A_1 + \frac{A_2}{s - s_2}(s - s_1) + \cdots + \frac{A_m}{s - s_m}(s - s_1) \quad . \tag{25}$$

If we let $s = s_1$, the right-hand side of Equation (25) reduces to A_1, while the left-hand side becomes indeterminate, that is, $\frac{0}{0}$. To evaluate this indeterminate form we use de l'Hospital's rule,

$$\lim_{s \to s_1} \frac{N(s)(s - s_1)}{M(s)} = \lim_{s \to s_1} \frac{N(s) + N'(s)(s - s_1)}{M'(s)} = \frac{N(s_1)}{M'(s_1)} \quad .$$

Hence,

$$A_1 = \frac{N(s_1)}{M'(s_1)} \quad .\dagger$$

Note that $M'(s_1)$ cannot be zero, for if $M'(s)$ had s_1 as a root, then s_1 would be a double root of $M(s)$—contrary to hypothesis. If we similarly treat $s_2, s_3, \cdots, s_m$, we arrive at the following theorem:

$\dagger$ Alternatively, since $M(s)$ contains the factor $(s - s_1)$ we may write $M(s) = (s - s_1)\mu(s)$ and hence

$$\frac{N(s)(s - s_1)}{M(s)} = \frac{N(s)}{\mu(s)} \quad .$$

Thus we have removed the indeterminacy by canceling $(s - s_1)$ and hence have eliminated the necessity for applying de l'Hospital's rule. Clearly $\mu(s_1) = M'(s_1)$ and

$$\frac{N(s_1)}{\mu(s_1)} \equiv \frac{N(s_1)}{M'(s_1)} = A_1 \quad .$$

THEOREM 1. Let $F(s) = \dfrac{N(s)}{M(s)}$ be a rational function of s where the degree m of the polynomial M exceeds the degree of the polynomial N. Let $s_1, s_2, \cdots,$ s_m be m distinct roots of $M(s) = 0$. Then $F(s)$ has the partial fraction decomposition

$$F(s) = \sum_{i=1}^{m} \frac{A_i}{s - s_i} \quad ,$$

where

$$A_i = \frac{N(s_i)}{M'(s_i)} \quad ,$$

$M'(s)$ being the derivative of $M(s)$.

Let us now consider the case where the roots of $M(s)$ are repeated. In order to keep the notation relatively simple, suppose that a is a root of multiplicity r. Then we may write

$$M(s) = (s - a)^r P(s) \quad ,$$

where $P(s)$ is a polynomial in s containing the other factors of $M(s)$. The rational function $F(s)$ then becomes

$$F(s) = \frac{N(s)}{M(s)} = \frac{N(s)}{(s - a)^r P(s)} = \frac{G(s)}{(s - a)^r} \quad ,$$

where $G(s) = \dfrac{N(s)}{P(s)}$ is a rational function of x. Now, in this case we may write

$$F(s) = \frac{G(s)}{(s - a)^r} = \frac{A_1}{s - a} + \frac{A_2}{(s - a)^2} + \cdots + \frac{A_r}{(s - a)^r} + H(s) \quad , \quad (26)$$

where $H(s)$ denotes the sum of the fractions corresponding to all other factors of $M(s)$. If we multiply Equation (26) by $(s - a)^r$

$$G(s) = A_1(s - a)^{r-1} + A_2(s - a)^{r-2} + \cdots + A_r + H(s)(s - a)^r \quad , (27)$$

and set s equal to a,

$$G(a) = A_r \quad .$$

To determine A_{r-1}, differentiate $G(s)$,

$$G'(s) = (r - 1)A_1(s - a)^{r-2} + (r - 2)A_2(s - a)^{r-3} + \cdots + A_{r-1}$$
$$+ r(s - a)^{r-1}H(s) + (s - a)^r H'(s) \quad ,$$

and again let $s = a$,

$$G'(a) = A_{r-1} \quad .$$

Continuing this process, namely, differentiating Equation (27) $r - k$ times and then setting s equal to a, we determine all the coefficients A_k,

$$A_k = \frac{G^{(r-k)}(a)}{(r-k)!} \quad , \quad k = 1, 2, \cdots, r \quad .$$

Thus we may state the following expansion theorem in the case of multiple roots:

THEOREM 2. If $F(s) = \dfrac{N(s)}{M(s)}$ is a rational function of s and $s = a$ is a root of $M(s) = 0$ of multiplicity r, then if we write $M(s) = (s - a)^r P(s)$,

$$F(s) = \sum_{k=1}^{r} \frac{A_k}{(s-a)^k} + H(s) \quad ,$$

where $H(s)$ denotes the sum of the fractions corresponding to all other factors of $M(s)$. The coefficients A_k are given by

$$A_k = \frac{G^{(r-k)}(a)}{(r-k)!} \quad ,$$

and

$$G(s) = \frac{N(s)}{P(s)} \quad .$$

The rational function $H(s)$ of the previous theorem can be further decomposed into partial fractions by applying Theorem 1 to the simple roots of $P(s) = 0$, and Theorem 2 to the multiple roots of $P(s) = 0$. In attempting to find the partial fraction decomposition of a rational function, invariably the most difficult part of the procedure is to find the roots of $M(s) = 0$.

As an illustration of the above theorem, let us decompose the rational function

$$F(s) = \frac{s^2 + 2}{(s - 1)^3} \tag{28}$$

into partial fractions. Applying Theorem 2,

$$F(s) = \frac{A_1}{s - 1} + \frac{A_2}{(s - 1)^2} + \frac{A_3}{(s - 1)^3} \quad ,$$

and $G(s) = s^2 + 2$. Hence

$$G'(s) = 2s \quad , \quad G''(s) = 2 \quad ,$$

and

$$A_1 = \frac{G''(1)}{2!} = \frac{2}{2} = 1$$

$$A_2 = \frac{G'(1)}{1!} = \frac{2}{1} = 2$$

$$A_3 = \frac{G(1)}{0!} = \frac{3}{1} = 3 \quad .$$

Thus $F(s)$ as given by Equation (28) may be written

$$F(s) = \frac{1}{s-1} + \frac{2}{(s-1)^2} + \frac{3}{(s-1)^3}$$

and

$$f(t) = \mathscr{L}^{-1}[F(s)] = e^t + 2te^t + \tfrac{3}{2}t^2e^t \quad .$$

The above general formulas represent a systematic procedure for obtaining the partial fraction expansion of a given rational function $R(s)$. However, in many elementary problems it is frequently more convenient to use the techniques described in the calculus. We illustrate this method by an example. Suppose we wish to expand

$$\frac{s^2 + 2}{(s-1)^2(s+2)}$$

into partial fractions. We write

$$\frac{s^2 + 2}{(s-1)^2(s+2)} = \frac{A}{s-1} + \frac{B}{(s-1)^2} + \frac{C}{s+2}$$

and then clear fractions by multiplying through by $(s-1)^2(s+2)$, thus obtaining the identity (in s),

$$s^2 + 2 \equiv A(s-1)(s+2) + B(s+2) + C(s-1)^2$$

$$\equiv (A+C)s^2 + (A+B-2C)s + (-2A+2B+C) \quad .$$

Equating coefficients of like powers of s, we get the system of linear algebraic equations

$$A \quad\quad + \; C = 1$$
$$A + \; B - 2C = 0$$
$$-2A + 2B + \; C = 2$$

on the coefficients A, B, C. These equations are readily solvable by the methods of Chapter 1, yielding

$$A = \tfrac{1}{3} \ , \quad B = 1 \ , \quad C = \tfrac{2}{3} \ .$$

Similarly, if $R(s)$ involves quadratic factors, say,

$$R(s) = \frac{N(s)}{(s - a)^3(s - b)(s^2 + cs + d)(s^2 + es + f)^2} \ ,$$

where $s^2 + cs + d = 0$ and $s^2 + es + f = 0$ have complex roots and $N(s)$ is a polynomial of degree less than ten, we may write

$$R(s) = \frac{A_1}{s - a} + \frac{A_2}{(s - a)^2} + \frac{A_3}{(s - a)^3} + \frac{B}{s - b} + \frac{Cs + D}{s^2 + cs + d}$$

$$+ \frac{E_1 s + F_1}{s^2 + es + f} + \frac{E_2 s + F_2}{(s^2 + es + f)^2} \ .$$

If we then clear fractions, we obtain a system of linear algebraic equations on the unknown constants A_1, A_2, A_3, B, C, D, E_1, F_1, E_2, F_2.

EXERCISES

Decompose the following rational functions into partial fractions:

1. $\dfrac{1}{s^3 + s^2 - 1}$

2. $\dfrac{s}{(s + 2)(s + 3)^2}$

3. $\dfrac{s^2 + 2}{s^2(s + 1)(s + 2)}$

4. $\dfrac{s^4 - 4s^3 - s^2 - 11s - 35}{(s^2 + 4)(s + 1)(s^2 + 4s + 5)}$

5. Periodic Functions

We have seen in earlier chapters that periodic functions frequently occur in engineering problems. The Fourier transform of a periodic function $x(t)$ does not exist, since, in particular, the condition

$$\lim_{t \to \infty} x(t) = 0$$

is not fulfilled; hence $x(t)$ is not absolutely integrable. However, because of the convergence factor $e^{-\sigma t}$ in the Laplace transform, we can find the Laplace transform of a periodic function. Of course, when we speak of a periodic function in connection with the Laplace transform, we mean a function $x(t)$ with the properties that

(i) $x(t)$ is defined for $0 < t < T$
(ii) $x(t + T) = x(t)$ for $t > 0$
(iii) $x(t) \equiv 0$ for $t < 0$.

Consider, then, a function $x(t)$ of period T (cf. Fig. 5.4) whose Laplace transform we wish to find. If we call $f(t)$ the function defined as

$$f(t) = x(t) \quad , \quad 0 < t < T$$
$$f(t) = 0 \quad , \quad \text{otherwise,}$$

then we shall show that the Laplace transform $X(s)$ of $x(t)$ may be written in terms of the Laplace transform $F(s)$ of $f(t)$.

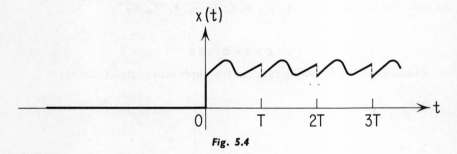

Fig. 5.4

By definition,

$$X(s) = \int_0^\infty x(t)e^{-st}dt$$

$$= \int_0^T x(t)e^{-st}dt + \int_T^{2T} x(t)e^{-st}dt + \cdots + \int_{kT}^{(k+1)T} x(t)e^{-st}dt + \cdots .$$

Now, let

$$\zeta = t - kT \quad , \quad k = 0, 1, 2, \cdots$$

in the kth integral, and $X(s)$ becomes

$$X(s) = \int_0^T x(\zeta)e^{-s\zeta}d\zeta + \int_0^T x(\zeta + T)e^{-s(\zeta + T)}d\zeta$$

$$+ \cdots + \int_0^T x(\zeta + kT)e^{-s(\zeta + kT)}d\zeta + \cdots . \quad (29)$$

But

$$f(\zeta) = x(\zeta) = x(\zeta + T) = \cdots = x(\zeta + kT) = \cdots \quad,$$

since the range of integration in each integral is from 0 to T. Thus Equation (29) becomes

$$X(s) = \int_0^T f(\zeta)e^{-s\zeta}d\zeta + e^{-sT}\int_0^T f(\zeta)e^{-s\zeta}d\zeta + \cdots + e^{-kTs}\int_0^T f(\zeta)e^{-s\zeta}d\zeta + \cdots$$

$$= F(s)[1 + e^{-sT} + \cdots + e^{-ksT} + \cdots] \quad.$$

The coefficient of $F(s)$ is a geometric series of ratio e^{-sT} and

$$|e^{-sT}| < 1$$

for $\Re(s) > 0$. Hence

$$X(s) = \frac{F(s)}{1 - e^{-sT}} \quad. \tag{30}$$

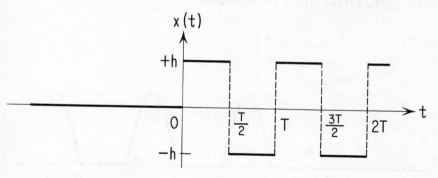

Fig. 5.5

For example, consider the square wave of Figure 5.5. Here the period is T and

$$f(t) = +h \quad , \quad 0 < t < \frac{T}{2}$$

$$f(t) = -h \quad , \quad \frac{T}{2} < t < T$$

$$f(t) = 0 \quad , \quad \text{otherwise} \quad .$$

Hence

$$F(s) = \int_0^\infty f(t)e^{-st}dt = \int_0^{T/2} he^{-st}dt + \int_{T/2}^T (-h)e^{-st}dt$$

$$= \frac{h}{s}(1 - e^{-sT/2})^2$$

and by Equation (30),

$$X(s) = \frac{\dfrac{h}{s}(1 - e^{-sT/2})^2}{1 - e^{-sT}} = \frac{h(1 - e^{-sT/2})}{s(1 + e^{-sT/2})} \quad .$$

If we multiply numerator and denominator by $e^{sT/4}$ and recall that

$$\tanh u = \frac{e^u - e^{-u}}{e^u + e^{-u}} \quad ,$$

we have

$$X(s) = \frac{h}{s} \tanh \frac{sT}{4} \tag{31}$$

as the Laplace transform of the square wave.

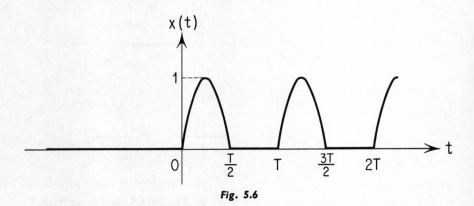

Fig. 5.6

As another example consider the half-wave rectified sine wave of Figure 5.6. In this case the period is T and

$$f(t) = \sin \frac{2\pi t}{T} \quad , \quad 0 < t < \frac{T}{2}$$

$$f(t) = 0 \qquad , \quad \text{otherwise} \quad .$$

Then, since

$$\mathscr{L}[f(t)] = \int_0^{T/2} \sin \frac{2\pi t}{T} e^{-st} dt = \frac{2\pi T}{s^2 T^2 + 4\pi^2}(1 + e^{-sT/2}) \quad ,$$

we have by Equation (30) that

$$X(s) = \frac{2\pi T}{s^2 T^2 + 4\pi^2} \frac{1 + e^{-sT/2}}{1 - e^{-sT}} = \frac{2\pi T}{s^2 T^2 + 4\pi^2} \frac{1}{1 - e^{-sT/2}} \quad . \tag{32}$$

In the next section we shall see an application of the Laplace transform of a periodic function in the solution of a partial differential equation.

EXERCISES

1. Find the Laplace transform of the full-wave rectified sine wave.
2. Find the Laplace transform of the triangular function sketched in Figure 5.7 below.

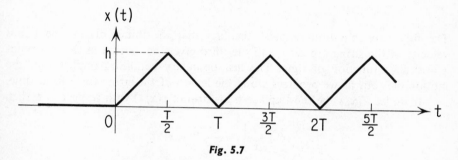

Fig. 5.7

3. Find the Laplace transform of the nonperiodic finite pulse $x(t)$ defined as

$$x(t) = h \quad , \quad a < t < b$$

$$x(t) = 0 \quad , \quad \text{otherwise} \quad .$$

4. Find the Laplace transform of the nonperiodic function

$$x(t) = 0 \qquad , \quad t < 1$$

$$x(t) = \frac{1}{\sqrt{t^2 - 1}} \quad , \quad t > 1 \quad .$$

6. Applications to Partial Differential Equations

The Laplace transform can be used to solve partial differential equations in much the same way that the Fourier transform was utilized. Let us take as our first example the problem of finding the motion of a semi-infinite vibrating string. The partial differential equation involved is

$$a^2 \frac{\partial^2 v}{\partial x^2} = \frac{\partial^2 v}{\partial t^2} \quad , \tag{33}$$

and we shall take boundary conditions of the form

$$v(x, 0) = 0$$

$$\frac{\partial}{\partial t} v(x, 0) = 0 \tag{34}$$

$$v(0, t) = f(t)$$

$$\lim_{x \to \infty} v(x, t) = 0 \quad .$$

The first two conditions express the fact that the initial displacement and velocity of the string are zero, and the third gives the motion of the end point $x = 0$ as a function of time. The last boundary condition implies that the motion dies out as we progress along the length of the string for a fixed time.

If we let $V(x, s)$ be the Laplace transform of $v(x, t)$ with respect to t, then

$$\mathscr{L}\left[\frac{\partial^2 v}{\partial x^2}\right] = \frac{\partial^2}{\partial x^2} V(x, s)$$

and

$$\mathscr{L}\left[\frac{\partial^2 v}{\partial t^2}\right] = s^2 V(x, s) - \frac{\partial}{\partial t} v(x, 0) - s v(x, 0)$$

$$= s^2 V(x, s) \quad ,$$

since by the first two boundary conditions of Equations (34), $v(x, 0) = \frac{\partial}{\partial t} v(x, 0) = 0$. Hence the partial differential equation of Equation (33) becomes the *ordinary* differential equation

$$a^2 \frac{d^2}{dx^2} V(x, s) = s^2 V(x, s) \tag{35}$$

on the transform $V(x, s)$, where we think of s as a parameter. The solution of Equation (35) is

$$V(x, s) = A(s) e^{\frac{s}{a} x} + B(s) e^{-\frac{s}{a} x} \quad , \tag{36}$$

where $A(s)$ and $B(s)$ are the "constants" of integration. Now, from the third boundary condition

$$F(s) = \mathcal{L}[f(t)] = \mathcal{L}[v(0, t)] = V(0, s) \quad,$$

and Equation (36) implies

$$F(s) = A(s) + B(s) \quad.$$

If the last boundary condition is to be satisfied, $A(s)$ must be zero, since $e^{sx/a}$ approaches infinity as $x \to \infty$ for $\Re(s) > 0$ and by the last boundary condition of Equations (34), $\lim_{x \to \infty} V(x, s) = 0$. Thus we have

$$A(s) = 0$$
$$B(s) = F(s) \quad,$$

and Equation (36) again implies

$$V(x, s) = F(s)e^{-\frac{x}{a}s} \quad.$$

From the table on page 205,

$$v(x, t) = \mathcal{L}^{-1}[V(x, s)] = f\left(t - \frac{x}{a}\right) u\left(t - \frac{x}{a}\right) \quad, \tag{37}$$

which is the solution of our boundary value problem.

As a second example, consider the equation

$$\frac{\partial v}{\partial t} = a^2 \frac{\partial^2 v}{\partial x^2} \quad, \tag{38}$$

which could represent the flow of heat or electricity. If the bar (or cable) is of length L, let us solve the equation with the boundary conditions

$$v(x, 0) = 0$$
$$v(0, t) = 0 \tag{39}$$
$$v(L, t) = f(t)$$

which expresses the facts that the initial temperature (voltage) is zero, that the end $x = 0$ is kept at zero temperature (grounded) for all time, and that the temperature (voltage) at the end $x = L$ is a given function of time.

If we transform Equation (38) with respect to t and let $V(x, s)$ be the

Laplace transform of $v(x, t)$, then Equation (38) becomes an equation on the transform V,

$$sV(x, s) = a^2 \frac{d^2}{dx^2} V(x, s) \quad,$$

whose solution is

$$V(x, s) = A(s)e^{\frac{x}{a}\sqrt{s}} + B(s)e^{-\frac{x}{a}\sqrt{s}} \quad. \tag{40}$$

From the condition $v(0, t) = 0$ we infer

$$0 = \mathscr{L}[v(0, t)] = V(0, s) = A(s) + B(s) \quad,$$

and, from the last boundary condition,

$$F(s) = \mathscr{L}[v(L, t)] = V(L, s) = A(s)e^{\frac{L}{a}\sqrt{s}} + B(s)e^{-\frac{L}{a}\sqrt{s}} \quad.$$

These last two equations determine $A(s)$ and $B(s)$, and Equation (40) assumes the form

$$V(x, s) = \frac{F(s)}{e^{\frac{L}{a}\sqrt{s}} - e^{-\frac{L}{a}\sqrt{s}}} (e^{\frac{x}{a}\sqrt{s}} - e^{-\frac{x}{a}\sqrt{s}})$$

$$= F(s) \frac{\sinh \frac{x}{a}\sqrt{s}}{\sinh \frac{L}{a}\sqrt{s}} \quad, \tag{41}$$

and $v(x, t)$ is the inverse transform of this function.

To evaluate $\mathscr{L}^{-1}[V(x, s)]$, introduce the change of variable

$$\frac{\sqrt{s}}{a} = \zeta \quad,$$

and write

$$V(x, s) = F(s)e^{-\zeta L} \frac{(e^{x\zeta} - e^{-x\zeta})}{(1 - e^{-2\zeta L})} \quad. \tag{42}$$

Then, if we expand $\dfrac{1}{1 - e^{-2\zeta L}}$ as an infinite series,

$$\frac{1}{1 - e^{-2\zeta L}} = 1 + e^{-2\zeta L} + e^{-4\zeta L} + \cdots \quad,$$

we may write Equation (42) as

$$V(x, s) = F(s)[e^{-\zeta(L-x)} - e^{-\zeta(L+x)}] \sum_{n=0}^{\infty} e^{-2n\zeta L}$$

$$= F(s) \sum_{m=1,3,5,\cdots}^{\infty} [e^{-\zeta(mL-x)} - e^{-\zeta(mL+x)}] \quad . \tag{43}$$

If, for example, $f(t)$ is the unit step function, then

$$F(s) = \frac{1}{s} \quad ,$$

and

$$\mathscr{L}^{-1}\left[\frac{1}{s} e^{-\zeta(mL-x)}\right] = \mathscr{L}^{-1}\left[\frac{1}{s} e^{-\sqrt{s}\left(\frac{mL-x}{a}\right)}\right] = \text{cerf}\left(\frac{mL-x}{2a\sqrt{t}}\right) \quad .\dagger \tag{44}$$

The function "cerf" is defined as one minus the error function,

$$\text{cerf } u = 1 - \text{erf } u = 1 - \frac{2}{\sqrt{\pi}} \int_0^u e^{-u^2} du = \frac{2}{\sqrt{\pi}} \int_u^\infty e^{-u^2} du \quad , \tag{45}$$

and is called the co-error function, (cf. Chap. 2, Sec. 3). Utilizing Equation (44), we may write the inverse transform of $V(x, s)$ as

$$v(x, t) = \sum_{m=1,3,5,\cdots}^{\infty} \left[\text{cerf}\left(\frac{mL-x}{2a\sqrt{t}}\right) - \text{cerf}\left(\frac{mL+x}{2a\sqrt{t}}\right)\right] \quad . \tag{46}$$

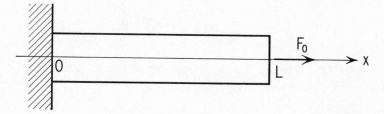

Fig. 5.8

As a final application to partial differential equations we shall consider the longitudinal vibrations of a bar of length L, fixed at the origin (cf. Fig. 5.8). The equation satisfied by the displacement $v(x, t)\ddagger$ is

$$a^2 \frac{\partial^2 v}{\partial x^2} = \frac{\partial^2 v}{\partial t^2} \quad . \tag{47}$$

---

† See Formula 83, C.RC., *Standard Mathematical Tables*, p. 312.
‡ Cf. Miller, *Partial Differential Equations in Engineering Problems*, Chap. 1.

If the beam is initially at rest and has zero initial velocity, then two boundary conditions are

$$v(x, 0) = 0$$

$$\frac{\partial}{\partial t} v(x, 0) = 0 \ .$$

Further, since the bar is fixed at the origin, we obtain the additional boundary condition

$$v(0, t) = 0 \ .$$

Now, suppose that a constant force of F_0 lbs./sq. in. is applied to the free end and we wish to determine the displacement $v(L, t)$ at this end. The stress σ equals

$$\sigma = \varepsilon E = E \frac{\partial v}{\partial x} \ ,$$

where $\varepsilon = \dfrac{\partial v}{\partial x}$ is the strain and E is Young's modulus. Since at $x = L$, $\sigma = F_0$, we have

$$F_0 = E \frac{\partial}{\partial x} v(L, t) \ ,$$

and our fourth boundary condition becomes

$$\frac{\partial}{\partial x} v(L, t) = \frac{F_0}{E} \ .$$

If we let $V(x, s)$ be the Laplace transform of $v(x, t)$ with respect to t, the transform of Equation (47) becomes

$$a^2 \frac{d^2}{dx^2} V(x, s) = s^2 V(x, s) - \frac{\partial}{\partial t} v(x, 0) - s v(x, 0)$$
$$= s^2 V(x, s) \ , \tag{48}$$

since by the first two boundary conditions, $v(x, 0) = \dfrac{\partial}{\partial t} v(x, 0) = 0$. Thus we may solve Equation (48) by considering s as a parameter and obtain

$$V(x, s) = A(s) e^{\frac{x}{a} s} + B(s) e^{-\frac{x}{a} s} \ , \tag{49}$$

where $A(s)$ and $B(s)$ are the "constants" of integration.

In order to determine A and B, we consider the transforms of the remaining two boundary conditions,

$$0 = \mathscr{L}[v(0, t)] = V(0, s) \tag{50}$$

and

$$\frac{F_0}{sE} = \mathscr{L}\left[\frac{F_0}{E}\right] = \mathscr{L}\left[\frac{\partial}{\partial x} v(L, t)\right] = \frac{d}{dx} V(L, s) \quad . \tag{51}$$

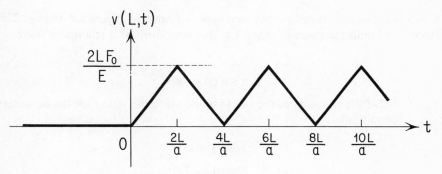

Fig. 5.9

If we use Equation (50) in Equation (49),

$$0 = A(s) + B(s) \quad , \tag{52}$$

and, since

$$\frac{dV}{dx} = \frac{s}{a} A(s)e^{\frac{s}{a}x} - \frac{s}{a} B(s)e^{-\frac{s}{a}x} \quad ,$$

Equation (51) implies

$$\frac{F_0}{sE} = \frac{s}{a} A(s)e^{\frac{s}{a}L} - \frac{s}{a} B(s)e^{-\frac{s}{a}L} \quad . \tag{53}$$

Together, Equations (52) and (53) imply

$$A(s) = - B(s) = \frac{F_0 a}{Es^2} \frac{1}{e^{\frac{L}{a}s} + e^{-\frac{L}{a}s}}$$

and, substituting in Equation (49),

$$V(x, s) = \frac{aF_0}{Es^2} \frac{e^{\frac{s}{a}x} - e^{-\frac{s}{a}x}}{e^{\frac{L}{a}s} + e^{-\frac{L}{a}s}} = \frac{aF_0}{Es^2} \frac{\sinh\frac{x}{a}s}{\cosh\frac{L}{a}s} \quad .$$

Now, if $x = L$,

$$V(L, s) = \frac{aF_0}{Es^2} \tanh \frac{L}{a} s \quad ;$$

and

$$v(L, t) = \mathcal{L}^{-1}[V(L, s)] \quad ,$$

which is the desired function, has the shape indicated in Figure 5.9 on page 227, since $(1/s^2) \tanh s$ is essentially the Laplace transform of a triangular wave.

EXERCISES

1. Solve the equation of the semi-infinite vibrating string for the boundary conditions

$$v(0, t) = 0$$

$$v(x, 0) = f(x)$$

$$\frac{\partial}{\partial t} v(x, 0) = 0$$

$$\lim_{x \to \infty} v(x, t) = 0 \quad .$$

2. Solve the one-dimensional heat equation

$$\frac{\partial v}{\partial t} = a^2 \frac{\partial^2 v}{\partial x^2}$$

for a semi-infinite insulated bar with the boundary conditions

$$v(x, 0) = 0$$

$$v(0, t) = f(t)$$

$$\lim_{x \to \infty} v(x, t) = 0 \quad .$$

3. Find the stress $\left(= E \dfrac{\partial v}{\partial x} \right)$ at $x = L$ in a bar of length L subject to longitudinal vibrations. The equation of motion is

$$a^2 \frac{\partial^2 v}{\partial x^2} = \frac{\partial^2 v}{\partial t^2} \quad .$$

Assume the boundary conditions

$$v(L, t) = 0$$

$$v(x, 0) = 0$$

$$\frac{\partial}{\partial t} v(x, 0) = V_0 \quad \text{(a constant)}$$

$$\frac{\partial}{\partial x} v(0, t) = 0 \quad .$$

7. Convolution

All of the properties of the Laplace transform that we have considered so far in this chapter have been almost immediate consequences of the very definition. We now wish to consider a nonobvious property of the Laplace transform which is of inestimable value in further applications. The result is simple to state; namely, if $F(s)$ is the Laplace transform of $f(t)$ and $G(s)$ is the Laplace transform of $g(t)$, then the inverse Laplace transform of $F(s)G(s)$ is

$$\mathcal{L}^{-1}[F(s)G(s)] = \int_0^t f(t - \zeta)g(\zeta)d\zeta \quad . \tag{54}$$

This integral is known as the *convolution integral*, and we shall derive a number of results that stem from this formula after we establish Equation (54).

Suppose $F(s)$ and $G(s)$ are as above. Then, by definition,

$$F(s)G(s) = \int_0^\infty f(t)e^{-st}dt \int_0^\infty g(z)e^{-sz}dz$$

$$= \int_0^\infty \int_0^\infty f(t)g(z)e^{-s(t+z)}dt\,dz \quad . \tag{55}$$

If we make the change of variable,

$$t = u - v$$

$$z = \quad v \quad ,$$

then we see that the Jacobian of this transformation is unity,

$$J\left(\frac{t, z}{u, v}\right) = 1 \quad .$$

Also, since t does not take on negative values, $u - v$ must be positive; that is,

$u > v$, and hence the variable v can range only from 0 to u. Thus Equation (55) becomes

$$F(s)G(s) = \int_0^\infty e^{-su} \left[\int_0^u f(u - v)g(v)dv \right] du \quad,$$

and therefore

$$\mathscr{L}^{-1}[F(s)G(s)] = \int_0^u f(u - v)g(v)dv \quad.$$

From the symmetry of Equation (55) we see the roles of f and g could be interchanged to obtain

$$\mathscr{L}^{-1}[G(s)F(s)] = \int_0^v g(v - u)f(u)du \quad.$$

As a first application of the convolution theorem, let us compute the Laplace transform of the error function

$$\text{erf } \sqrt{t} = \frac{2}{\sqrt{\pi}} \int_0^{\sqrt{t}} e^{-x^2}dx \quad,$$

which we may write as

$$\text{erf } \sqrt{t} = \frac{1}{\sqrt{\pi}} \int_0^t \frac{e^{-z}}{\sqrt{z}} dz$$

by making the change of variable $z = x^2$. Now, if we let

$$f(z) = e^z$$

and

$$g(z) = \frac{1}{\sqrt{z}} \quad;$$

then

$$\mathscr{L}[f(z)] = \frac{1}{s - 1} \quad,$$

and

$$\mathscr{L}[g(z)] = \frac{\sqrt{\pi}}{\sqrt{s}} \quad,$$

and by Equation (54),

$$\mathscr{L}^{-1}\left[\frac{1}{s - 1} \frac{\sqrt{\pi}}{\sqrt{s}} \right] = \int_0^t \frac{e^{(t-\zeta)}}{\sqrt{\zeta}} d\zeta = \sqrt{\pi}e^t \text{ erf } \sqrt{t} \quad,$$

or

$$\mathscr{L}[e^t \operatorname{erf} \sqrt{t}] = \frac{1}{\sqrt{s}(s-1)} \quad . \tag{56}$$

Using the translation formula from the table on page 205, namely,

$$\mathscr{L}[e^{-at}f(t)] = F(s + a) \quad ,$$

we conclude that

$$\mathscr{L}[\operatorname{erf} \sqrt{t}] = \frac{1}{s\sqrt{s+1}} \quad . \tag{57}$$

However, we have more interesting problems that can be solved by means of convolution. For example, consider the second problem of Section 3, which solved the equation of motion of the damped vibrating mass [cf. Equations (16) and (17)]. Let us now solve this problem without making any explicit assumptions regarding the function $f(t)$. Then the transform of

$$\ddot{x} + \dot{x} + x = f(t)$$

[Equation (16)], with the boundary conditions

$$x(0) = \dot{x}(0) = 0$$

[Equation (17)], is

$$s^2 X(s) + s X(s) + X(s) = F(s) \quad , \tag{58}$$

where $X(s) = \mathscr{L}[x(t)]$ and $F(s) = \mathscr{L}[f(t)]$. We can solve Equation (58) for $X(s)$,

$$X(s) = \frac{1}{s^2 + s + 1} F(s) \quad .$$

Now, we cannot explicitly find $x(t)$ unless $f(t)$ and, therefore, $F(s)$ is known. However, using convolution, we may write

$$x(t) = \int_0^t g(t - \zeta)f(\zeta)d\zeta \quad , \tag{59}$$

where $g(t) = \mathscr{L}^{-1}\left[\dfrac{1}{s^2 + s + 1}\right]$. But this is a known function, namely,

$$g(t) = \mathscr{L}^{-1}\left[\frac{1}{(s + \tfrac{1}{2})^2 + \tfrac{3}{4}}\right] = \frac{2\sqrt{3}}{3} e^{-\frac{1}{2}t} \sin \frac{\sqrt{3}}{2} t \quad ;$$

hence Equation (59) becomes

$$x(t) = \frac{2\sqrt{3}}{3} \int_0^t f(\zeta) e^{-\frac{1}{2}(t-\zeta)} \sin \frac{\sqrt{3}}{2} (t - \zeta) d\zeta \quad , \tag{60}$$

which expresses $x(t)$ in terms of known functions for any forcing function $f(t)$. If the reader refers to Chapter 3 he will see a strong resemblance between Equations (59) and (60) and the one-sided Green's function method employed there. We shall continue the discussion of this similarity in the next chapter.

Another important application of the convolution theorem is to the solution of integral equations. By an *integral equation* we mean an equation of the form

$$f(t) = \phi(t) + \int_a^\xi g(t, x) f(x) dx \quad , \tag{61}$$

where $f(t)$ is the unknown function we are searching for, $\phi(t)$ is a known function, and $g(t, x)$ is also a known function called the *kernel* of the integral equation. If ξ is a constant, say, $\xi = b$, then we call Equation (61) an *integral equation of Fredholm type*; if $\xi = t$, we call Equation (61) a *Volterra type integral equation*

In many important physical problems the kernel of the integral equation is simply a function of the *difference* of the arguments; that is,

$$g(t, x) \equiv g(t - x) \quad .$$

Hence, if we have a Volterra type integral equation of the form

$$f(t) = \phi(t) + \int_0^t g(t - x) f(x) dx \quad , \tag{62}$$

we see it is admirably adapted to solution by convolution. For, if we take the Laplace transform of Equation (62),

$$F(s) = \Phi(s) + G(s)F(s) \quad ,$$

where $F(s) = \mathscr{L}[f(t)]$, $\Phi(s) = \mathscr{L}[\phi(t)]$, $G(s) = \mathscr{L}[g(t)]$. Then

$$F(s) = \frac{\Phi(s)}{1 - G(s)} \quad ,$$

and

$$f(t) = \mathscr{L}^{-1}\left[\frac{\Phi(s)}{1 - G(s)}\right] \quad . \tag{63}$$

Since ϕ and g are known functions, Φ and G are also known; hence $f(t)$ is given by Equation (63) in terms of known functions.

For example, if

$$f(t) = t + \int_0^t (t - x)f(x)dx \quad,$$

then

$$f(t) = \mathcal{L}^{-1}\left[\frac{\mathcal{L}[t]}{1 - \mathcal{L}[t]}\right] = \mathcal{L}^{-1}\left[\frac{1}{s^2 - 1}\right] = \sinh t$$

is the desired solution.

As an example of the way in which integral equations arise in physical situations we give the classical problem of Abel. Consider a wire resting in the vertical plane (cf. Fig. 5.10) upon which a small bead of mass m is permitted

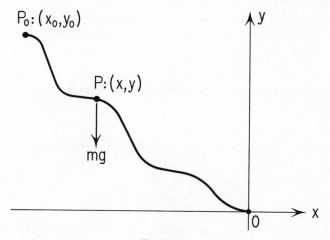

Fig. 5.10

to slide. If the bead is released from the point P_0, its time of descent to the point 0 can be measured as a function of y_0, say, $T = \phi(y_0)$. The problem posed by Abel was to find the shape of the wire in order that the time of descent be a specified function of y_0.

To set up the problem we shall assume that the bead is released from rest at the point P_0, and that the initial velocity is zero. Also we shall assume the bead has zero potential energy at the origin. Then the total energy of the bead is the sum of its kinetic energy, $\frac{1}{2}mv^2$, and its potential energy, mgy, and this sum is mgy_0,

$$\tfrac{1}{2}mv^2 + mgy = mgy_0 \quad. \tag{64}$$

Noting that the velocity v at any point P is

$$v = -\frac{d\lambda}{dt} \quad,$$

where λ is the arc length measured from the point 0, we may write Equation (64) as

$$dt = -\frac{d\lambda}{\sqrt{2g(y_0 - y)}} \quad. \tag{65}$$

If we integrate,

$$T = \int_0^T dt = -\int_{\lambda_0}^0 \frac{d\lambda}{\sqrt{2g(y_0 - y)}} \quad, \tag{66}$$

where λ_0 is the arc length from 0 to P_0.

Now, the arc length λ at any point P is some function of y, say,

$$\lambda = f(y) \quad,$$

where f is the unknown function we wish to find. Hence

$$d\lambda = f'(y)dy \quad,$$

and, noting that $T = \phi(y_0)$, we may write Equation (66) as

$$\phi(y_0) = \int_0^{y_0} \frac{f'(y)dy}{\sqrt{2g(y_0 - y)}} \quad. \tag{67}$$

Equation (67) can be solved for the unknown function $f(y)$ by using the convolution formula:

$$\Phi(s) = \frac{1}{\sqrt{2g}} \mathscr{L}\left[\frac{1}{\sqrt{t}}\right] \mathscr{L}[f'(t)]$$

$$= \frac{1}{\sqrt{2g}} \sqrt{\frac{\pi}{s}} \, [sF(s) - f(0)] \quad.$$

But $f(0) = 0$, since the arc length is measured from 0. Hence

$$\Phi(s) = \sqrt{\frac{\pi}{2g}} \, \sqrt{s} \, F(s) \quad,$$

and

$$F(s) = \sqrt{\frac{2g}{\pi}} \frac{1}{\sqrt{s}} \Phi(s) \quad . \tag{68}$$

Again using the convolution integral, we can find the inverse Laplace transform of Equation (68),

$$f(t) = \frac{\sqrt{2g}}{\pi} \int_0^t \frac{1}{\sqrt{t-\zeta}} \phi(\zeta) d\zeta \quad , \tag{69}$$

which is the desired solution.

If, for example,

$$T = \alpha \sqrt{y_0} \quad ,$$

where α is a constant, then

$$\phi(y_0) = \alpha \sqrt{y_0} \quad ,$$

and

$$\begin{aligned}
f(t) &= \frac{\sqrt{2g}}{\pi} \int_0^t \frac{1}{\sqrt{t-\zeta}} \alpha \sqrt{\zeta} \, d\zeta \\
&= \alpha \frac{\sqrt{2g}}{\pi} \left[-\sqrt{\zeta}\sqrt{t-\zeta} - t \arcsin\sqrt{\frac{t-\zeta}{t}} \right] \Big|_0^t \\
&= \alpha \frac{\sqrt{2g}}{\pi} t \frac{\pi}{2} = \alpha \sqrt{\frac{g}{2}} t \quad .
\end{aligned} \tag{70}$$

Hence the arc length λ_0 is

$$\lambda_0 = \alpha \sqrt{\frac{g}{2}} y_0 \quad .$$

Thus, if the equation of the wire is

$$x_0 = h(y_0) \quad ,$$

then

$$d\lambda_0 = \sqrt{1 + [h'(y_0)]^2} \, dy_0 = \alpha \sqrt{\frac{g}{2}} \, dy_0 \quad ,$$

and

$$h'(y_0) = \sqrt{\frac{\alpha^2 g - 2}{2}} \quad,$$

or

$$x_0 = \sqrt{\frac{\alpha^2 g - 2}{2}} \, y_0 + C \quad.$$

Since we have assumed that the curve passes through the origin, the constant of integration C is zero, and

$$y_0 = \sqrt{\frac{2}{\alpha^2 g - 2}} \, x_0 \tag{71}$$

is the equation of the wire.

EXERCISES

1. Prove that

$$\mathscr{L}[t^{-\frac{3}{2}} e^{-k^2/4t}] = \frac{2\sqrt{\pi}}{k} e^{-k\sqrt{s}} \quad, \quad k > 0 \quad.$$

2. Solve the differential equation

$$\ddot{x} + 2\dot{x} + 3x = g(t)$$

with the boundary conditions

$$x(0) = 1 \quad, \quad \dot{x}(0) = 2 \quad,$$

where $g(t)$ is arbitrary.

3. Solve the integral equation

$$f(t) = e^{-2t} + \int_0^t f(\tau) \sin(t - \tau) d\tau \quad.$$

4. Find $f(t)$ where $f(t)$ satisfies the integral equation

$$f(t) = \cos t - t - 2 - \int_0^t f(\tau)(t - \tau) d\tau \quad.$$

5. Show that the solution of the Abel integral equation

$$\phi(t) = \int_0^t \frac{f(\lambda)}{(t - \lambda)^\alpha} \, d\lambda \quad , \quad 0 < \alpha < 1$$

is

$$f(t) = \frac{\sin \pi\alpha}{\pi} \left[\int_0^t \frac{\phi'(\lambda)}{(t - \lambda)^{1-\alpha}} \, d\lambda \right] \, .$$

6. A *tautochrone* is a curve which has the property that a body sliding on it from a state of rest under the action of a given force reaches its lowest point in a time independent of the starting point. Show that if the force is gravity, g, and the time of descent is T_0, then the tautochrone is a cycloid generated by a circle of radius gT_0^2/π^2.

Although the Laplace transform is an admirable tool in many applications and leads to a methodical way of solving differential equations, it is not a panacea. If we can solve a differential equation by the Laplace transform technique, we can solve it by classical methods (cf. Chap. 3). In various instances, of course, one method may prove superior to the other because of its greater ease of applicability. This is particularly true in certain problems involving discontinuous functions, and in certain integral equations. However, it would be foolhardy to discard entirely either the standard methods or the operational methods in favor of the other.

Besides the Fourier and Laplace transforms which we have studied there are others of varying usefulness. Three of the most important may be mentioned here.

One of these is the *Fourier sine and cosine transforms* (cf. Sec. 5, Chap. 4)

$$F(\omega) = \int_0^\infty f(t) \sin \omega t \, dt \tag{72}$$

and

$$F(\omega) = \int_0^\infty f(t) \cos \omega t \, dt \quad , \tag{73}$$

where inverse transforms are

$$f(t) = \frac{2}{\pi} \int_0^\infty F(\omega) \sin \omega t \, d\omega \tag{74}$$

and

$$f(t) = \frac{2}{\pi} \int_0^\infty F(\omega) \cos \omega t \, d\omega \quad , \tag{75}$$

respectively. The *Hankel transform* is

$$F(s) = \int_0^\infty f(t)tJ_\nu(st)dt \quad , \tag{76}$$

and the inversion formula is

$$f(t) = \int_0^\infty F(s)sJ_\nu(st)ds \quad . \tag{77}$$

In both Equations (76) and (77), J_ν is the Bessel function of the first kind and order ν. The Hankel transform stands in the same relation to Fourier-Bessel series as the Fourier transform does to Fourier series. Finally, we mention the *Mellin transform*

$$F(s) = \int_0^\infty f(t)t^{s-1}dt \tag{78}$$

and its inverse

$$f(t) = \frac{1}{2\pi j} \int_{\sigma-j\infty}^{\sigma+j\infty} F(s)t^{-s}ds \quad , \quad t > 0 \quad . \tag{79}$$

REFERENCES

Churchill, R. V., *Modern Operational Mathematics in Engineering*. New York: McGraw-Hill Book Co., Inc., 1944.

Miller, K. S., *Partial Differential Equations in Engineering Problems*. New York: Prentice-Hall, Inc., 1953.

Sneddon, I. N., *Fourier Transforms*. McGraw-Hill Book Co., Inc., 1951.

Tranter, C. J., *Integral Transforms in Mathematical Physics*. New York: John Wiley & Sons, Inc., 1951.

Chapter Six | **NETWORK THEORY**

1. Introduction

A physical, lumped-constant electrical network consists of an interconnection of a number of elements—voltage generators, current generators, resistors, capacitors, inductors, and transformers. In this chapter we wish to discuss these components, analyze various circuits, and investigate some of the main problems associated with networks in general. We shall see that such mathematical concepts as matrix theory, Fourier analysis, and Laplace transform are indispensable as background material in such a treatment.

The first step in analyzing a physical problem is to approximate the given physical network by an *idealized* linear network. The basic elements of idealized networks are assumed to be limited to voltage sources, current sources, resistances, capacitances, inductances, and ideal transformers. It is assumed that two or more inductances possess *mutual inductance*. The first approximation to a given physical network is obtained by substituting the *ideal element* for the *physical* element, as indicated in the table on page 240.

Generally, a physical network can be approximated to any desired degree of accuracy by an idealized network. For example, an inductor can be approximated very accurately by an idealized network consisting of an inductance and resistance in series shunted by a capacitance (cf. Fig. 6.1). Although we are presumably analyzing *physical* networks, all mathematical operations are performed on the associated *idealized* com-

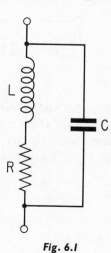

Fig. 6.1

ponents. Thus the domain of network theory is limited to the consideration of idealized elements only.

Elements of a physical network	*Ideal elements*
Resistor	Resistance
Capacitor	Capacitance
Inductor	Inductance
Transformer	Ideal transformer
Voltage generator	Voltage source
Current generator	Current source

2. Electrical Characteristics of Basic Network Elements

Two leads connected to any two points of a network are called *terminals*. The voltage $v(t)$ across a two-terminal network N is illustrated in Figure 6.2.

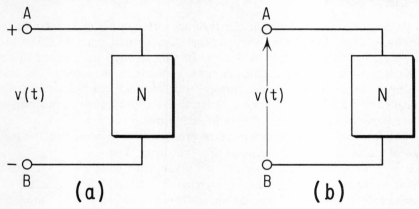

Fig. 6.2

The plus and minus sign or an arrow indicate the polarity of the source at any instant at which $v(t)$ has a positive value. Figures 6.2a and 6.2b represent the same polarity. The *potential difference* between the points A and B, written V_{AB} or $V_A - V_B$, is related to $v(t)$ by the equation

$$V_{AB} = \pm\, v(t) \quad,\tag{1}$$

where the plus sign is chosen if the plus sign of $v(t)$ is at A. For example, in Figure 6.2

$$V_{AB} = +\, v(t) \quad,$$

whereas in Figure 6.3,

$$V_{AB} = -v(t) \quad .$$

The current $i(t)$ through N is illustrated in Figure 6.4. The arrow shows the direction of flow of positive charge at any instant at which $i(t)$ has a positive value.

A voltage $v(t)$ across N is said to be a *voltage drop* if the $\pm$ signs of $v(t)$

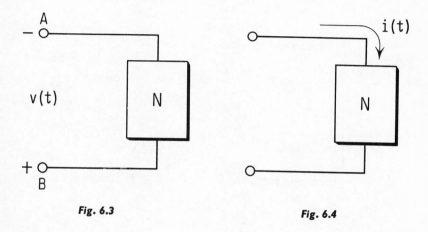

Fig. 6.3   **Fig. 6.4**

are related to the arrow of $i(t)$, as indicated in Figure 6.5a. If the $\pm$ signs are related to the arrow as in Figure 6.5b, then $v(t)$ is said to be a *voltage rise* with

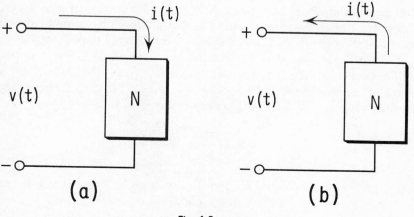

(a)   **(b)**

Fig. 6.5

respect to $i(t)$. Considering v as a voltage drop with respect to i, the volt-ampere characteristics of the first three basic elements are expressed in the following form:

$$\begin{cases} \text{Resistance, } R & v = Ri \\ \text{Conductance, } G & i = Gv \end{cases} \qquad RG = 1$$

$$\begin{cases} \text{Capacitance, } C & i = C\dfrac{dv}{dt} \\ \text{Elastance, } S & v = v_0 + S\displaystyle\int_0^t i\,dt \end{cases} \qquad CS = 1$$

$$\begin{cases} \text{Inductance, } L & v = L\dfrac{di}{dt} \\ \text{Inverse inductance, } \Gamma & i = i_0 + \Gamma\displaystyle\int_0^t v\,dt \end{cases} \qquad L\Gamma = 1 \quad ,$$

Fig. 6.6

where R, C, L, G, S, Γ are constants independent of i and v.

Whenever two inductances possess mutual inductance, they are represented diagramatically as in Figure 6.7. The significance of the "dots" is as follows: Current entering either inductance through the dot marked terminal produces a magnetic flux in the same direction as that produced by current entering the other coil through its dot marked terminal. By Faraday's law it follows that if i_2 is increasing in magnitude the dot marked terminal of L_1 becomes positive with respect to the unmarked terminal, and vice versa. The volt-ampere characteristic of a pair of inductances possessing mutual inductance M is defined in the following manner: The voltage drop v_1 across L_1 is

$$v_1 = L_1\frac{di_1}{dt} \pm M\frac{di_2}{dt} \quad ,$$

where M is a positive constant, and the plus sign is chosen if the currents in both coils enter or leave through the dot marked terminals.

If one of the currents *enters* through the dot marked terminal, while the other current *leaves* through the dot marked terminal, then the minus sign should be chosen. Similarly,

$$v_2 = L_2 \frac{di_2}{dt} \pm M \frac{di_1}{dt} \quad ,$$

where the sign before M is the same as for v_1. For the case illustrated in Figure 6.7,

$$v_1 = L_1 \frac{di_1}{dt} + M \frac{di_2}{dt}$$

$$v_2 = L_2 \frac{di_2}{dt} + M \frac{di_1}{dt} \quad , \tag{2}$$

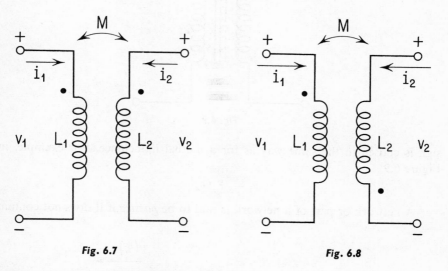

Fig. 6.7   Fig. 6.8

and for the case illustrated in Figure 6.8,

$$v_1 = L_1 \frac{di_1}{dt} - M \frac{di_2}{dt}$$

$$v_2 = L_2 \frac{di_2}{dt} - M \frac{di_1}{dt} \quad .$$

In brief, then, if Figure 6.7 is taken as standard, the equations for v_1 and v_2 are given by Equation (2) and,

(i) If we change a dot, we change the sign of M.

(ii) If we reverse the direction of i_k, we change the sign of di_k/dt, $k = 1, 2$.

(iii) If we reverse the plus and minus signs on v_k, we change the sign of v_k, $k = 1, 2$.

An ideal transformer is represented diagramatically in Figure 6.9. The dot convention has the same significance as in the case of mutual inductances. Its volt-ampere characteristics are defined in the following manner: The voltage drop v_1 produced by a voltage drop v_2 is given by the equation

$$v_1 = \pm nv_2 \quad ,\qquad\qquad\qquad (3)$$

where n is a positive constant called the *turns ratio*, and the positive or negative

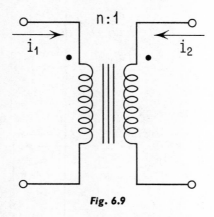

Fig. 6.9

sign is chosen in the same way as for a mutual inductance. For example, in Figure 6.9,

$$v_1 = + nv_2 \quad .$$

A network or part of a network is said to be *passive* if it does not contain

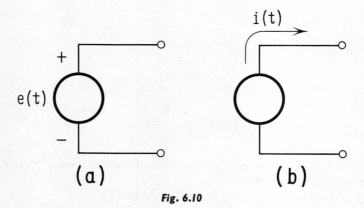

Fig. 6.10

any internal voltage or current sources. Otherwise it is said to be *active*. (Voltage sources are diagramed in Fig. 6.10a and current sources in Fig. 6.10b.)

The circuit diagram of a network consists of a definite number of *nodes* which are interconnected by *branches*. Any two-terminal network which connects two nodes constitutes a branch. A branch may be passive or active. The simplest active branches are voltage and current sources. Any closed path by

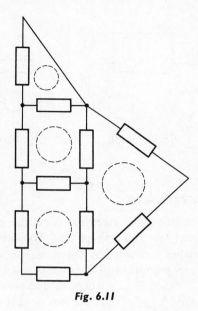

Fig. 6.11

way of two or more branches constitutes a *loop*. If a network is mappable on the plane, its loops can be chosen as shown in Figure 6.11. In this case they are called *meshes*. A network is said to consist of separate parts if no current is

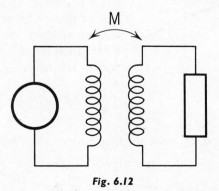

Fig. 6.12

flowing from one part into the other. For example, the network of Figure 6.12 consists of two parts. A network is said to be *k-terminal* if the total number of input and output terminals is equal to k. Some examples are shown in Figure 6.13.

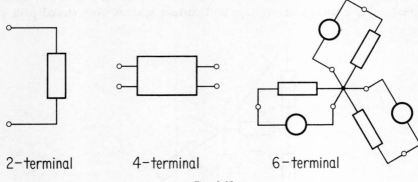

| 2-terminal | 4-terminal | 6-terminal |

Fig. 6.13

3. Kirchhoff's Current Law

The differential equations of electrical networks can be formulated by using Kirchhoff's current law and voltage law. The current law can be stated as follows: In the branches connected to a common node, the algebraic sum of the currents whose arrows point toward the node is equal to that of the currents whose arrows point away from the node.

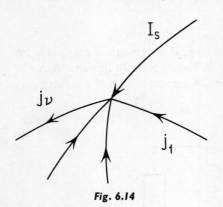

A current is said to *enter* a node if its arrow points toward that node, and is said to *leave* a node if its arrow points away from that node.

Let $\mathfrak{N}$ be a network having n' nodes and b branches; let j_ν be the branch current of the νth branch and I_s the source current entering the sth node (cf. Fig. 6.14). Then for this node the Kirchhoff current law reads

Fig. 6.14

$$I_s = \alpha_{s1} j_1 + \alpha_{s2} j_2 + \cdots + \alpha_{sb} j_b ,$$

where

$$\alpha_{s\nu} = 0 \text{ if } j_\nu \text{ does not terminate on the } s^{\text{th}} \text{ node}$$

$$\alpha_{s\nu} = -1 \text{ if } j_\nu \text{ enters the } s^{\text{th}} \text{ node}$$

$$\alpha_{s\nu} = +1 \text{ if } j_\nu \text{ leaves the } s^{\text{th}} \text{ node}.$$

We may write down similar equations for each of the nodes, thus obtaining the following system of algebraic equations:

$$I_1 = \alpha_{11}j_1 + \alpha_{12}j_2 + \cdots + \alpha_{1b}j_b$$

$$I_2 = \alpha_{21}j_1 + \alpha_{22}j_2 + \cdots + \alpha_{2b}j_b$$

$$\cdots \cdots \cdots \cdots \cdots \cdots \cdots \qquad (4)$$

$$I_{n'} = \alpha_{n'1}j_1 + \alpha_{n'2}j_2 + \cdots + \alpha_{n'b}j_b \quad .$$

Now, considering the network as a whole, it follows from Kirchhoff's law that the total source current entering the network must be zero; that is,

$$I_1 + I_2 + \cdots + I_{n'} = 0 \quad . \qquad (5)$$

Thus Equations (4) are not linearly independent. On the other hand, if only $n' - 1$ of Equations (4) are considered, that is, if the current law for a node k is not included, then each branch current which terminates on the kth node will appear in only one of the remaining $n' - 1$ equations, and therefore the equations will be linearly independent. In other words, a network having n' nodes has $n = n' - 1$ independent nodes. If a network consists of s separate parts, then in each of the separate parts there is one "dependent" node. Hence we have the following theorem.

THEOREM 1. A network which consists of s separate parts and has a total of n' nodes, has $n = n' - s$ independent nodes.

It is customary to describe a network by the number of its independent nodes rather than by the total number of nodes. Thus an n-node network is understood to have n independent nodes.

Any current distribution which satisfies the current law equation can be obtained by the superposition of a definite number of so-called *loop currents*. We can obtain a clear understanding of the mechanism of loop currents through the following reasoning: Let l loops be chosen in such a way that every branch of the network is traversed by at least one loop. With each loop we associate a current i_v which circulates solely in that loop, and choose a positive sense of circulation (indicated by an arrow, as in Fig. 6.15). In this way the μth loop becomes associated with a loop current i_μ. We can imagine the branch current j_v of the vth branch as due to the superposition of all the loop currents which traverse the vth branch. In other words,

$$j_v = \varepsilon_{v1}i_1 + \varepsilon_{v2}i_2 + \cdots + \varepsilon_{vl}i_l \quad , \quad v = 1, 2, \cdots, b \quad , \qquad (6)$$

where

$\varepsilon_{v\mu} = 0$ if i_μ does not traverse the vth branch

$\varepsilon_{v\mu} = +1$ if i_μ traverses the vth branch in the positive sense of j_v

$\varepsilon_{v\mu} = -1$ if i_μ traverses the vth branch in the negative sense of j_v .

We can easily verify that when j_ν is expressed in terms of loop currents as in Equation (6), then the current law equation is automatically satisfied at every node of the network. Thus we are justified in making the following statement: *Any current distribution which satisfies the current law equations can be obtained by the superposition of a definite number of loop currents.*

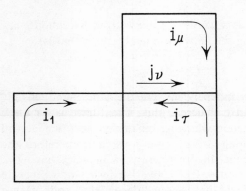

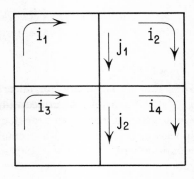

Fig. 6.15   **Fig. 6.16**

It is evident that there is a lower as well as an upper bound to the number of loop currents which can be associated with a given network. The lower limit l_1 is called the *number of independent* loops of the network. A network is called an *l-loop network* if it has l independent loops. To determine l in terms of the number of independent nodes, n, and the number of branches, b, we consider the n equations which express the current law at each one of the n independent nodes of the network [cf. Equations (4)]:

$$I_1 = \alpha_{11}j_1 + \alpha_{12}j_2 + \cdots + \alpha_{1b}j_b$$
$$I_2 = \alpha_{21}j_1 + \alpha_{22}j_2 + \cdots + \alpha_{2b}j_b$$
$$\cdot \quad \cdot \quad \cdot \quad \cdot \quad \cdot \quad \cdot \quad \cdot \quad \cdot \quad \cdot \quad \cdot \quad \cdot \quad \cdot \tag{7}$$
$$I_n = \alpha_{n1}j_1 + \alpha_{n2}j_2 + \cdots + \alpha_{nb}j_b \quad .$$

There are b unknown branch currents and n linearly independent equations among them. Thus the number of independent unknowns is equal to $b - n$. But from the theory of linear equations (cf. Chap. 1) we know that $b - n$ independent variables cannot be expressed in terms of less than $b - n$ other variables. Thus the least number of loop currents l is $b - n$.

THEOREM 2. In an *n*-node, *l*-loop, *b*-branch network,

$$l = b - n \quad .$$

Whenever a network is mappable, it is customary to choose meshes as loops with the positive sense of the loop current in the clockwise direction.

Thus every branch current is equal to the difference between the loop currents of the loops to which it is common. For example, in Figure 6.16,

$$j_1 = i_1 - i_2$$
$$j_2 = i_3 - i_4 \quad .$$

4. Kirchhoff's Voltage Law

Let the nodes of the branches forming the sth loop be numbered consecutively from 1 to t in clockwise or counterclockwise direction, as in Figure 6.17.

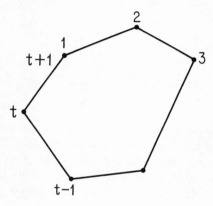

Fig. 6.17

Let the difference of potential between k and $k + 1$ be denoted by V_k. Then Kirchhoff's voltage law may be written

$$\sum_{k=1}^{t} V_k \equiv 0 \quad . \tag{8}$$

It is convenient to formulate the voltage law in terms of branch voltage drops. Thus, expressing every V_k in terms of the corresponding voltage drop v_k, we can substitute in Equation (8) to obtain

$$e_s = \beta_{s1}v_1 + \beta_{s2}v_2 + \cdots + \beta_{sb}v_b \quad , \quad s = 1, 2, \cdots, l \quad , \tag{9}$$

where e_s is the sum of voltage rises (with respect to the loop currents) of active branches in the sth loop and

$\beta_{s\nu} = 0$ if the νth branch is not a part of the sth loop

$\beta_{s\nu} = +1$ if the positive sense of the branch current j_ν is the same as that of the loop current i_s

$\beta_{s\nu} = -1$ if the positive sense of the branch current j_ν is opposite to that of the loop current i_s.

For example, for the loop shown in Figure 6.18,

$$-e_1 = -v_1 + v_2 + v_3 \quad .$$

In the previous section we saw that any branch current could be expressed as a linear combination of loop currents; and that, in particular, any branch

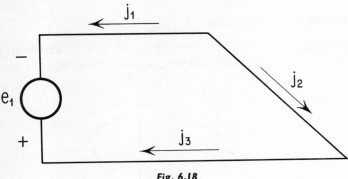

Fig. 6.18

current could be expressed as a difference of two mesh currents. Now it will be shown that any branch voltage can be expressed as a difference of two *node voltages*. To do this, we choose an arbitrary node of the network and let the potential of this node be taken as reference. We call this reference node *datum node* or simply *datum*. If we denote the potential of the μth node with respect

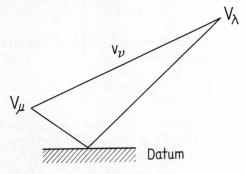

Fig. 6.19

to datum by V_μ, and let v_ν be the voltage drop of the branch which contains the μ and λ node, then (cf. Fig. 6.19)

$$v_\nu = \gamma_{\nu 1} V_1 + \gamma_{\nu 2} V_2 + \cdots + \gamma_{\nu n} V_n \quad , \quad \nu = 1, 2, \cdots, b \quad , \tag{10}$$

where all the terms except $\gamma_{\nu\mu}$ and $\gamma_{\nu\lambda}$ are zero and

$$-\gamma_{\nu\lambda} = \gamma_{\nu\mu} = +1 \text{ if } v_\nu = V_\mu - V_\lambda$$
$$-\gamma_{\nu\lambda} = \gamma_{\nu\mu} = -1 \text{ if } v_\nu = -(V_\mu - V_\lambda) \quad .$$

Node voltages serve the same purposes as loop currents; that is, they make possible the expression of b branch voltage drops in terms of n node voltages.

5. Matrix Formulation

In order to derive the general equilibrium equations of networks, it is necessary to reduce the branches to their simplest form, that is, to consider every passive element as a branch. The active elements are assumed to be distributed throughout the loops of which they are a part, and are not considered as branches. The most compact way of deriving the general form of the equilibrium equations of networks is through the use of matrix notation. We do this by first reformulating the branch volt-ampere characteristics as well as the voltage and current laws in matrix form.

Consider, then, a b-branch, n-node, l-loop network $\mathfrak{N}$ which has no ideal transformers. Let the λ inductance branches be numbered consecutively from 1 to λ, the ρ resistance branches from $\lambda + 1$ to $\lambda + \rho$, and the σ elastance branches from $\lambda + \rho + 1$ to b. The voltage drop v_ν across an inductance $l_{\nu\nu}$ is

$$v_\nu = l_{\nu 1}\frac{dj_1}{dt} + l_{\nu 2}\frac{dj_2}{dt} + \cdots + l_{\nu b}\frac{dj_b}{dt} \quad ,$$

where $l_{\nu\mu}$ is the coefficient of mutual inductance between branches ν and μ and its sign is determined as in Section 2. The branch voltage drops for these λ inductance branches are given by the following system of equations:

$$v_1 = l_{11}\frac{dj_1}{dt} + l_{12}\frac{dj_2}{dt} + \cdots + l_{1\lambda}\frac{dj_\lambda}{dt}$$

$$v_2 = l_{21}\frac{dj_1}{dt} + l_{22}\frac{dj_2}{dt} + \cdots + l_{2\lambda}\frac{dj_\lambda}{dt}$$

$$\cdots \cdots \cdots \cdots \cdots \cdots \tag{11}$$

$$v_\lambda = l_{\lambda 1}\frac{dj_1}{dt} + l_{\lambda 2}\frac{dj_2}{dt} + \cdots + l_{\lambda\lambda}\frac{dj_\lambda}{dt} \quad .$$

If we use p to denote the differential operator $\dfrac{d}{dt}$, then Equations (11) may be written in matrix form as

$$\left\|\begin{array}{c} v_1 \\ v_2 \\ \vdots \\ v_\lambda \end{array}\right\| = \left\|\begin{array}{cccc} l_{11} & l_{12} & \cdots & l_{1\lambda} \\ l_{21} & l_{22} & \cdots & l_{2\lambda} \\ \cdot & \cdot & \cdots & \cdot \\ l_{\lambda 1} & l_{\lambda 2} & \cdots & l_{\lambda\lambda} \end{array}\right\| \cdot \left\|\begin{array}{c} pj_1 \\ pj_2 \\ \vdots \\ pj_\lambda \end{array}\right\| \tag{12}$$

or, still more compactly, as

$$\|v\|_\lambda = \|l\|_{\lambda\lambda} \cdot p \|j\|_\lambda \quad , \tag{13}$$

where the subscripts λ on $\|v\|$ and $\|j\|$ indicate that these are column vectors with λ components, while the double subscript $\lambda\lambda$ on $\|l\|$ indicates that $\|l\|_{\lambda\lambda}$ is a square matrix with λ rows and columns. The matrix $\|l\|_{\lambda\lambda}$ is called the *branch inductance matrix*. By definition of mutual inductance,

$$l_{\nu\mu} = l_{\mu\nu} \quad .$$

Thus $\|l\|_{\lambda\lambda}$ is a *symmetric matrix*.

In a similar manner the volt-ampere characteristics of the ρ resistance branches and σ elastance branches may be expressed in the form

$$\|v\|_\rho = \|r\|_{\rho\rho} \cdot \|j\|_\rho \quad , \tag{14}$$

where

$$\|r\|_{\rho\rho} = \begin{Vmatrix} r_{\lambda+1} & 0 & \cdots & 0 \\ 0 & r_{\lambda+2} & \cdots & 0 \\ \cdot & \cdot & \cdots & \cdot \\ 0 & 0 & \cdots & r_{\lambda+\rho} \end{Vmatrix} \tag{15}$$

is called the *branch resistance matrix* and

$$\|v\|_\sigma = \|s\|_{\sigma\sigma} \cdot p^{-1} \|j\|_\sigma \quad , \tag{16}$$

where†

$$\|s\|_{\sigma\sigma} = \begin{Vmatrix} s_{\lambda+\rho+1} & 0 & \cdots & 0 \\ 0 & s_{\lambda+\rho+2} & \cdots & 0 \\ \cdot & \cdot & \cdots & \cdot \\ 0 & 0 & \cdots & s_b \end{Vmatrix} \tag{17}$$

is called the *branch elastance matrix*.

---

† The symbol $p = \dfrac{d}{dt}$ used in Equation (13) is called the *Heaviside operator*. We use the symbol p^{-1} to mean $p^{-1}(\ ) = \displaystyle\int_0^t (\ )dt$ with the tacit assumption that it is applied only to functions $x(t)$ with the property that $x(0) = 0$. For in this case $pp^{-1}x = p^{-1}px = x$. Later in this chapter we shall consider the relation between p and the Laplace transform variable s.

The combined volt-ampere characteristics of the b-branches can be expressed by defining the *branch operator matrix* $\|\theta\|_{bb}$ as

$$
\|\theta\|_{bb} = \left\|\begin{array}{c:c:c}
\|l\|_{\lambda\lambda}p & \|0\|_{\lambda\rho} & \|0\|_{\lambda\sigma} \\ \hdashline
\|0\|_{\rho\lambda} & \|r\|_{\rho\rho} & \|0\|_{\rho\sigma} \\ \hdashline
\|0\|_{\sigma\lambda} & \|0\|_{\sigma\rho} & \|s\|_{\sigma\sigma}p^{-1}
\end{array}\right\| , \tag{18}
$$

where $\|l\|_{\lambda\lambda}$, $\|r\|_{\rho\rho}$, $\|s\|_{\sigma\sigma}$ and the zero matrices $\|0\|_{\lambda\rho}$, $\|0\|_{\lambda\sigma}$, and so forth are submatrices of $\|\theta\|_{bb}$. The complete set of b equations expressing branch voltage drops in terms of branch currents may thus be expressed in matrix form as

$$
\|v\|_b = \|\theta\|_{bb} \cdot \|j\|_b , \tag{19}
$$

which is the combined branch volt-ampere characteristics. Note that $\|\theta\|_{bb}$ is a symmetric matrix.

The matrix form of the *voltage law* can be written [cf. Equations (9)]

$$
\|e\|_l = \|\beta\|_{lb} \cdot \|v\|_b , \tag{20}
$$

and the *current law* equation may be expressed in matrix form as [cf. Equations (7)]

$$
\|I\|_n = \|\alpha\|_{nb} \cdot \|j\|_b . \tag{21}
$$

Expressing the branch currents in terms of loop currents [cf. Equation (6)] we obtain

$$
\|j\|_b = \|\varepsilon\|_{bl} \cdot \|i\|_l , \tag{22}
$$

and expressing the branch voltage drops in terms of node voltages [cf. Equation (10)], we obtain

$$
\|v\|_b = \|\gamma\|_{bn} \cdot \|V\|_n . \tag{23}
$$

6. The Equilibrium Equations of Networks

The equilibrium equations of a network consist of a set of equations interrelating the known and unknown variables in the network. They can be formulated either on the *loop basis* or the *node basis*. First let us formulate these equations on the *loop basis*.

We shall assume the network to have no current sources and no ideal transformers. Then from Equations (20), (19), (22),

$$\| e \|_l = \| \beta \|_{lb} \cdot \| \theta \|_{bb} \cdot \| \varepsilon \|_{bl} \cdot \| i \|_l \quad , \tag{24}$$

and, if we define the matrix $\| Z \|_{ll}$ as

$$\| Z \|_{ll} = \| \beta \|_{lb} \cdot \| \theta \|_{bb} \cdot \| \varepsilon \|_{bl} \quad , \tag{25}$$

Equation (24) becomes

$$\| e \|_l = \| Z \|_{ll} \cdot \| i \|_l \tag{26}$$

or, in expanded form,

$$e_1 = Z_{11} i_1 + Z_{12} i_2 + \cdots + Z_{1l} i_l$$
$$e_2 = Z_{21} i_1 + Z_{22} i_2 + \cdots + Z_{2l} i_l \tag{27}$$
$$\cdot \quad \cdot \quad \cdot \quad \cdot \quad \cdot \quad \cdot \quad \cdot \quad \cdot \quad \cdot \quad \cdot \quad \cdot \quad \cdot$$
$$e_l = Z_{l1} i_1 + Z_{l2} i_2 + \cdots + Z_{ll} i_l \quad .$$

The set of l equations represented by Equations (27) constitutes the equilibrium equations of a given network on the loop basis. They express the l voltage law equations for l independent loops in terms of associated loop currents. Additional information about $\| Z \|_{ll}$ is obtained by dividing the matrices $\| \beta \|_{lb}$, $\| \theta \|_{bb}$ and $\| \varepsilon \|_{bl}$ into appropriate submatrices. We write

$$\| \beta \|_{lb} = \left\| \; \| \beta \|_{l\lambda} \; \vdots \; \| \beta \|_{l\rho} \; \vdots \; \| \beta \|_{l\sigma} \; \right\|_{lb} , \tag{28}$$

where $\| \beta \|_{l\lambda}$ denotes a submatrix of $\| \beta \|_{lb}$ composed of the first l rows and λ columns, $\| \beta \|_{l\rho}$ is a submatrix composed of the first l rows and $\lambda + 1, \cdots, \lambda + \rho$ columns, and $\| \beta \|_{l\sigma}$ is a submatrix composed of the first l rows and the $\lambda + \rho + 1, \cdots, b$ columns. The matrix $\| \theta \|_{bb}$ is defined by Equation (18); and we write

$$\| \varepsilon \|_{bl} = \left\| \begin{array}{c} \| \varepsilon \|_{\lambda l} \\ \hline \| \varepsilon \|_{\rho l} \\ \hline \| \varepsilon \|_{\sigma l} \end{array} \right\|_{bl} , \tag{29}$$

where $\| \varepsilon \|_{\lambda l}$, $\| \varepsilon \|_{\rho l}$ and $\| \varepsilon \|_{\sigma l}$ are defined in the expected fashion.

Performing the operation indicated by Equation (25), we may write

$$\| Z \|_{ll} = [\| \beta \|_{l\lambda} \cdot \| l \|_{\lambda\lambda} \cdot \| \varepsilon \|_{\lambda l}] p + [\| \beta \|_{l\rho} \cdot \| r \|_{\rho\rho} \cdot \| \varepsilon \|_{\rho l}]$$
$$+ [\| \beta \|_{l\sigma} \cdot \| s \|_{\sigma\sigma} \cdot \| \varepsilon \|_{\sigma l}] p^{-1} \quad . \tag{30}$$

If we define

$$\|L\|_{u} = \|\beta\|_{u\lambda} \cdot \|l\|_{\lambda\lambda} \cdot \|\varepsilon\|_{\lambda l} \tag{31}$$

as the loop inductance-parameter matrix,

$$\|R\|_{u} = \|\beta\|_{l\rho} \cdot \|r\|_{\rho\rho} \cdot \|\varepsilon\|_{\rho l} \tag{32}$$

as the loop resistance-parameter matrix, and

$$\|S\|_{u} = \|\beta\|_{l\sigma} \cdot \|s\|_{\sigma\sigma} \cdot \|\varepsilon\|_{\sigma l} \tag{33}$$

as the loop elastance-parameter matrix, then $\|Z\|_{u}$ may be written

$$\|Z\|_{u} = \|L\|_{u}p + \|R\|_{u} + \|S\|_{u}p^{-1} \quad . \tag{34}$$

$\|Z\|_{u}$ is called the *impedance matrix*, and it is readily verified that $\|Z\|_{u}$ is a symmetric matrix. The equilibrium equations then assume the matrix form

$$\|e\|_{l} = \{\|L\|_{u}p + \|R\|_{u} + \|S\|_{u}p^{-1}\}\|i\|_{l} \tag{35}$$

or, in expanded form they become identical with Equations (27), where

$$Z_{\nu\mu} = L_{\nu\mu}p + R_{\nu\mu} + S_{\nu\mu}p^{-1} \quad . \tag{36}$$

We call $Z_{\nu\mu}$ the *mutual impedance* of loops ν and μ ($\nu \neq \mu$), and $Z_{\nu\nu}$ is called the *self-impedance* of the νth loop.

EXERCISE

The matrix A^{t} is said to be the *transpose* of the matrix $A = \|a_{ij}\|$ if $A^{t} = \|a_{ji}\|$; that is, rows and columns have been interchanged. Show that

$$\|Z\|_{u} = \|\beta\|_{lb} \cdot \|\theta\|_{bb} \cdot \|\beta\|_{lb}^{t} \quad ;$$

that is, show that

$$\|\varepsilon\|_{bl} = \|\beta\|_{lb}^{t} \quad .$$

Also prove that $\|\alpha\|_{nb}$ is the transpose of $\|\gamma\|_{bn}$.

The above formulas indicate that in order to derive the equilibrium equations of a network on the loop basis [Equations (27)], it is sufficient to write down the β and θ matrices by inspection, perform the multiplications indicated by Equation (25), and substitute the values of L, R, and S thus obtained into Equation (27).

As an example, let us determine the θ, β, and ε matrices of the network illustrated in Figure 6.20 below, where

$$L_1 = 1 \quad , \quad L_2 = 1 \quad , \quad L_3 = 2 \quad , \quad L_4 = 1 \quad , \quad L_5 = 2$$
$$M_{12} = 1 \quad , \quad M_{15} = 2 \quad , \quad M_{34} = 1$$
$$R_6 = 1 \quad , \quad R_7 = 1 \quad , \quad S_8 = 1 \quad .$$

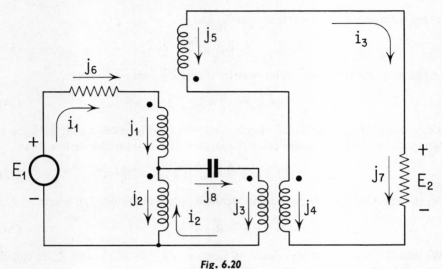

Fig. 6.20

By inspection we immediately see that

$$\|\theta\|_{bb} = \left\|\begin{array}{ccccc|ccc}
p & p & 0 & 0 & -2p & 0 & 0 & 0 \\
p & p & 0 & 0 & 0 & 0 & 0 & 0 \\
0 & 0 & 2p & p & 0 & 0 & 0 & 0 \\
0 & 0 & p & p & 0 & 0 & 0 & 0 \\
-2p & 0 & 0 & 0 & 2p & 0 & 0 & 0 \\ \hline
0 & 0 & 0 & 0 & 0 & 1 & 0 & 0 \\
0 & 0 & 0 & 0 & 0 & 0 & 1 & 0 \\
0 & 0 & 0 & 0 & 0 & 0 & 0 & p^{-1}
\end{array}\right\| \quad , \quad (37)$$

$$\|\beta\|_{lb} = \left\|\begin{array}{ccccc|cc|c}
1 & 1 & 0 & 0 & 0 & 1 & 0 & 0 \\
0 & -1 & 1 & 0 & 0 & 0 & 0 & 1 \\
0 & 0 & 0 & -1 & -1 & 0 & 1 & 0
\end{array}\right\| \quad , \quad (38)$$

and

$$\|\varepsilon\|_{bl} = \|\beta\|_{lb}^{t} = \begin{Vmatrix} 1 & 0 & 0 \\ 1 & -1 & 0 \\ 0 & 1 & 0 \\ 0 & 0 & -1 \\ 0 & 0 & -1 \\ 1 & 0 & 0 \\ 0 & 0 & 1 \\ 0 & 1 & 0 \end{Vmatrix}.$$

With these matrices we can compute the impedance matrix by Equation (25):

$$\|Z\|_{ll} = \|\beta\|_{lb} \cdot \|\theta\|_{bb} \cdot \|\beta\|_{lb}^{t} = \begin{Vmatrix} 4p+1 & -2p & 2p \\ -2p & 3p+p^{-1} & -p \\ 2p & -p & 3p+1 \end{Vmatrix}$$

and thus find the equilibrium equations on the loop basis.

Finally, if we consider the circuit of Figure 6.20 as a four-terminal network with input E_1 and output voltage E_2 developed across R_7, then

$$E_2 = R_7 i_3 = i_3 = \frac{\begin{vmatrix} 4p+1 & -2p & E_1 \\ -2p & 3p+p^{-1} & 0 \\ 2p & -p & 0 \end{vmatrix}}{\begin{vmatrix} 4p+1 & -2p & 2p \\ -2p & 3p+p^{-1} & -p \\ 2p & -p & 3p+1 \end{vmatrix}}$$

$$= \frac{-E_1(4p^2+2)}{16p^3 + 16p^2 + 11p + 7 + p^{-1}},$$

and

$$\frac{E_2}{E_1} = \frac{-p(4p^2+2)}{16p^4 + 16p^3 + 11p^2 + 7p + 1}. \tag{39}$$

This last formula presents an interesting result. If we call the right-hand side of Equation (39), $H(p)$, then we may write the equation

$$E_2 = H(p)E_1 \quad , \tag{40}$$

which expresses the output voltage as a function of the input voltage. We shall call $H(p)$ the *system function of the network*. In general, if we have a passive

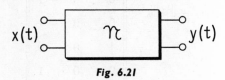

Fig. 6.21

four-terminal network $\mathfrak{N}$ as in Figure 6.21, then we can associate with it a *system function $H(p)$* which is a rational function of p and write

$$y(t) = H(p)x(t) \quad . \tag{41}$$

We shall return to this interesting concept after formulating the equilibrium equations on the *node basis*.

To determine the equilibrium equations on the node basis we shall assume that the network contains no voltage sources and no ideal transformers. From Equation (21)

$$\| I \|_n = \| \alpha \|_{nb} \cdot \| j \|_b \quad ,$$

and from Equation (19)

$$\| v \|_b = \| \theta \|_{bb} \cdot \| j \|_b \quad ,$$

or

$$\| j \|_b = \| \theta \|_{bb}^{-1} \cdot \| v \|_b \quad ,$$

where $\| \theta \|_{bb}^{-1}$ is the inverse matrix of $\| \theta \|_{bb}$. Finally, from Equation (23),

$$\| v \|_b = \| \gamma \|_{bn} \cdot \| V \|_n \quad ,$$

and, if these results are combined,

$$\| I \|_n = \| \alpha \|_{nb} \cdot \| \theta \|_{bb}^{-1} \cdot \| \gamma \|_{bn} \cdot \| V \|_n \quad . \tag{42}$$

If we define the matrix $\| Y \|_{nn}$ as

$$\| Y \|_{nn} = \| \alpha \|_{nb} \cdot \| \theta \|_{bb}^{-1} \cdot \| \gamma \|_{bn} \quad ,$$

then we call $\| Y \|_{nn}$ the *admittance matrix* (note that $\| Y \|_{nn}$ is always a symmetric matrix), and Equation (42) becomes

$$\| I \|_n = \| Y \|_{nn} \cdot \| V \|_n \quad . \tag{43}$$

In expanded form this reads

$$
\begin{aligned}
I_1 &= Y_{11}V_1 + Y_{12}V_2 + \cdots + Y_{1n}V_n \\
I_2 &= Y_{21}V_1 + Y_{22}V_2 + \cdots + Y_{2n}V_n \\
&\; \cdot \quad \cdot \quad \cdot \quad \cdot \quad \cdot \quad \cdot \quad \cdot \quad \cdot \quad \cdot \quad \cdot \quad \cdot \quad \cdot \quad \cdot \\
I_n &= Y_{n1}V_1 + Y_{n2}V_2 + \cdots + Y_{nn}V_n \quad .
\end{aligned}
\tag{44}
$$

The set of n equations represented by Equations (44) constitute the *equilibrium equations* of a given network on the *node basis*. They express the n current law equations for n independent nodes in terms of associated node voltages.

By the same procedure as that we used to treat the impedance matrix, we arrive at the result that $\| \gamma \|_{bn}$ is the transpose of $\| \alpha \|_{nb}$, that is,

$$\| \gamma \|_{bn} = \| \alpha \|_{nb}^t \quad ,$$

and that $\| Y \|_{nn}$ may be written in the form

$$\| Y \|_{nn} = \| \Gamma \|_{nn} p^{-1} + \| G \|_{nn} + \| C \|_{nn} p \quad , \tag{45}$$

where

$$\| \Gamma \|_{nn} = \| \alpha \|_{n\lambda} \cdot \| l \|_{\lambda\lambda}^{-1} \cdot \| \alpha \|_{n\lambda}^t \tag{46}$$

$$\| G \|_{nn} = \| \alpha \|_{n\rho} \cdot \| r \|_{\rho\rho}^{-1} \cdot \| \alpha \|_{n\rho}^t \tag{47}$$

$$\| C \|_{nn} = \| \alpha \|_{n\sigma} \cdot \| s \|_{\sigma\sigma}^{-1} \cdot \| \alpha \|_{n\sigma}^t \quad . \tag{48}$$

Equation (43) may thus be written

$$\| I \|_n = \{\| \Gamma \|_{nn} p^{-1} + \| G \|_{nn} + \| C \|_{nn} p\} \| V \|_n \quad , \tag{49}$$

or in expanded form they become identical with Equations (44), where

$$Y_{\nu\mu} = \Gamma_{\nu\mu} p^{-1} + G_{\nu\mu} + C_{\nu\mu} p \quad . \tag{50}$$

We call $Y_{\nu\mu}$ the *mutual admittance* of nodes ν and μ $(\nu \neq \mu)$ and $Y_{\nu\nu}$ is called the *self-admittance* of the νth node.

As an example, consider the circuit of Figure 6.22 where the values of the parameters are

$$L_1 = 1 \quad, \quad L_2 = 2 \quad, \quad L_3 = 2$$
$$M_{12} = 1 \quad, \quad M_{13} = 2 \quad, \quad M_{23} = 1$$
$$S_4 = \tfrac{1}{2} \quad, \quad S_5 = 1 \quad, \quad S_6 = 1 \quad .$$

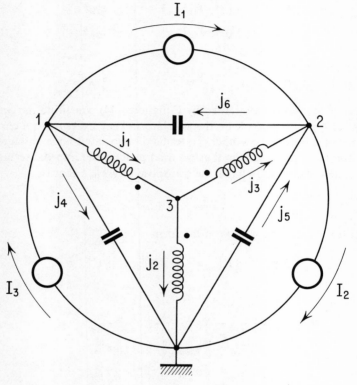

Fig. 6.22

Then by inspection the θ matrix reads

$$\|\theta\| = \left\|\begin{array}{ccc:ccc} p & -p & -2p & 0 & 0 & 0 \\ -p & 2p & p & 0 & 0 & 0 \\ -2p & p & 2p & 0 & 0 & 0 \\ \hdashline 0 & 0 & 0 & \tfrac{1}{2}p^{-1} & 0 & 0 \\ 0 & 0 & 0 & 0 & p^{-1} & 0 \\ 0 & 0 & 0 & 0 & 0 & p^{-1} \end{array}\right\|$$

and

$$\|\theta\|^{-1} = \begin{Vmatrix} -p^{-1} & 0 & -p^{-1} & 0 & 0 & 0 \\ 0 & \frac{2}{3}p^{-1} & -\frac{1}{3}p^{-1} & 0 & 0 & 0 \\ -p^{-1} & -\frac{1}{3}p^{-1} & -\frac{1}{3}p^{-1} & 0 & 0 & 0 \\ \hdashline 0 & 0 & 0 & 2p & 0 & 0 \\ 0 & 0 & 0 & 0 & p & 0 \\ 0 & 0 & 0 & 0 & 0 & p \end{Vmatrix}.$$

(As a check, we may verify that $\|\theta\| \cdot \|\theta\|^{-1} = \|\delta\|$ where $\|\delta\|$ is the identity matrix.) The α matrix is found to be

$$\|\alpha\| = \begin{Vmatrix} 1 & 0 & 0 & 1 & 0 & -1 \\ 0 & 0 & -1 & 0 & -1 & 1 \\ -1 & 1 & 1 & 0 & 0 & 0 \end{Vmatrix}$$

and

$$\|Y\| = \|\alpha\| \cdot \|\theta\|^{-1} \cdot \|\alpha\|^t = \begin{Vmatrix} -p^{-1} + 3p & p^{-1} - p & 0 \\ p^{-1} - p & -\frac{1}{3}p^{-1} + 2p & -\frac{1}{3}p^{-1} \\ 0 & -\frac{1}{3}p^{-1} & \frac{2}{3}p^{-1} \end{Vmatrix}. \qquad (51)$$

The equilibrium equations on the node basis are then

$$\begin{aligned} I_3 - I_1 &= (-p^{-1} + 3p)V_1 + & (p^{-1} - p)V_2 \\ I_1 - I_2 &= (p^{-1} - p)V_1 & + (-\tfrac{1}{3}p^{-1} + 2p)V_2 - \tfrac{1}{3}p^{-1}V_3 \\ 0 &= & -\tfrac{1}{3}p^{-1}V_2 + \tfrac{2}{3}p^{-1}V_3 . \end{aligned} \qquad (52)$$

EXERCISES

1. Determine the θ, β, and Z matrices for the circuit of Figure 6.23, and write the equilibrium equations on the loop basis. Assume the following values of the parameters:

$$\begin{aligned} L_1 &= 1 , & L_2 &= 3 , & L_3 &= 2 , & L_4 &= 1 \\ M_{12} &= 1 , & M_{24} &= 1 , & M_{23} &= 1 , & M_{14} &= 1 \\ R_5 &= 2 , & S_6 &= 4 . \end{aligned}$$

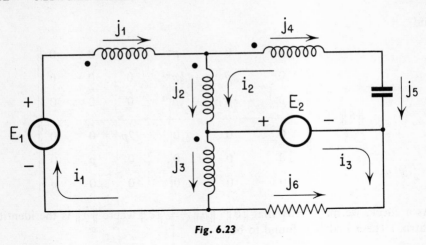

Fig. 6.23

2. Determine by inspection $\|\theta\|$, $\|\alpha\|$, $\|\gamma\|$, and verify that $\|\gamma\|$ is the transpose of $\|\alpha\|$ for the network of Figure 6.24. Form the admittance matrix

$$\|Y\| = \|\alpha\| \cdot \|\theta\|^{-1} \cdot \|\gamma\| \quad,$$

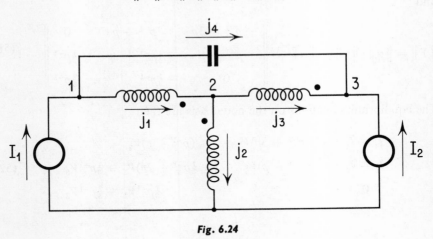

Fig. 6.24

and thus obtain the equilibrium equations on the node basis. Let the elements have the following numerical values:

$$L_1 = 1 \quad , \quad L_2 = 2 \quad , \quad L_3 = 2$$
$$M_{13} = 1 \quad , \quad M_{12} = 1 \quad , \quad M_{23} = 1$$
$$S_4 = 2 \quad .$$

3. Find the voltage ratio E_2/E_1 for the circuit of Figure 6.25, where

$$L_1 = 4 \quad , \quad L_2 = 1 \quad , \quad M_{12} = 1$$
$$R_3 = 2 \quad , \quad R_4 = 1$$
$$S_5 = 1 \quad , \quad I = 2V \quad .$$

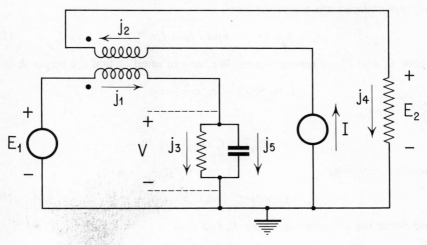

Fig. 6.25

7. The System Function

Ordinarily we are interested in the steady state response of a network to sinusoidally varying voltage and current sources, that is, in particular solutions of the equilibrium equations for

$$e_s = E_s^0 \cos(\omega t + \phi) \quad \text{or} \quad I_s = I_s^0 \cos(\omega t + \theta) \quad . \tag{53}$$

The conventional way for finding the network response to sinusoidally varying sources is through the use of the complex exponential $e^{j\omega t}$. Its use is based on the following property of linear operators: if T is a linear operator and $f(t)$ is a complex valued function of the real variable t, then

$$\Re[Tf(t)] = T\Re[f(t)] \quad .$$

We recall that multiplication by a real function of t, differentiation, integration, the Fourier and Laplace transforms are all linear operators. Since, in particular,

$$E^0 \cos(\omega t + \phi) = \Re[E^0 e^{j(\omega t + \phi)}] \quad , \tag{54}$$

it follows that in order to find the response to $E^0 \cos(\omega t + \phi)$ it is sufficient to find the response to $E^0 e^{j(\omega t + \phi)}$ and then evaluate the real part. Thus it is always assumed that the applied voltages (or currents), as well as their responses, are of the form $E^0 e^{j(\omega t + \phi)}$. It is tacitly understood that the actual applied voltages and their responses are the *real* parts of the complex voltages and their complex responses, respectively.

In the case of the equilibrium equations we assume that the applied voltages and currents are of the form

$$e'_s = E_s^0 e^{j(\omega t + \phi)} \quad \text{and} \quad i'_s = I_s^0 e^{j(\omega t + \theta)} \quad , \tag{55}$$

where E_s^0 and I_s^0 are real constants. We have in mind to find the response to

$$e_s = \Re[e'_s] = E_s^0 \cos(\omega t + \phi)$$

or

$$i_s = \Re[i'_s] = I_s^0 \cos(\omega t + \theta) \quad .$$

Now we may write

$$e'_s = (E_s^0 e^{j\phi}) e^{j\omega t} \quad \text{and} \quad i'_s = (I_s^0 e^{j\theta}) e^{j\omega t} \tag{56}$$

and define the *complex amplitudes* E'_s and I'_s as

$$E'_s = E_s^0 e^{j\phi} \quad \text{and} \quad I'_s = I_s^0 e^{j\theta} \quad .$$

We have

$$e'_s = E'_s e^{j\omega t} \quad \text{and} \quad i'_s = I'_s e^{j\omega t} \quad , \tag{57}$$

with the understanding that the real voltages and currents are

$$e_s = \Re[E'_s e^{j\omega t}] \quad \text{and} \quad I_s = \Re[I'_s e^{j\omega t}] \quad .$$

Substituting Equation (57) into the equilibrium equations on the loop basis [Equations (27)], we get

$$E'_1 = Z_{11} I'_1 + Z_{12} I'_2 + \cdots + Z_{1l} I'_l$$
$$E'_2 = Z_{21} I'_1 + Z_{22} I'_2 + \cdots + Z_{2l} I'_l$$
$$\cdot \quad \cdot \quad \cdot \quad \cdot \quad \cdot \quad \cdot \quad \cdot \quad \cdot \quad \cdot \quad \cdot \quad \cdot \quad \cdot \quad \cdot \tag{58}$$
$$E'_l = Z_{l1} I'_1 + Z_{l2} I'_2 + \cdots + Z_{ll} I'_l \quad ,$$

where

$$Z_{\nu\mu} = Z_{\mu\nu} = L_{\nu\mu} j\omega + R_{\nu\mu} + \frac{S_{\nu\mu}}{j\omega} \quad . \tag{59}$$

We see that the expression for $Z_{\nu\mu}$ is identical with Equation (36) with p replaced by $j\omega$. In particular, in the example treated in the previous section, we may write Equation (39) as

$$\frac{E_2}{E_1} = \frac{-(j\omega)[4(j\omega)^2 + 2]}{16(j\omega)^4 + 16(j\omega)^3 + 11(j\omega)^2 + 7(j\omega) + 1} \quad ,$$

which expresses the complex amplitude ratio as a function of $j\omega$. We see therefore, that if p is replaced by $j\omega$, Equation (40) becomes

$$E_2 = H(j\omega)E_1 \quad ,$$

where $H(j\omega)$, the system function, is just the ratio of complex amplitudes. Thus, if we analyze a network on the sinusoidal or, as it is frequently called, the *steady state* basis, then we can easily compute $H(j\omega)$. More generally, if $\mathfrak{N}$ is a passive four-terminal network (cf. Fig. 6.21), then we define the *system function* $H(j\omega)$ as

$$H(j\omega) = \frac{y(t)}{x(t)}\bigg|_{x = e^{j\omega t}} \quad . \tag{60}$$

It is tacitly assumed that $H(j\omega)$ is calculated after a long period of time so that in a physically realizable system any initial "transients" due, for example, to initial charges on condensers, have all died down. In terms of the Heaviside operator $p = d/dt$ we may write

$$H(p) = \frac{N(p)}{M(p)} \quad , \tag{61}$$

where N and M are polynomials in p. Then it follows from Equation (41) that

$$M(p)y(t) = N(p)x(t) \quad , \tag{62}$$

where M and N are now linear differential operators. Equation (62) expresses the fact that the output, y, acted on by the linear differential operator M is equal to the input x acted on by the linear differential operator N. If we are to solve uniquely for y, by the Green's function method, for instance, then boundary conditions must be associated with M.

If we take the Fourier transform of both sides of Equation (62), we get

$$M(j\omega)Y(j\omega) = N(j\omega)X(j\omega)$$

or

$$Y(j\omega) = H(j\omega)X(j\omega) \quad , \tag{63}$$

where $X(j\omega) = \mathscr{F}[x(t)]$ and $Y(j\omega) = \mathscr{F}[y(t)]$. Also, if we take the Laplace transform of both sides of Equation (62) and assign to $N(p)$ the boundary conditions $x^{(\beta)}(0) = 0$, $\beta = 0, 1, \cdot \cdot \cdot, n - 1$, and the boundary conditions $y^{(\alpha)}(0) = 0$, $\alpha = 0, 1, \cdot \cdot \cdot, m - 1$ to $M(p)$ where n is the degree of N and m is the degree of M, then

$$M(s)Y(s) = N(s)X(s)$$

or

$$Y(s) = H(s)X(s) \quad , \tag{64}$$

where $X(s) = \mathscr{L}[x(t)]$ and $Y(s) = \mathscr{L}[y(t)]$.

We see therefore that if $\mathfrak{N}$ is a passive four-terminal network, then the *system function H* can be interpreted as

(i) A complex voltage ratio,

$$\frac{y(t)}{x(t)} \bigg|_{x = e^{j\omega t}} = H(j\omega) \quad ,$$

where ω is angular frequency.

(ii) A differential equation

$$y(t) = H(p)x(t) \quad ,$$

where $p = \dfrac{d}{dt}$ is the Heaviside operator.

(iii) A Fourier transform

$$Y(j\omega) = H(j\omega)X(j\omega) \quad ,$$

where $Y(j\omega) = \mathscr{F}[y(t)]$, $X(j\omega) = \mathscr{F}[x(t)]$.

(iv) A Laplace transform

$$Y(s) = H(s)X(s) \quad ,$$

where $X(s) = \mathscr{L}[x(t)]$, $Y(s) = \mathscr{L}[y(t)]$.

All in all, it appears that H is a very versatile function to associate with a network, for a knowledge of H completely determines $\mathfrak{N}$ in the sense that, given any input $x(t)$, the output $y(t)$ is uniquely specified.

8. The Delta Function

One of the fundamental problems in the theory of communication systems is to characterize a network $\mathfrak{N}$ (cf. Fig. 6.21). We have seen that a knowledge of the *transfer function* or system function $H(j\omega)$ is sufficient to characterize $\mathfrak{N}$. We recall that $H(j\omega)$ can be interpreted as the ratio of complex amplitudes, and we have called $H(j\omega)e^{j\omega t}$ the *steady state* response. There are other ways of characterizing $\mathfrak{N}$. For example, we can consider the response of $\mathfrak{N}$ to the unit step function $u(t)$ or the *ramp function* $tu(t)$. In this case we generally call the response a *transient* response. One can of course consider other functions as inputs. Perhaps the most important is the response of a network to a *delta function* input. In this case, the response is called the *impulsive response*. We shall see in the next section that the impulsive response completely characterizes $\mathfrak{N}$. For the present, however, let us define and examine a few properties of the "delta function."

The engineer usually defines the so-called *delta function* or *unit impulse function* $\delta(t)$ by the three equations

$$\delta(t) = 0 \quad , \quad t \neq 0$$

$$\delta(t) = \infty \quad , \quad t = 0 \tag{65}$$

$$\int_{-\infty}^{\infty} \delta(t)dt = 1 \quad .$$

That is, $\delta(t)$ is a function which is zero everywhere except at the origin and the value of its integral is one. A physical interpretation of the delta function can be obtained by considering the limit of a finite pulse $p(t)$ of unit area as the

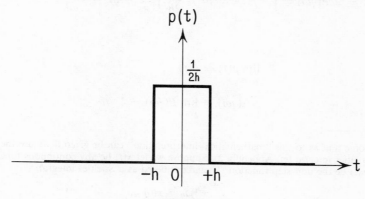

Fig. 6.26

height of the pulse becomes infinite. Referring to Figure 6.26, we see that for any $h > 0$,

$$p(t) = 0 \quad , \quad |t| > h$$

$$p(t) = \frac{1}{2h} \quad , \quad |t| < h$$

$$\int_{-\infty}^{\infty} p(t)dt = 1 \quad .$$

Now, as $h \to 0$, $p(t) \to \delta(t)$, if we allow

$$\lim_{h \to 0} \int_{-\infty}^{\infty} p(t)dt = \int_{-\infty}^{\infty} \lim_{h \to 0} p(t)dt \ .$$

However, this interchange of limits is not valid, and, mathematically speaking, to say a function is zero everywhere except at a single point and has a non-zero integral is sheer nonsense.

Since, however, the delta function is such a useful tool in the theory of communications and other branches of engineering, it is the task of the mathematician to overcome the difficulties mentioned above and place the delta function on a sound mathematical foundation. Such an analysis has been achieved and it is called "the theory of distributions." But it is beyond the scope of this book to present it in detail.† In this section we shall derive various properties of the delta function. Our mathematical manipulations will be purely formal, and we shall appeal to the theory of distributions for a precise mathematical interpretation of our results.

Consider again the pulse of Figure 6.26. Its Fourier transform $P(j\omega)$ is given by

$$P(j\omega) = \int_{-\infty}^{\infty} p(t)e^{-j\omega t}dt = \frac{1}{2h}\int_{-h}^{h}e^{-j\omega t}dt = \frac{\sin \omega h}{\omega h} \ .$$

Now

$$\lim_{h \to 0} p(t) = \delta(t) \quad,$$

$$\Delta(j\omega) = \lim_{h \to 0} P(j\omega) = 1 \quad.$$

---

† Some hint as to this "mathematical interpretation" can be given if we use the concept of the Stieltjes integral (cf. Appendix 2). Suppose we let $x(t)$ be any continuous function of t and let $u(t)$ be the unit step function. Then, considered as a Stieltjes integral,

$$\int_{-\infty}^{\infty} x(t)du = x(0) \quad.$$

If we interpret du as a differential and write formally $d\,u(t) = \delta(t)\,dt$, then the above equation may be written as

$$\int_{-\infty}^{\infty} x(t)\delta(t)dt = x(0) \quad.$$

Clearly the function $\delta(t)$ must have the properties

$$\delta(t) = 0 \quad, \quad t \neq 0$$
$$\delta(t) = \infty \quad, \quad t = 0 \quad,$$

and, if we let $x(t) \equiv 1$, we may write

$$\int_{-\infty}^{\infty} \delta(t)dt = 1 \quad.$$

Hence we shall say that the Fourier transform $\Delta(j\omega)$ of the delta function $\delta(t)$ is 1. By applying the translation property of the Fourier transform, namely,

$$\mathscr{F}[x(t + \tau)] = e^{j\omega\tau}\mathscr{F}[x(t)] \quad,$$

we conclude that

$$\mathscr{F}[\delta(t - \tau)] = e^{-j\omega\tau} \quad.$$

A formal application of the inverse Fourier transform gives

$$\delta(t) = \frac{1}{2\pi} \int_{-\infty}^{\infty} \Delta(j\omega)e^{j\omega t}d\omega \quad,$$

and, since $\Delta(j\omega) = 1$,

$$\int_{-\infty}^{\infty} e^{j\omega t}d\omega = 2\pi\, \delta(t) \quad. \tag{66}$$

Replacing ω by $-\omega$ in the above equation,

$$\int_{-\infty}^{\infty} e^{-j\omega t}d\omega = 2\pi\, \delta(t) \quad, \tag{67}$$

and adding Equation (66) and (67), we have

$$\int_{-\infty}^{\infty} \cos \omega t \, d\omega = 2\pi\, \delta(t) \quad.$$

We recall that

$$\int_{-\infty}^{\infty} \delta(t)dt = 1 \quad.$$

Clearly,

$$\int_{-\varepsilon}^{\varepsilon} \delta(t)dt = 1 \tag{68}$$

for every $\varepsilon > 0$, since $\delta(t) = 0$ for $t \neq 0$. Also,

$$\int_{-\infty}^{0} \delta(t)dt = \int_{-\varepsilon}^{0} \delta(t)dt = \tfrac{1}{2} = \int_{0}^{\varepsilon} \delta(t)dt = \int_{0}^{\infty} \delta(t)dt \tag{69}$$

for any $\varepsilon > 0$, as can readily be seen by considering the limit of $p(t)$ as h approaches zero. [That is, only half the area of $p(t)$ is included in $(-\infty, 0)$ or $(0, \infty)$.]

An important property of the delta function is that it acts as a *reproducing kernel*. For example, consider

$$\int_{-\infty}^{\infty} x(t)\delta(t)dt \quad .$$

This may be written as

$$\int_{-\varepsilon}^{\varepsilon} x(t)\delta(t)dt$$

for any $\varepsilon > 0$, since the integrand is zero for $t \neq 0$. Now, using the mean value theorem for integrals, we have

$$\int_{-\varepsilon}^{\varepsilon} x(t)\delta(t)dt = x(\theta)\int_{-\varepsilon}^{\varepsilon} \delta(t)dt = x(\theta) \quad ,$$

where $-\varepsilon \leq \theta \leq \varepsilon$. Since the above formula is true for all $\varepsilon > 0$,

$$\int_{-\infty}^{\infty} x(t)\delta(t)dt = x(0) \quad . \tag{70}$$

An immediate generalization is

$$\int_{-\infty}^{\infty} x(t)\delta(t - \tau)dt = x(\tau) \quad . \tag{71}$$

The unit impulse function $\delta(t)$ can be regarded as the derivative of the unit step function. If we write the Fourier transform of $u(t)$ as $U(j\omega) = \dfrac{1}{j\omega}$, then the Fourier transform of the derivative of $u(t)$ is $j\omega U(j\omega) = 1 = \Delta(j\omega)$, and

$$u'(t) = \delta(t) \quad .$$

Derivatives of the delta function itself are also useful. Physically speaking, $\delta'(t)$ might represent a unit doublet. One of the most important properties of the derivatives of the delta function is their reproducing properties: namely,

$$\int_{-\infty}^{\infty} x(t)\delta^{(k)}(t - \xi)dt = (-1)^k x^{(k)}(\xi) \quad .$$

The formal proof is by integration by parts. Consider $k = 1$,

$$\int_{-\infty}^{\infty} x(t)\delta'(t - \xi)dt = \int_{-\infty}^{\infty} x(t)d\delta(t - \xi)$$

$$= x(t)\delta(t - \xi)\Big|_{-\infty}^{\infty} - \int_{-\infty}^{\infty} x'(t)\delta(t - \xi)dt \quad .$$

Now, since $t - \xi \neq 0$ at $t = \pm \infty$, $x(t)\delta(t - \xi) = 0$ at $t = \pm \infty$. Also from Equation (71),

$$\int_{-\infty}^{\infty} x'(t)\delta(t - \xi)dt = x'(\xi) \quad ,$$

and, therefore,

$$\int_{-\infty}^{\infty} x(t)\delta'(t - \xi)dt = - x'(\xi)$$

A similar proof applies to the kth derivative.

EXERCISES

1. Verify the following formulas:

(i) $\delta(t - \xi) = \delta(\xi - t)$.

(ii) $\displaystyle\int_{-\infty}^{\infty} \cos \omega t \, dt = 2\pi \, \delta(\omega)$.

(iii) $t \, \delta(t) = 0$.

(iv) $\displaystyle\int_{-\infty}^{\infty} \delta(\zeta - t)\delta(t - \xi)dt = \delta(\zeta - \xi)$.

(v) $x(t)\delta(t - \xi) = x(\xi)\delta(t - \xi)$.

(vi) $\delta(t^2 - \xi^2) = \dfrac{1}{2\xi} [\delta(t - \xi) + \delta(t + \xi)]$, $\xi > 0$.

(vii) $\delta(t) = a \, \delta(at)$, $a > 0$.

(viii) $\displaystyle\int_{-\infty}^{\infty} \cos \omega t \cos \Omega t \, dt = \pi[\delta(\omega + \Omega) + \delta(\omega - \Omega)]$.

(ix) $\displaystyle\int_{0}^{\infty} \cos \omega t \cos \Omega t \, dt = \dfrac{\pi}{2} \delta(\omega - \Omega)$, $\omega \geq 0, \Omega > 0$.

2. In Section 5 of Chapter 4 we considered the problem of an infinite beam resting on an elastic foundation with a concentrated load of P pounds at the origin. Show that this differential equation can be written

$$EIy^{(4)} + Ky = P \, \delta(x) \quad ,$$

where $\delta(x)$ is the delta function. Since $y(x)$ and $y'(x)$ both vanish at

$x = \pm \infty$, show that the solution to the above differential equation with these boundary conditions is

$$y(x) = \frac{PQ}{2K} (\sin Qx + \cos Qx)e^{-Qx} \quad , \quad x > 0$$

$$y(x) = \frac{PQ}{2K} (-\sin Qx + \cos Qx)e^{Qx} \quad , \quad x < 0 \quad ,$$

where

$$Q = \sqrt[4]{\frac{K}{4EI}} \quad .$$

(Note that $y(x)$ satisfies the differential equation because of the discontinuity in its third derivative.) In Section 5 of Chapter 4 [cf. Equation (32)] we showed that

$$y(x) = \frac{P}{\pi} \int_0^\infty \frac{\cos \omega x}{EI\omega^4 + K} \, d\omega$$

Using the above formulas, prove that

$$\int_0^\infty \frac{\cos \omega x}{\omega^4 + 4} \, d\omega = \frac{\pi}{8} (\cos x + \sin x)e^{-x} \quad , \quad x > 0 \quad ,$$

a result usually derived in the theory of the complex variable.

9. The Impulsive Response

Let us now turn to the problem of characterizing a network $\mathfrak{N}$ in terms of its impulsive response. If H is the system function of our network, then

$$y(t) = H(p)x(t) \quad , \tag{72}$$

where y is the output and x the input (cf. Fig. 6.21). Writing Equation (72) in terms of Fourier transforms, we have

$$Y(j\omega) = H(j\omega)X(j\omega) \quad , \tag{73}$$

where $Y(j\omega) = \mathscr{F}[y(t)]$ and $X(j\omega) = \mathscr{F}[x(t)]$. If, in particular, $x(t)$ is a unit delta function, $\delta(t)$, then

$$X(j\omega) = \mathscr{F}[\delta(t)] = 1$$

and $Y(j\omega)$,

$$Y(j\omega) = H(j\omega) \cdot 1 \tag{74}$$

becomes the Fourier transform of the response to a unit impulse function. That is, $y(t) = \mathscr{F}^{-1}[Y(j\omega)]$ is the *impulsive response* of the network. We see from Equation (74) that the system function $H(j\omega)$ and the impulsive response $W(t)$ are Fourier transform pairs. Thus

$$H(j\omega) = \int_{-\infty}^{\infty} W(t)e^{-j\omega t}dt \quad , \tag{75}$$

and

$$W(t) = \frac{1}{2\pi} \int_{-\infty}^{\infty} H(j\omega)e^{j\omega t}d\omega \quad . \tag{76}$$

Since a knowledge of $H(j\omega)$ completely describes $\mathfrak{N}$, and since $H(j\omega)$ is known if $W(t)$ is [cf. Equation (75)], we conclude that the impulsive response also completely characterizes $\mathfrak{N}$. There are, however, other forms showing how the impulsive response is related to the input and output of $\mathfrak{N}$. One form can be deduced by taking the Laplace transform of both sides of Equation (72),

$$Y(s) = H(s)X(s) \quad ,$$

where $Y(s) = \mathscr{L}[y(t)]$ and $X(s) = \mathscr{L}[x(t)]$. Then, by the convolution theorem,

$$y(t) = \int_0^t W(t - \lambda)x(\lambda)d\lambda \quad , \tag{77}$$

which clearly shows the dependence of the output on the impulsive response.

The impulsive response is sometimes called the *weighting function*, and the convolution integral is sometimes called the *superposition integral*. We shall show the origin of such terms by essentially rederiving the convolution theorem,

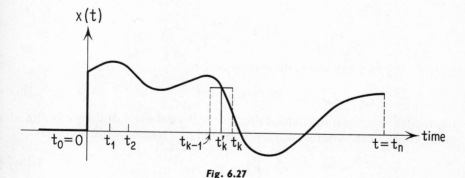

Fig. 6.27

using the notion of delta functions. Consider, then, the input $x(t)$ to $\mathfrak{N}$, which we assume is zero for negative time, and divide the interval from 0 to t into n smaller pieces by the points of subdivision $0 = t_0, t_1, \cdots, t_n = t$ (cf. Fig. 6.27). Let $\Delta t_k = t_k - t_{k-1}$, and let t'_k be any point between t_{k-1} and t_k. Then each rectangle can be approximated by the delta function

$$[x(t'_k)\Delta t_k]\delta(t - t'_k)$$

and

$$x(t) \doteq \sum_{k=1}^{n} x(t'_k)\delta(t - t'_k)\Delta t_k \quad . \tag{78}$$

Now the response of $\mathfrak{N}$ to $\delta(t - \lambda)$ is by definition the impulsive response $W(t - \lambda)$. Hence the response of $\mathfrak{N}$ to $x(t)$ is approximately

$$y(t) \doteq \sum x(t'_k)\Delta t_k W(t - t'_k) \quad ;$$

that is, the output $y(t)$ is a *weighted sum* of the inputs—the weight factors being the impulsive response W. If we let max $\Delta t_k \to 0$, then the above sum approaches the convolution integral

$$y(t) = \int_0^t W(t - \lambda)x(\lambda)d\lambda \quad . \tag{79}$$

The term *superposition integral* stems from the fact that $y(t)$ can be considered as the superposition of responses to delta functions $\delta(t - t'_k)$.

Finally, we should like to make precise the relation between the impulsive response or weighting function and the one-sided Green's function introduced in Chapter 3. To do this we write

$$y(t) = H(p)x(t)$$

as

$$M(p)y(t) = N(p)x(t) \quad , \tag{80}$$

where

$$H(p) = \frac{N(p)}{M(p)} \quad .$$

If $N(p) \equiv 1$, then Equation (80) may be written

$$M(p)y(t) = x(t) \quad , \tag{81}$$

where $M(p)$ is a linear differential operator with constant coefficients. If $H(t, \lambda)$ is the Green's function for M, then Equation (81) may be written

$$y(t) = \int_0^t H(t, \lambda)x(\lambda)d\lambda \quad . \tag{82}$$

If $x(t)$ is a sinusoidal function, then the output $y(t)$ obtained from Equation (82) will differ from the output obtained by using the complex voltage ratio only to the extent that the boundary conditions differ.

From Equation (79) we see that for $t > \lambda$,

$$W(t - \lambda) \equiv H(t, \lambda) \quad . \tag{83}$$

That is, the impulsive response and Green's function are identical. Note that Equation (83) also implies that H is a function only of the *difference* of its arguments: $H(t, \lambda) \equiv H(t - \lambda)$. But if $t < \lambda$, Equation (83) is no longer true. For, whereas $H(t, \lambda)$ is defined regardless of whether or not t exceeds λ, for a physically realizable system

$$W(t - \lambda) = 0 \quad , \quad t < \lambda \quad .$$

This is reasonable, since if the input $x(t)$ is applied at $t = 0$ there can be no response to x *until* $t = 0$.

In the general case [Equation 80)], one can also write

$$y(t) = \int_0^t H(t, \lambda) N(p) x(\lambda) d\lambda \quad ,$$

which expresses the output in terms of the input via the Green's function. However, to compare $W(t - \lambda)$ with $H(t, \lambda)$ we must first eliminate $N(p)$. This can be done by using the notion of the *adjoint operator†*; however, we shall not embark on such a discussion here.

EXERCISES

1. Show the Green's function $H(t, \lambda)$ of a linear differential operator with *constant* coefficients is a function only of the *difference* of the arguments; that is, $H(t, \lambda) = H(t - \lambda)$.

2. A network is said to be an *ideal low pass filter* if (i) the magnitude of its transfer function $H(j\omega)$ is a constant up to a certain frequency, say Ω, and is zero for $\omega > \Omega$; and (ii) its phase varies linearly with frequency. Show that the impulsive response of an ideal low pass filter is

$$W(t) = \frac{K}{\pi} \frac{\sin \Omega(t - \tau)}{t - \tau} \quad ,$$

where K is the magnitude, $\theta = -\tau\omega$ is the phase angle, and Ω is the cutoff frequency. Show also that its response to a step input $u(t)$ is

$$y(t) = K \left[\frac{1}{2} + \frac{1}{\pi} \text{Si } (t - \tau)\Omega \right] \quad ,$$

where Si is the sine-integral function (cf. Chap. 2). (Since it is not possible to specify phase and amplitude of a network independently, the "ideal" low pass filter is not physically realizable. This accounts for the fact that $W(t)$ and $y(t)$ do not vanish for negative time.)

---

† Cf. Ince, *Ordinary Differential Equations*, p. 123.

3. If $f(t)$ is a signal whose highest frequency component is W cycles per second, prove that the function $f(t)$ can be recovered from the amplitude modulated signal $g(t) = A(t)f(t)$ by using a low pass filter, provided the fundamental frequency of $A(t)$ is greater than or equal to $2W$.

4. If N and M are linear differential operators with Green's functions $H_N(x, \xi)$ and $H_M(x, \xi)$ respectively, show that the Green's function $H(x, \xi)$ of the operator MN is

$$H(x, \xi) = \int_\xi^x H_N(x, \zeta)H_M(\zeta, \xi)d\zeta \quad .$$

10. Periodic Components in Random Functions

In our analysis of power spectra and correlation functions in Sections 8 and 9 of Chapter 4 we tacitly assumed that $x(t)$ contained no DC or periodic components. Another way of stating this is to say that $x(t)$ has no pulses in its spectrum; that is, the energy in any frequency band $(f, f + df)$ approaches zero as df tends to zero. Physically, if we have a periodic component of some fixed frequency f', then $w(f')$ is infinite, while $w(f) = 0$ for $f \neq f'$. However, again from physical considerations, we also know that the total power $\rho = \int_0^\infty w(f)df$ is finite. It appears, therefore, that the appropriate tool to use in treating periodic components is the delta function.

Suppose, as a first example, that $x(t)$ contains a DC component $x_1(t)$,

$$x_1(t) = A \quad \text{(a constant)} \quad .$$

Then, by definition of the autocorrelation function,

$$\psi_1(\tau) = \lim_{T \to \infty} \frac{1}{T} \int_{-T/2}^{T/2} x_1(t)x_1(t + \tau)dt = \lim_{T \to \infty} \frac{1}{T} \int_{-T/2}^{T/2} A^2 dt = A^2 \quad ,$$

and its power spectrum is obtained from the Wiener-Khintchine relations as

$$w_1(f) = 4 \int_0^\infty \psi(\tau) \cos \omega\tau \, d\tau = 4 \int_0^\infty A^2 \cos \omega\tau \, d\tau = 4A^2[\pi\delta(\omega)]$$

(cf. Exercise 1 of Sec. 8). But even though the power spectrum is infinite, we know physically that the total power ρ_1 is finite. This is verified mathematically by

$$\rho_1 = \int_0^\infty w_1(f)df = 4A^2\pi \int_0^\infty \delta(\omega)df = 2A^2 \int_0^\infty \delta(\omega)d\omega$$

$$= 2A^2[\tfrac{1}{2}] = A^2 = \psi_1(0) \quad .$$

Similarly, if $x(t)$ contains a periodic component $x_2(t)$,

$$x_2(t) = B \cos \Omega t \quad,$$

where Ω is some fixed frequency, then

$$\psi_2(\tau) = \lim_{T \to \infty} \frac{1}{T} \int_{-T/2}^{T/2} x_2(t) x_2(t + \tau) dt = \lim_{T \to \infty} \frac{1}{T} \int_{-T/2}^{T/2} B^2 \cos \Omega t \cos \Omega(t + \tau) dt$$

$$= \lim_{T \to \infty} \frac{B^2}{2} \left[\cos \Omega \tau + \frac{\sin \Omega(T + \tau) - \sin \Omega(-T + \tau)}{2\Omega T} \right]$$

$$= \frac{B^2}{2} \cos \Omega \tau \quad,$$

and the power spectrum $w_2(f)$ becomes infinite at $\omega = \Omega$;

$$w_2(f) = 4 \int_0^\infty \psi_2(\tau) \cos \omega \tau \, d\tau = \frac{4B^2}{2} \int_0^\infty \cos \Omega \tau \cos \omega \tau \, d\tau$$

$$= 2B^2(\tfrac{1}{4})[\delta(\omega - \Omega)]2\pi = \pi B^2 \delta(\omega - \Omega) \quad.$$

However, as physically anticipated, the total power, ρ_2, is finite,

$$\rho_2 = \int_0^\infty w_2(f) df = \pi B^2 \int_0^\infty \delta(\omega - \Omega) \frac{d\omega}{2\pi} = \frac{B^2}{2} = \psi_2(0) \quad.$$

Finally, let us consider a nontrivial example where $x(t)$ is a square wave defined analytically by

$$x(t) = h \quad, \quad 0 < t < a$$

$$x(t) = 0 \quad, \quad a < t < 2a$$

$$x(t + 2a) = x(t)$$

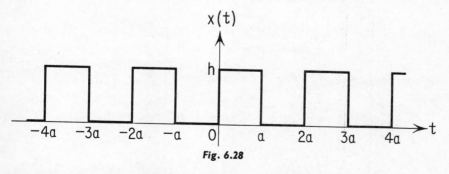

Fig. 6.28

and sketched in Figure 6.28 above. Its autocorrelation function is found to be a Fourier series:

$$\psi(\tau) = \frac{h^2}{4} + \frac{2h^2}{\pi^2} \sum_{n=1,3,5,\cdots}^{\infty} \frac{1}{n^2} \cos \frac{n\pi\tau}{a} \quad , \tag{84}$$

which is sketched in Figure 6.29.

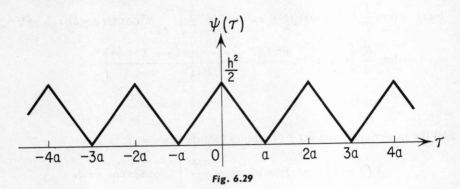

Fig. 6.29

The power spectrum is

$$w(f) = 4 \int_0^\infty \psi(\tau) \cos \omega\tau \, d\tau$$

$$= h^2 \int_0^\infty \cos \omega\tau \, d\tau + \frac{8h^2}{\pi^2} \sum_{n=1,3,5,\cdots}^{\infty} \frac{1}{n^2} \int_0^\infty \cos \frac{n\pi\tau}{a} \cos \omega\tau \, d\tau$$

$$= h^2 \pi \delta(\omega) + \frac{8h^2}{\pi^2} \sum_{n=1,3,5,\cdots}^{\infty} \frac{1}{n^2} \frac{\pi}{2} \delta\left(\frac{n\pi}{a} - \omega\right) \quad . \tag{85}$$

One could also compute the power spectrum of $x(t)$ directly (that is, instead of using the Wiener-Khintchine relations). To do this, we first consider the Fourier series expansion for $x(t)$. It is given by

$$x(t) = \frac{h}{2} + \frac{2h}{\pi} \sum_{n=1,3,5,\cdots}^{\infty} \frac{1}{n} \sin \frac{n\pi t}{a} \quad .$$

The contribution to $w(f)$ due to the component

$$\frac{2h}{\pi n} \sin \frac{n\pi t}{a} \quad , \quad n = 1, 3, 5, \cdots$$

is

$$\pi \left(\frac{2h}{\pi n}\right)^2 \delta\left(\omega - \frac{n\pi}{a}\right) = \frac{4h^2}{\pi n^2} \delta\left(\frac{n\pi}{a} - \omega\right) \quad .$$

The contribution to $w(f)$ due to the component $\frac{1}{2}h$ is

$$4\pi \left(\frac{h}{2}\right)^2 \delta(\omega) = h^2 \pi \, \delta(\omega) \quad .$$

Hence

$$w(f) = h^2\pi \, \delta(\omega) + \frac{4h^2}{\pi} \sum_{n=1,3,5,\ldots}^{\infty} \frac{1}{n^2} \delta \left(\frac{n\pi}{a} - \omega\right) \quad ,$$

which is the same as Equation (85).

The power ρ can be computed a number of ways. The simplest is to write

$$\rho = \lim_{T \to \infty} \frac{1}{T} \int_{-T/2}^{T/2} x^2(t)dt = \frac{1}{2a} \int_0^{2a} x^2(t)dt \quad ,$$

since $x(t)$ is periodic of period $2a$. But

$$\rho = \frac{1}{2a} \int_0^{2a} x^2(t)dt = \frac{1}{2a} \int_0^a h^2 dt = \frac{h^2}{2} \quad . \tag{86}$$

Also, we may write

$$\rho = \int_0^{\infty} w(f)df = \frac{1}{2\pi} \left[\pi h^2 \left(\frac{1}{2}\right) + \frac{4h^2}{\pi} \sum_{n=1,3,5,\ldots}^{\infty} \frac{1}{n^2} (1) \right]$$

$$= \frac{h^2}{4} + \frac{2h^2}{\pi^2} \sum_{n=1,3,5,\ldots}^{\infty} \frac{1}{n^2}$$

and, from Equation (84),

$$\psi(0) = \frac{h^2}{4} + \frac{2h^2}{\pi^2} \sum_{n=1,3,5,\ldots}^{\infty} \frac{1}{n^2} \quad .$$

But, from Figure 6.29,

$$\psi(0) = \frac{h^2}{2} \quad .$$

EXERCISES

1. Prove that

$$\sum_{k=1}^{\infty} \frac{1}{k^2} = \frac{\pi^2}{6}$$

and

$$\sum_{n=1,3,5,\ldots}^{\infty} \frac{1}{n^2} = \frac{\pi^2}{8} \quad .$$

2. Compute the power spectrum and autocorrelation functions of
   (i) $x_1(t) = \sin t + \cos 2t$,
   (ii) $x_2(t) = e^{-|t|}$.

II. Input and Output Spectral Densities

If we have a passive linear network such as that illustrated in Figure 6.21 we know that the output is uniquely determined (for a given input) if the system function $H(j\omega)$ is known. The problem we now wish to consider is as follows: Let the input $x(t)$ have a spectral density $S_x(\omega)$ and the output $y(t)$ have a spectral density $S_y(\omega)$. Since given x and H, we can find y, is it possible to find $S_y(\omega)$, knowing S_x and H? The answer is yes; in fact, the relation is quite simple; namely,

$$S_y(\omega) = |H(j\omega)|^2 S_x(\omega) \quad .$$

We shall derive this equation using the concept of the autocorrelation function. Referring to Figure 6.21, we know that the output $y(t)$ is related to the input $x(t)$ by the functional equation

$$y(t) = H(p)x(t) \quad .$$

We also recall that the impulsive response $W(t)$ of $\mathfrak{N}$ is the inverse Fourier transform of $H(j\omega)$; that is,

$$H(j\omega) = \int_{-\infty}^{\infty} W(t)e^{-j\omega t}dt \quad , \tag{87}$$

and, finally, by the superposition theorem,

$$y(t) = \int_0^t W(t - \lambda)x(\lambda)d\lambda = \int_0^t W(\zeta)x(t - \zeta)d\zeta \quad .$$

This last equation may be written

$$y(t) = \int_{-\infty}^{\infty} W(\zeta)x(t - \zeta)d\zeta \quad , \tag{88}$$

since for a physically realizable network $W(\zeta) = 0$ for $\zeta < 0$ and $x(t - \zeta) = 0$ for $t < \zeta$.

Hence, if $\psi_y(\tau)$ is the autocorrelation function of $y(t)$, then by definition of the autocorrelation function,

$$\psi_y(\tau) = \lim_{T \to \infty} \frac{1}{T} \int_{-T/2}^{T/2} \left[\int_{-\infty}^{\infty} W(\zeta)x(t - \zeta)d\zeta \right] \left[\int_{-\infty}^{\infty} W(\xi)x(t + \tau - \xi)d\xi \right] dt$$

$$= \int_{-\infty}^{\infty} \int_{-\infty}^{\infty} W(\zeta)W(\xi) \left[\lim_{T \to \infty} \frac{1}{T} \int_{-T/2}^{T/2} x(t - \zeta)x(t + \tau - \xi)dt \right] d\zeta \, d\xi \quad . \tag{89}$$

If we make the change of variables $u = t - \zeta$, $\zeta = \zeta$, $\xi = \xi$, the Jacobian of the transformation is unity, and

$$\lim_{T \to \infty} \frac{1}{T} \int_{-T/2}^{T/2} x(t - \zeta)x(t + \tau - \xi)dt$$

becomes

$$\lim_{T \to \infty} \frac{1}{T} \int_{-T/2-\zeta}^{T/2-\zeta} x(u)x(u + \tau + \zeta - \xi)du = \psi_x(\tau + \zeta - \xi) \quad , \qquad (90)$$

where ψ_x is the autocorrelation function of $x(t)$. Substituting Equation (90) into Equation (89), we obtain

$$\psi_y(\tau) = \int_{-\infty}^{\infty} \int_{-\infty}^{\infty} W(\zeta)W(\xi)\psi_x(\tau + \zeta - \xi)d\zeta \, d\xi \quad .$$

Now the Fourier transform of $\psi_y(\tau)$ is its spectral density $S_y(\omega)$, and

$$S_y(\omega) = 2\int_{0}^{\infty} \psi_y(\tau) \cos \omega\tau \, d\tau = \int_{-\infty}^{\infty} \psi_y(\tau) \cos \omega\tau \, d\tau \quad .$$

Hence

$$S_y(\omega) = \int_{-\infty}^{\infty} \left[\int_{-\infty}^{\infty} \int_{-\infty}^{\infty} W(\zeta)W(\xi)\psi_x(\tau + \zeta - \xi)d\zeta \, d\xi \right] \cos \omega\tau \, d\tau \quad .$$

If we make the change of variable $v = \tau + \zeta - \xi$, $\zeta = \zeta$, $\xi = \xi$ with unity Jacobian, there results

$$S_y(\omega) = \int_{-\infty}^{\infty} \int_{-\infty}^{\infty} \int_{-\infty}^{\infty} W(\zeta)W(\xi)\psi_x(v) \cos \omega(v - \zeta + \xi)d\zeta \, d\xi \, dv \quad . \quad (91)$$

Now, if we replace the cosine term by complex exponentials, Equation (91) breaks up into the product of integrals:

$$S_y(\omega) = \frac{1}{2} \left[\int_{-\infty}^{\infty} W(\zeta)e^{-j\omega\zeta}d\zeta \right] \left[\int_{-\infty}^{\infty} W(\xi)e^{j\omega\xi}d\xi \right] \left[\int_{-\infty}^{\infty} \psi_x(v)e^{j\omega v}dv \right]$$

$$+ \frac{1}{2} \left[\int_{-\infty}^{\infty} W(\zeta)e^{j\omega\zeta}d\zeta \right] \left[\int_{-\infty}^{\infty} W(\xi)e^{-j\omega\xi}d\xi \right] \left[\int_{-\infty}^{\infty} \psi_x(v)e^{-j\omega v}dv \right] \quad ,$$

and, using Equation (87), we may write

$$S_y(\omega) = \tfrac{1}{2}H(j\omega)H(-j\omega)\int_{-\infty}^{\infty} \psi_x(v)e^{j\omega v}dv$$

$$+ \tfrac{1}{2}H(-j\omega)H(j\omega)\int_{-\infty}^{\infty} \psi_x(v)e^{-j\omega v}dv \quad ,$$

Combining terms, we have

$$S_y(\omega) = \tfrac{1}{2}|H(j\omega)|^2 \int_{-\infty}^{\infty} \psi_x(v)[e^{j\omega v} + e^{-j\omega v}]dv$$

$$= |H(j\omega)|^2 \int_{-\infty}^{\infty} \psi_x(v)\cos \omega v\, dv$$

$$= |H(j\omega)|^2 S_x(\omega) \quad . \tag{92}$$

Thus we have shown that the output spectral density is simply equal to the square of the modulus of the transfer function times the input spectral density.

It follows immediately from this relation that

$$w_y(f) = |H(j\omega)|^2 w_x(f) \quad , \quad f \geq 0 \quad , \tag{93}$$

where $w_y(f)$ and $w_x(f)$ are the corresponding power spectra of the output and input signals, respectively.

As an application of the above formulas we wish to consider the case of *white noise*. This type of noise is characterized by having a flat power spectrum (cf. Fig. 6.30), $w(f) = K$, $f \geq 0$. In many respects white noise is easier to

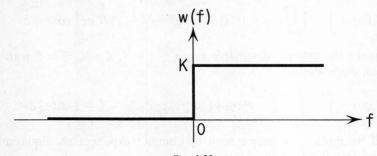

Fig. 6.30

analyze than other types with a more complicated spectrum. It can also be regarded as the limiting case of Markoffian noise (cf. Sec. 9 of Chap. 4) as the half-power point $\omega = a$ approaches infinity. Hence it is also of "practical" value, since it can be regarded as an idealized case.

By the Wiener-Khintchine formulas, its autocorrelation function is a delta function,

$$\psi(\tau) = \int_0^{\infty} w(f)\cos \omega\tau\, df = \int_0^{\infty} K \cos \omega\tau\, \frac{d\omega}{2\pi} = \frac{K}{2}\,\delta(\tau) \quad ,$$

and, as expected, the total power is infinite:

$$\rho = \psi(0) = \frac{K}{2}\,\delta(0) = \infty$$

$$= \int_0^\infty w(f)\,df = K\int_0^\infty df = \infty \ .$$

Generally white noise is the easiest to generate in a laboratory, or more practically, one can generate a noise with a spectrum which is flat up to any desired finite frequency. Suppose in some application *Markoffian noise* is

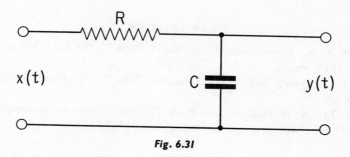

Fig. 6.31

required. Then, if we pass the white noise, say of amplitude K through a simple *RC*-network (cf. Fig. 6.31), the power spectrum of the output noise, $y(t)$, will be

$$w_y(f) = \left|\frac{1}{1 + j\omega RC}\right|^2 K = \frac{K}{1 + R^2 C^2 \omega^2} \ ,$$

since the transfer function of the network is

$$H(j\omega) = \frac{1}{1 + j\omega RC} \ .$$

The output power spectrum is therefore Markoffian,

$$w_y(f) = \frac{K/T^2}{\omega^2 + 1/T^2} \ , \quad f \geq 0 \ ,$$

with amplitude K/T^2 and half-power point $\omega = 1/T$, where $T = RC$ is the time constant of the circuit.

In general, then, if we wish to generate a noise with a given power spectrum $w(f)$, all we must do is construct a network whose transfer function $H(j\omega)$ has the property that $|H(j\omega)|^2 = w(f)$. Then, if we pass white noise of unit amplitude through this network, the output power spectrum will be $w(f)$. From a practical point of view, one can synthesize a passive network that approximates any given function [in this case, $w(f)$] to any degree of precision.

EXERCISE

A certain function of time $x(t)$ has a power spectrum

$$w(f) = 1 + \omega^2 \quad , \quad 0 \leqq \omega \leqq 1$$
$$w(f) = 0 \qquad , \qquad \omega > 1 \quad .$$

If $x(t)$ is passed through an RC-circuit with time constant $T = 1$, find the power spectrum and autocorrelation function of the output.

REFERENCES

Guillemin, E. A., *Communication Networks*. New York: John Wiley & Sons, Inc., 1935, Vol. 2.

Ince, E. L., *Ordinary Differential Equations*. New York: Dover Publications, 1944.

James, H. M., N. B. Nichols, and R. S. Phillips, *Theory of Servomechanisms*. New York: McGraw-Hill Book Co., Inc., 1947.

Chapter Seven

RANDOM FUNCTIONS

1. Foundations of Probability Theory

In Section 8 of Chapter 4 we mentioned that probability theory was a prerequisite to the study of amplitude distributions of random time functions. In the first few sections of this chapter we shall develop those portions of the theory necessary to give an adequate treatment of random phenomena. It is not our intention to develop probability theory in its full axiomatic generality, but rather to develop it as a practical tool useful in solving engineering problems. A certain abstractness in the formulation of the theory is useful, however, as it leads to a clear-cut picture of the notion of probability and avoids many of the apparent paradoxes.

Suppose, now, that we conduct an *experiment E*—using the word "experiment" in the most general sense of the term. There is a cause and an effect, or if we like, an input and an output (cf. Fig. 7.1). It may be that the output

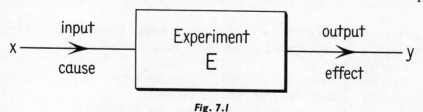

Fig. 7.1

depends precisely on the input; that is, the output, y, equals a definite function of the input x. In this case we shall write $y = F(x)$ and say that the experiment is *deterministic*. As an example, if the experiment is to determine the response of an *RC*-network, then once the input and initial conditions are given, the output is completely and uniquely determined. On the other hand, there are many experiments which are not deterministic. For example, let the experiment E consist in tossing a coin, and let the output consist in determining whether heads or tails appear. Certainly, in this case, the output cannot be expressed as a definite function of the input. It is in experiments of this general character that we are interested; and probability theory furnishes one of the most powerful tools for its treatment.

Before laying down the axioms of our theory we shall consider an intuitive model (repetition of trials) and an abstract model (sample space). These will give motivation to the definitions used in the axioms. That is, the axioms will not violate our intuitive notion of probability. However, once the axioms have been laid down, all our deductions will be made from the axioms. If any deduction violates intuitive notions, it does not mean that the result is incorrect, but only that the axioms we have chosen do not fit the physical world around us.

Suppose, now, we have tossed a coin N times and heads have appeared H times. Then one might say that the probability that heads occur, $p(H)$, is approximately H/N, where N is assumed large. Or we might write, equivalently,

$$p(H) = \lim_{N \to \infty} \frac{H}{N} \ .$$

In general, then, if an experiment E has n possible outcomes

$$E_1, E_2, \cdots, E_n \ ,$$

we shall say

$$p(E_k) = \lim_{N \to \infty} \frac{N_k}{N} \ , \quad k = 1, 2, \cdots, n \ ,$$

where N_k is the number of times E_k occurred in N trials. Clearly,

$$N_1 + N_2 + \cdots + N_n = N \ .$$

Now suppose that in a series of N observations (where we assume N very large) two events A and B can occur or not occur. Four possibilities arise:

Case (i) A occurs   and B occurs
Case (ii) A occurs   and B does not occur
Case (iii) A does not occur and B occurs
Case (iv) A does not occur and B does not occur.

Suppose that Case (i) occurred N_1 times, Case (ii) occurred N_2 times, Case (iii) occurred N_3 times and Case (iv) occurred N_4 times. Of course

$$N = N_1 + N_2 + N_3 + N_4 \ .$$

We now introduce some notation. By $p(A)$ we shall mean the probability that A has occurred, by $P(B)$, the probability that B has occurred. These are called *a priori* or *absolute probabilities*. We shall use the symbol $p(A, B)$ to mean the probability that *both* A and B have occurred. $p(A, B)$ is known as the *joint probability* of A and B. By $p(A + B)$ we shall mean the probability that either A or B or both has occurred. Finally, by $p_B(A)$ we shall mean the probability of A occurring, knowing that B has occurred, and by $p_A(B)$, the probability of B occurring, knowing that A has occurred. These are called *conditional probabilities*. Sometimes we say "$p_B(A)$ is the probability of A occurring on the hypothesis B (has occurred)" with a similar statement for $p_A(B)$.

With the above definitions, it is clear that

$$p(A) = \frac{N_1 + N_2}{N}$$

$$p(B) = \frac{N_1 + N_3}{N}$$

$$p(A, B) = \frac{N_1}{N}$$

$$p_B(A) = \frac{N_1}{N_1 + N_3}$$

$$p_A(B) = \frac{N_1}{N_1 + N_2}$$

$$p(A + B) = \frac{N_1 + N_2 + N_3}{N}$$

are good approximations when N is large. From these results we can deduce the following formulas,

$$p(A + B) = \frac{N_1}{N} + \frac{N_2}{N} + \frac{N_3}{N} = p(A) + p(B) - p(A, B)$$

$$p_A(B)p(A) = \frac{N_1}{N_1 + N_2} \frac{N_1 + N_2}{N} = \frac{N_1}{N} = p(A, B)$$

$$p_B(A)p(B) = \frac{N_1}{N_1 + N_3} \frac{N_1 + N_3}{N} = \frac{N_1}{N} = p(A, B) \quad .$$

If the occurrence of A precludes the occurrence of B and conversely, we shall say that the two events A and B are *mutually exclusive*. In this case $p(A, B) = 0$, $p(A + B) = p(A) + p(B)$, and $p_A(B) = 0 = p_B(A)$. If the occurrence or nonoccurrence of A [B] has no effect on the occurrence or nonoccurrence of B [A], we shall say A and B are *stochastically independent* or *statistically independent* or simply *independent*. In this case, $p_B(A) = p(A)$, $p_A(B) = p(B)$, $p(A, B) = p(A)p(B)$.

A more mathematical model is furnished by the notion of a *sample space*. This sample space is a set which has as its elements *sample points*. We shall assume that every thinkable outcome of an experiment is completely and uniquely described by one and only one sample point. Given a sample space, S, with the sample points $E_1, E_2, \cdots$, we shall associate with each point E_j a nonnegative number called the *probability* of E_j, which we denote by $p(E_j)$. The numbers $p(E_j)$ enjoy the property that

$$\sum_j p(E_j) = 1 \quad ,$$

where the summation is extended over all sample points.

So far, probability has been defined in a purely arbitrary manner except for the above trivial requirements. For example, consider the experiment of tossing a coin. There might be three thinkable outcomes:

1. Heads
2. Tails
3. The coin rests on its circumference.

Then our sample space will have three points, say, E_1, E_2, E_3. Theoretically, we may assign any nonnegative numbers to E_1, E_2, E_3 such that their sum is one. These three numbers would meet all the conditions of being probabilities. However, if we wish our probability space to coincide with the physical world around us (cf. our intuitive model of repetition of trials), we feel that the numbers 1/2, 1/2, 0 should be assigned. That is,

$$p(E_1) = \tfrac{1}{2}$$
$$p(E_2) = \tfrac{1}{2}$$
$$p(E_3) = 0 \quad .$$

If A is a set of sample points $E_1, E_2, \cdots, E_n$ in a space S, then by the probability of A we shall mean

$$p(A) = p(E_1) + p(E_2) + \cdots + p(E_n) \quad .$$

This expresses the fact that probability is an additive function. The word "event" will be used synonomously with a *set of sample points*.

We shall say that two events A_1 and A_2 are *mutually exclusive* if their intersection is empty; that is, if $E_{i_1}, E_{i_2}, \cdots, E_{i_m}$ are the sample points in A_1 and $E_{j_1}, E_{j_2}, \cdots, E_{j_n}$ are the sample points in A_2, then no E_{i_r} is equal to any E_{j_s}, $r = 1, 2, \cdots, m$; $s = 1, 2, \cdots, n$. Looking at the situation physically, we see that if the outcome E_{i_k} occurs, then, since E_{i_k} is not an element of A_2, the event A_2 cannot occur. In the contrary case, if A_1 and A_2 have common points, then the events are not mutually exclusive.

By the *joint probability* of two events A_1 and A_2 we mean the probability of the simultaneous occurrence of *both* A_1 and A_2. In terms of sample points,

$$p(A_1, A_2) = p(E_1) + p(E_2) + \cdots + p(E_\beta) \quad,$$

where $E_1, E_2, \cdots, E_\beta$ is that aggregate of sample points belonging to *both* A_1 and A_2. If A_1 and A_2 are mutually exclusive, $p(A_1, A_2) = 0$.

After the above intuitive remarks we lay down the following axioms of our theory.

AXIOM 1. The value of a probability p is some number between zero and one. The probability of a certain event is one, the probability of an impossible event is zero.

AXIOM 2. The probability of two events A and B occurring is equal to the product of the probability of one times the conditional probability of the other,

$$p(A, B) = p_A(B)p(A) = p_B(A)p(B) \quad.$$

AXIOM 3. The probability of A and/or B occurring is

$$p(A + B) = p(A) + p(B) - p(A, B) \quad.$$

We also lay down the following definitions: (i) Two events A and B are said to be *stochastically independent* if

$$p(A, B) = p(A)p(B) \quad.$$

From this follows $p(A) = p_B(A)$, $p(B) = p_A(B)$. (ii) Two events A and B are said to be *mutually exclusive* if

$$p(A, B) = 0 \quad.$$

From this it follows that $p(A + B) = p(A) + p(B)$.

2. Random Variables

Suppose X is a variable which can take on the values

$$x_1, x_2, \cdots, x_n \quad,$$

with the respective probabilities of assuming these values of

$$p(x_1), p(x_2), \cdots, p(x_n) \quad.$$

Of course $\Sigma p(x_i) = 1$. Then X is called a *chance variable* or a *random variable* or a *stochastic variable* or a *variate*.

Before discussing any properties of random variables, let us consider a physical problem whose analogy to probability theory will facilitate the assimilation of future concepts. Suppose we have a unit mass which we proceed to break up into n smaller (not necessarily equal) masses $m_1, m_2, \cdots, m_n$. Evidently

$$m_1 + m_2 + \cdots + m_n = 1 \quad .$$

Let these masses be arbitrarily distributed along the x-axis (cf. Fig. 7.2). The distance to any mass from the origin will be denoted by x_k. From elementary mechanics

$$x_{cg} = \text{center of mass} = m_1 x_1 + m_2 x_2 + \cdots + m_n x_n \quad \text{(first moment)}$$

$$I = \text{moment of inertia} = m_1 x_1^2 + m_2 x_2^2 + \cdots + m_n x_n^2 \quad \text{(second moment)} \quad .$$

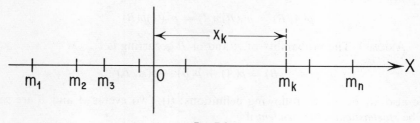

Fig. 7.2

Probabilities can be concretely interpreted in terms of this mass distribution. For example, if X is a chance variable assuming the values $x_1, x_2, \cdots, x_n$ with respective probabilities $p(x_1), p(x_2), \cdots, p(x_n)$, then the *expected value*, $E[X]$, of X is defined as

$$\text{Mean value} = \text{average value} = \text{expected value} = E[X]$$

$$= \sum_{i=1}^{n} x_i p(x_i) \quad . \tag{1}$$

In the light of the above example,

$$E[X] = x_{cg} \quad , \quad E[X - x_{cg}] = 0 \quad .$$

We see that by the introduction of a new variable $X' = X - x_{cg}$, we have $E[X'] = 0$. That is, X' is a stochastic variable with mean zero. It is evident that this can always be done, and that we can always reduce our problem to one of "mean zero." In terms of our mass distribution, this means referring the origin of our system to its center of gravity.

In general, we define the expected value of a deterministic function of X by the equation

$$E[f(X)] = \sum_{i=1}^{n} f(x_i)p(x_i) \quad . \tag{2}$$

If in particular $f(X) = X$, we obtain the previous formula,

$$E[X] = \Sigma x_i p(x_i) \quad .$$

We shall now take Equation (2) as our definition of the expected value, from which Equation (1) follows as a corollary. Note that if we take Equation (1) as our definition of the expected value, $E[f(X)]$ is already defined, namely,

$$E[f(X)] = \Sigma f(x_i)p(f(x_i)) \quad . \tag{3}$$

This is not the same form as Equation (2) although it can be shown that Equations (2) and (3) are equal. However, by choosing our definition as in Equation (2) we avoid this situation (cf. Exercise 10 at the end of Sec. 5).

As an example of Equation (2), consider $E[(X - a)^2]$ where a is a constant:

$$\begin{aligned}
E[(X - a)^2] &= \Sigma(x_i - a)^2 p(x_i) = \Sigma(x_i^2 - 2x_i a + a^2)p(x_i) \\
&= \Sigma x_i^2 p(x_i) - 2a\Sigma x_i p(x_i) + a^2 \Sigma p(x_i) \\
&= E[X^2] - 2aE[X] + a^2 \quad .
\end{aligned}$$

In mechanics, it is customary to refer the moment of inertia of a body to its center of gravity. The same is done in probability theory. Let X be a stochastic variable with mean a, $E[X] = a$. Then the expected value of $(X - a)^2$, namely, $E[(X - a)^2]$, is called the *dispersion* or *variance* D_x of the stochastic variable X,

$$\sigma_x^2 = D_x = E[(X - a)^2] \quad ,$$

and σ_x is called the *standard deviation* or *root mean square* (r.m.s.) value of the variate X. In terms of our mass distribution, σ_x is the radius of gyration. From the above definition, $E[X] = a$, we have

$$E[(X - a)^2] = E[X^2] - a^2 \quad .$$

Physically speaking, in terms of our distribution of mass, this amounts to the parallel axis theorem of mechanics.

The function $p(X)$ which takes on the discrete values $p(x_1), p(x_2), \cdots$, $p(x_n)$ at the points $x_1, x_2, \cdots, x_n$, respectively, is often called the *frequency function* (fr.f.) or probability function of the distribution. We write

$$p(x_i) = \text{Prob. } [X = x_i] \quad .$$

Clearly,

$$\sum_{i=1}^{n} p(x_i) = 1 \quad .$$

Another important function associated with a variate X is the *distribution function* (d.f.), $P(x)$. It is defined as

$$P(x) = \text{Prob. } [X \leq x] = \sum_{x_i \leq x} p(x_i)$$

and is read "$P(x)$ is the probability that X be less than or equal to x." From the definition of the fr.f. $p(X)$ we see that $P(x)$ is a step function (cf. Fig. 7.3) whose jumps are equal to $p(x_i)$.

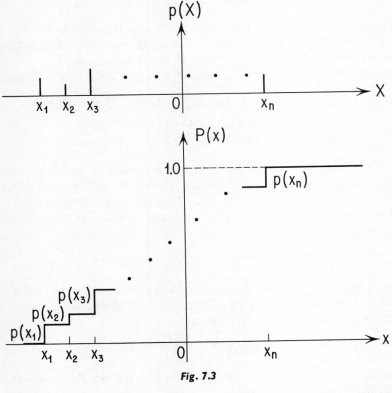

Fig. 7.3

A simple inequality based on the concept of fr.f. can now be easily deduced. It is called the Bienaymé-Tschebyscheff inequality [cf. Equation (4)] and is of considerable practical value. Suppose X is a variate which assumes the values $x_1, x_2, \cdots, x_n$ with probabilities $p(x_1), p(x_2), \cdots, p(x_n)$, respectively. Let $E[X] = 0$, $E[X^2] = \Sigma x_i^2 p(x_i) = s^2$. Let a be any positive constant. Then

$$s^2/a^2 = \Sigma p(x_i)x_i^2/a^2 \quad .$$

Consider the subset $x_{i_1}, x_{i_2}, \cdots, x_{i_m}$ of $x_1, x_2, \cdots, x_n$ with the property that

$$|x_{i_j}| \geq a \quad , \quad j = 1, 2, \cdots, m \quad .$$

Now $x_{i_j}^2/a^2 \geq 1$ and

$$s^2/a^2 \geq \sum_j p(x_{i_j})x_{i_j}^2/a^2 \quad .$$

If we replace $x_{i_j}^2/a^2$ by 1, then the above inequality is strengthened, namely,

$$s^2/a^2 \geq \sum_j p(x_{i_j}) \quad .$$

But $\sum_j p(x_{i_j})$ is the probability that X have a value $\geq a$ or $\leq -a$. Hence

$$\text{Prob. } [|X| \geq a] \leq s^2/a^2 \quad . \tag{4}$$

Suppose now we consider *two* random variables X and Y. Let X be defined as above, and let Y assume the values

$$y_1, y_2, \cdots, y_m$$

with respective probabilities

$$q(y_1), q(y_2), \cdots, q(y_m) \quad .$$

Then we are invited to consider the *joint probability* $p(X, Y)$ of X and Y simultaneously, assuming certain values. For example, $p(x_i, y_j)$ is the probability that $X = x_i$ and $Y = y_j$. We write this as

$$p(x_i, y_j) = \text{Prob. } [X = x_i, Y = y_j] \quad .$$

Since (x_i, y_j), $i = 1, 2, \cdots, n$; $j = 1, 2, \cdots, m$ exhaust all possible values that can be assumed by the pair (X, Y), we must have

$$\sum_{i=1}^{n} \sum_{j=1}^{m} p(x_i, y_j) = 1 \quad .$$

The distribution function $P(x, y)$ associated with the joint fr.f. $p(X, Y)$ defined above is

$$P(x, y) = \text{Prob. } [X \leq x, Y \leq y] = \sum_{x_i \leq x} \sum_{y_j \leq y} p(x_i, y_j) \quad .$$

Now,

$$P(x) = \text{Prob. } [X \leq x] = P(x, \infty) = \text{Prob. } [X \leq x, \ Y < \infty]$$

$$= \sum_{x_i \leq x} \sum_{j=1}^{m} p(x_i, y_j) = \sum_{x_i \leq x} p(x_i) \quad ,$$

which shows the relation between the d.f. of X and the joint d.f. $P(x, y)$. When a d.f. is determined from a joint d.f. in this manner, we call it a *marginal distribution*. The corresponding marginal fr.f. is given by

$$p(x_i) = \text{Prob. } [X = x_i, \ Y < \infty] = \sum_{j=1}^{m} p(x_i, y_j) \quad .$$

Of course, similar definitions apply with the variables X and Y interchanged.

From Axiom 2 we can define the *conditional probability* $p_{y_j}(x_i)$ as the probability that $X = x_i$, knowing $Y = y_j$, or explicitly,

$$p_{y_j}(x_i) = \frac{\text{Prob. } [X = x_i, \ Y = y_j]}{\text{Prob. } [Y = y_j]} = \frac{p(x_i, y_j)}{q(y_j)} \quad .$$

A similar formula holds for the conditional probability $q_{x_i}(y_j)$. The corresponding conditional d.f. $P_y(x)$ is given by

$$P_{y_j}(x) = \frac{\text{Prob. } [X \leq x, \ Y = y_j]}{\text{Prob. } [Y = y_j]} = \frac{\sum_{x_i \leq x} p(x_i, y_j)}{q(y_j)}$$

with the expected formula for the d.f. $Q_x(y)$.

The expected value of a function of X and Y is defined by

$$E[f(X, Y)] = \sum_{i=1}^{n} \sum_{j=1}^{m} f(x_i, y_j) p(x_i, y_j) \quad .$$

For example,

$$E[X + Y] = \sum_{i, j} (x_i + y_j) p(x_i, y_j)$$

$$= \sum_{j} y_j \sum_{i} p(x_i, y_j) + \sum_{i} x_i \sum_{j} p(x_i, y_j)$$

$$= \sum_{j} y_j q(y_j) + \sum_{i} x_i p(x_i)$$

$$= E[X] + E[Y] \quad .$$

Hence the sum of the expected values of two random variables is equal to the expected value of their sum. Similarly, we can show that

$$E[XY] = E[X] \cdot E[Y]$$

if X and Y are *independent*.

A distribution of great practical and theoretical importance (cf. Sec. 6) is the *binomial distribution*. Let X be a variate which assumes the integral values

$$0, 1, 2, \cdots, n$$

with the respective probabilities

$$B_0, B_1, B_2, \cdots, B_n$$

of assuming these values, where

$$B_r = \binom{n}{r} p^r(1 - p)^{n-r} \quad ,$$

p being some number between 0 and 1 and $\binom{n}{r}$ the binomial coefficient

$$\frac{n!}{r!(n - r)!} \quad .$$

Then we say X is *binomially distributed*. We shall find the mean and variance of X; which results will be used in our derivation of the normal distribution.

First, we must show that

$$\sum_{r=0}^{n} B_r = 1 \quad .$$

For convenience, introduce the notation

$$q = 1 - p \quad .$$

Then, by the binomial theorem,

$$(px + q)^n = \sum_{r=0}^{n} \binom{n}{r} p^r q^{n-r} x^r \quad . \tag{5}$$

If we let $x = 1$ in the above expression, we have

$$(p + q)^n = 1 = \sum_{r=0}^{n} \binom{n}{r} p^r q^{n-r} = \sum_{r=0}^{n} B_r \quad .$$

To determine $E[X]$, differentiate Equation (5) with respect to x,

$$n(px + q)^{n-1}p = \sum_{r=0}^{n} r \binom{n}{r} p^r q^{n-r} x^{r-1} \quad , \tag{6}$$

and then let $x = 1$,

$$n(p + q)^{n-1}p = np = \sum_{r=0}^{n} r \binom{n}{r} p^r q^{n-r} = E[X] \quad .$$

Hence the mean value of X is np, which could be expected from intuitive considerations.

To calculate the variance σ^2, we need only compute $E[X^2]$, since

$$\sigma^2 = E[(X - np)^2] = E[X^2] - (np)^2 \quad .$$

If we multiply the generating function of Equation (6) by x and again differentiate, there results, on letting $x = 1$:

$$n(n - 1)p^2 + np = \sum_{r=0}^{n} r^2 \binom{n}{r} p^r q^{n-r} = E[X^2] \quad .$$

We have, therefore,

$$\sigma^2 = E[(X - np)^2] = E[X^2] - (np)^2$$
$$= n(n - 1)p^2 + np - (np)^2 = npq \quad ,$$

and

$$\sigma = \sqrt{npq} \quad .$$

3. Continuous Distributions

In the previous discussions we assumed that our variate X could take on only a finite number of discrete values. We could, without difficulty, extend our finite sums to enumerably infinite sums. However, this is a trivial generalization. The important cases are those involving a *continuous distribution*. Consider, then, our mass analogy. Suppose that instead of being discretely distributed over the x-axis, the mass is *continuously* distributed. Then we cannot speak of the mass at any *one* point, since it is zero, but we can speak of the mass Δm lying in some small interval Δx of the x-axis. If the limit

$$\frac{\Delta m}{\Delta x}$$

exists as $\Delta x \to 0$, we call it the density of mass $\rho(x)$ (or mass density) at x. The mass contained in any interval $[a, b]$ is therefore given by the integral

$$\int_a^b \rho(x)dx \quad .$$

In an analogous fashion we define $p(X)$, the mass density or *probability density* of the variate X, by the relation

$$p(x) = \lim_{\Delta x \to 0} \frac{\text{Prob. } [x \leqq X \leqq x + \Delta x]}{\Delta x} \quad .$$

Hence

$$\text{Prob. } [a \leqq X \leqq b] = \int_a^b p(X)dX \quad .$$

Of course,

$$\int_{-\infty}^{\infty} p(X)dX = 1 \quad .$$

In terms of the "Prob." description, it is frequently convenient to write $p(X)$ in the form

$$p(x)dx = \text{Prob. } [x \leqq X \leqq x + dx] \quad ,$$

it being understood that $dx \to 0$.

The function $p(X)$ defined above is also called, as before, a frequency function (fr.f.), while the corresponding distribution function $P(x)$ is given by

$$P(x) = \text{Prob. } [X \leqq x] \quad .$$

We recall the definition of sample space in the discrete case. Here in the continuous case we must in general consider a continuum of values. For example, as used above, our space could consist of the x-axis R_1. Then instead of considering events as sets of sample points, we must consider subsets of R_1. The natural concept is to consider the space R_1 upon which a p-measure has been defined and to use the class of all Borel measurable sets (cf. Appendix 1).

The d.f. of a continuous variate X has been defined as

$$P(x) = \text{Prob. } [X \leqq x] = \int_{-\infty}^x p(X)dX \quad ,$$

and, if $p(X)$ is continuous,

$$\frac{d}{dx} P(x) = p(x) \quad .$$

However, $p(X)$ may not be continuous. For example, referring to the distribution of mass, the mass may be in part continuously distributed and in part discretely distributed. In this case it is necessary to use a Stieltjes integral (cf. Appendix 2),

$$P(x) = \int_{-\infty}^{x} dP(x) \quad . \tag{7}$$

If the distribution is concentrated at, say, n mass points x_i, then $P(x)$ is the step function of Figure 7.3. If $P(x)$ is differentiable, then

$$dP(x) = p(x)dx \quad .$$

In the combined case we obtain an integral *and* a sum from the Stieltjes integral representation of Equation (7).

With a view to simplicity we shall consider only continuous distributions. If our results are interpreted as Stieltjes integrals, then the formulas we derive in this section as well as the equations of earlier sections can be considered as special cases of the Stieltjes integral representation.

Let X and Y be two random variables of the continuous type. Then the joint fr.f. $p(X, Y)$ may be described as

$$p(x, y)dx\, dy = \text{Prob. } [x \leq X \leq x + dx, y \leq Y \leq y + dy] \quad ,$$

while the corresponding joint d.f. $P(x, y)$ is

$$P(x, y) = \text{Prob. } [X \leq x, Y \leq y] = \int_{-\infty}^{y} \int_{-\infty}^{x} p(X, Y)dX\, dY \quad .$$

Thus

$$p(x, y) = \frac{\partial^2}{\partial x\, \partial y} P(x, y) \quad .$$

Of course,

$$\int_{-\infty}^{\infty} \int_{-\infty}^{\infty} p(X, Y)dX\, dY = 1 \quad .$$

The *marginal distribution* $P(x)$ of X is given by

$$P(x) = \text{Prob. } [X \leq x, Y < \infty] = \text{Prob. } [X \leq x] = P(x, \infty)$$

$$= \int_{-\infty}^{\infty} \int_{-\infty}^{x} p(X, Y)dX\, dY = \int_{-\infty}^{x} p(X)dX \quad ,$$

where $p(X)$ is the fr.f. of X. A similar definition holds for the marginal distribution $Q(y)$ of Y. The marginal fr.f. of X is $p(X)$,

$$p(x) = \frac{\partial}{\partial x} P(x, \infty) = \int_{-\infty}^{\infty} p(x, Y) dY \quad,$$

with a similar definition for the fr.f. $q(Y)$ of Y.

The *conditional* d.f. of X relative to the hypothesis that $Y = y$ is given by Axiom 2 as

$$P_y(x) = \lim_{\Delta y \to 0} \frac{\text{Prob. } [X \leq x, \, y \leq Y \leq y + \Delta y]}{\text{Prob. } [y \leq Y \leq y + \Delta y]}$$

$$= \lim_{\Delta y \to 0} \frac{\int_{-\infty}^{x} \int_{y}^{y+\Delta y} p(X, Y) dX \, dY}{\int_{y}^{y+\Delta y} q(Y) dY} = \frac{\int_{-\infty}^{x} p(X, y) dX}{q(y)} \quad,$$

while the corresponding conditional fr.f. $p_Y(X)$ is

$$p_y(x) = \frac{\partial}{\partial x} P_y(x) = \frac{p(x, y)}{q(y)} \quad.$$

In terms of the "Prob." description we may write

$$p_y(x) dx = \frac{\text{Prob. } [x \leq X \leq x + dx, \, y \leq Y \leq y + dy]}{\text{Prob. } [y \leq Y \leq y + dy]}$$

$$= \frac{\int_{x}^{x+dx} \int_{y}^{y+dy} p(X, Y) dX \, dY}{\int_{y}^{y+dy} q(Y) dY}$$

$$= \frac{p(x, y) dx \, dy}{q(y) dy} = \frac{p(x, y) dx}{q(y)} \quad.$$

Similar expressions of course exist for $Q_x(y)$ and $q_X(Y)$.

The expected value of a function of a continuous variate X is defined as

$$E[f(X)] = \int_{-\infty}^{\infty} f(X) p(X) dX \quad,$$

where $p(X)$ is the fr.f. of X. One could also write

$$E[f(X)] = \int_{-\infty}^{\infty} f(X) dP(X)$$

in terms of d.f. Actually, this latter formula is more general if interpreted as a Stieltjes integral. As a special case of the above definition, the expected value of the variate X is given by

$$E[X] = \int_{-\infty}^{\infty} Xp(X)dX \quad .$$

If we are dealing with two continuous variates X and Y with joint fr.f. $p(X, Y)$, then the expected value of $f(X, Y)$ is defined as

$$E[f(X, Y)] = \int_{-\infty}^{\infty} \int_{-\infty}^{\infty} f(X, Y)p(X, Y)dX\,dY \quad .$$

One can readily show that

$$E[X + Y] = E[X] + E[Y] \quad .$$

If X and Y are *independent*, then

$$E[XY] = E[X] \cdot E[Y] \quad .$$

Proof. By definition

$$E[XY] = \int_{-\infty}^{\infty} \int_{-\infty}^{\infty} XYp(X, Y)dX\,dY \quad .$$

If X and Y are independent, $p(X) = p_Y(X)$, $q(Y) = q_X(Y)$ and

$$p(X, Y) = p(X)q(Y) \quad .$$

Thus

$$E[XY] = \int_{-\infty}^{\infty} \int_{-\infty}^{\infty} XYp(X)q(Y)dX\,dY = \int_{-\infty}^{\infty} Xp(X)dX \int_{-\infty}^{\infty} Yq(Y)dY$$
$$= E[X] \cdot E[Y] \quad .$$

We conclude this section with a discussion of the *correlation coefficient*. Let X and Y be stochastic variables with means a and b, respectively, $E[X] = a$, $E[Y] = b$. Also let

$$E[(X - a)^2] = \sigma_x^2$$
$$E[(Y - b)^2] = \sigma_y^2 \quad .$$

Let us consider the expected value of $(X - a)(Y - b)$. We shall use

$$E[(X - a)(Y - b)] = \tau\sigma_x\sigma_y$$

as the defining equation of the correlation coefficient τ and prove that $|\tau| \leq 1$. (The expression $E[(X - a)(Y - b)]$ is frequently called the *covariance* of X and Y.)

To do this, consider the expression

$$[(X - a)\xi + (Y - b)]^2 \quad.$$

Certainly

$$E[\{(X - a)\xi + (Y - b)\}^2] \geq 0$$

for any real number ξ. Hence

$$\xi^2 E[(X - a)^2] + 2\xi E[(X - a)(Y - b)] + E[(Y - b)^2] \geq 0 \quad,$$

or

$$\xi^2 \sigma_x^2 + 2\xi\tau\sigma_x\sigma_y + \sigma_y^2 \geq 0 \quad.$$

Then

$$\sigma_x^2\xi^2 + 2\tau\sigma_x\sigma_y\xi + \sigma_y^2 = w$$

is a parabola convex upward, and, if $w \geq 0$, the roots of

$$\sigma_x^2\xi^2 + 2\tau\sigma_x\sigma_y\xi + \sigma_y^2 = 0$$

must be imaginary or equal. That is,

$$\tau^2\sigma_x^2\sigma_y^2 - \sigma_x^2\sigma_y^2 \leq 0 \quad,$$

or

$$\tau^2 \leq 1 \quad.$$

Thus the correlation coefficient τ is less than or equal to one in absolute value.

If X and Y are independent,

$$E[(X - a)(Y - b)] = E[X - a]E[Y - b] = 0 \quad,$$

and $\tau = 0$. If $Y = \pm X$, then

$$E[(X - a)(Y - b)] = \pm E[(X - a)^2] = \pm \sigma_x^2 = \pm \sigma_x\sigma_y \quad,$$

and $\tau = \pm 1$.

If X and Y are independent, we have seen that $\tau = 0$; that is, X and Y are *uncorrelated*. In general, the converse is not true; that is, $\tau = 0$ does *not* imply that X and Y are independent. However, in certain very important and practical cases (the normal distribution, to be introduced later), zero correlation *does* imply statistical independence.

4. Functions of Random Variables

If X is a random variable and $Y = f(X)$ a deterministic function of X, then Y is also a random variable. The problem of determining the d.f. of Y when we know the d.f. of X frequently arises. We proceed to solve this problem.

Let X be a variate defined on a set A and let $Y = f(X)$ be a real, single-valued function of X. As X ranges in A, let Y range in a point set B. Then, if A' is any subset of A, and B' the corresponding subset of B, we have†

$$\text{Prob. } [X \varepsilon A'] = \text{Prob. } [Y \varepsilon B'] \quad . \tag{8}$$

Now, let B' be the set of points $(-\infty, y)$. Then

$$\int_{A'} p(X)dX = \text{Prob. } [X \varepsilon A'] = \text{Prob. } [Y \varepsilon B'] = \text{Prob. } [Y \leqq y]$$

$$= \int_{-\infty}^{y} q(Y)dY = Q(y) \quad ;$$

where $Q(y)$ is the d.f. of Y, $p(X)$ the fr.f. of X, and $q(Y)$ the fr.f. of Y.

As an example, let

$$Y = \alpha^2 X + \beta \quad ,$$

where α and β are real constants. Let $P(x)$ and $Q(y)$ be the d.f. and $p(X)$ and $q(Y)$ the corresponding fr.f. of X and Y, respectively. Then

$$Q(y) = \text{Prob. } [Y \leqq y] = \text{Prob. } \left[X \leqq \frac{y - \beta}{\alpha^2} \right] = P\left(\frac{y - \beta}{\alpha^2} \right) \quad .$$

In terms of fr.f.,

$$q(Y) = \frac{1}{\alpha^2} p\left(\frac{Y - \beta}{\alpha^2} \right) \quad .$$

We may write, in general, in terms of fr.f., that

$$p(x)|dx| = \text{Prob. } [x \leqq X \leqq x + |dx|] = \text{Prob. } [y \leqq Y \leqq y + |dy|] = q(y)|dy|$$

or

$$p(x) = q(y)\left| \frac{dy}{dx} \right| \quad . \tag{9}$$

---

† The notation "$X \varepsilon A'$" means "X is a point in A'" or "X is an element of the set A'."

Equation (8) is also valid if X and Y are interpreted as n-dimensional variates and A and B as n-dimensional point sets. The analog of Equation (9) is

$$p(x_1, x_2, \cdots, x_n) = q(y_1, y_2, \cdots, y_n) J\left(\frac{y_1, y_2, \cdots, y_n}{x_1, x_2, \cdots, x_n}\right) \ , \tag{10}$$

where J is the Jacobian of the transformation

$$y_i = y_i(x_1, x_2, \cdots, x_n) \ , \quad i = 1, 2, \cdots, n \ .$$

Care must be exercised in formally using Equation (10), and it is generally best to use the fundamental formula, Equation (8). For example, let

$$Y = X^2 \ .$$

Formal application of Equation (10) yields

$$p(x) = 2xq(y) \ ,$$

which is incorrect, since due attention was not paid to the fact that X can be positive or negative, while Y must always be nonnegative. From Equation (8),

$$Q(y) = \text{Prob.} [Y \leq y] = \text{Prob.} [-\sqrt{y} \leq X \leq +\sqrt{y}]$$
$$= \text{Prob.} [X \leq +\sqrt{y}] - \text{Prob.} [X \leq -\sqrt{y}]$$
$$= P(\sqrt{y}) - P(-\sqrt{y}) \ , \quad y \geq 0 \ ,$$

and is zero for negative values of y. The fr.f. equation is

$$\frac{dQ}{dy} = q(y) = \frac{1}{2\sqrt{y}} [p(\sqrt{y}) + p(-\sqrt{y})] \ , \quad y \geq 0 \ , \tag{11}$$

and is zero for $y < 0$. A *careful* application of Equation (9) would also yield Equation (11).

In the case

$$Y = X^2 \ , \quad X \geq 0$$
$$Y = 0 \ , \quad X < 0 \ ,$$

the d.f. of Y is

$$Q(y) = \text{Prob.} [Y \leq y] = \text{Prob.} [X \leq +\sqrt{y}] = P(\sqrt{y}) \ , \quad y \geq 0$$
$$Q(y) = 0 \qquad\qquad\qquad\qquad\qquad\qquad , \quad y < 0 \ .$$

Note in particular that

$$Q(0) = \text{Prob. } [Y \leq 0] = \text{Prob. } [X \leq 0] = P(0) \quad,$$

which in general is not zero. Since $Q(y)$ is not continuous at $y = 0$ if $P(0) \neq 0$, the fr.f. $q(Y)$ of Y is

$$q(Y) = \frac{1}{2\sqrt{Y}} p(\sqrt{Y}) \quad, \quad Y > 0$$

$$q(Y) = P(0)\delta(Y) \quad\quad, \quad Y = 0$$

$$q(Y) = 0 \quad\quad\quad\quad, \quad Y < 0 \quad,$$

where $\delta(Y)$ is the delta function. Clearly,

$$1 = \int_{-\infty}^{\infty} q(Y)dY = \lim_{\substack{\varepsilon \to 0 \\ \varepsilon > 0}} \left[\int_{-\infty}^{-\varepsilon} 0 \, dY + \int_{-\varepsilon}^{\varepsilon} P(0)\delta(Y)dY + \int_{\varepsilon}^{\infty} \frac{1}{2\sqrt{Y}} p(\sqrt{Y})dY \right]$$

$$= 0 + P(0) + \lim_{\substack{\varepsilon \to 0 \\ \varepsilon > 0}} \int_{\sqrt{\varepsilon}}^{\infty} p(u)du = P(0) + [1 - P(0)] = 1 \quad.$$

As remarked earlier, X and Y can be treated as more than one-dimensional. Suppose, for example, X and Y are each two-dimensional: $X = (X_1, X_2)$, $Y = (Y_1, Y_2)$. Then, if A is a set in *two*-dimensional euclidean space and B is the set corresponding to $Y = f(X)$ [which now becomes

$$Y_1 = f_1(X_1, X_2)$$

$$Y_2 = f_2(X_1, X_2) \quad],$$

then we still have

$$\text{Prob. } [(X_1, X_2) \, \varepsilon \, A'] = \text{Prob. } [(Y_1, Y_2) \, \varepsilon \, B'] \quad.$$

Suppose, now, X and Y are two variates and we wish to find the d.f. $R(z)$ of

$$Z = f(X, Y) \quad.$$

By definition of a d.f.,

$$R(z) = \text{Prob. } [Z \leq z] = \text{Prob. } [(X, Y) \, \varepsilon \, A] \quad,$$

where A is the region in (x, y)-space determined by the inequality

$$f(X, Y) \leq z \quad.$$

But, again by definition,

$$\text{Prob. }[(X,\,Y)\,\varepsilon\,A] = \int\!\!\int_A p(X,\,Y)dS \quad,$$

where $p(X,\,Y)$ is the joint fr.f. of X and Y. Hence

$$R(z) = \int\!\!\int_A p(X,\,Y)dS \quad, \tag{12}$$

and

$$r(z) = \frac{\partial}{\partial z}\int\!\!\int_A p(X,\,Y)dX\,dY \quad, \tag{13}$$

where $r(Z)$ is the fr.f. of Z.

Another approach based on Equation (10), is to set

$$U = g(X,\,Y)$$

along with

$$Z = f(X,\,Y)$$

such that the Jacobian of the transformation is nonsingular. Then

$$q(Z,\,U) = J\left(\frac{X,\,Y}{Z,\,U}\right)p(X,\,Y) \quad,$$

where $q(Z,\,U)$ is the joint fr.f. of Z and U. The marginal distribution $r(Z)$ of Z is given by

$$r(Z) = \int_{-\infty}^{\infty} q(Z,\,U)dU = \int_{-\infty}^{\infty} J\left(\frac{X,\,Y}{Z,\,U}\right)p(X,\,Y)dU \quad. \tag{14}$$

(The fr.f. q is assumed to be defined for $-\infty < U < \infty$, possibly as zero in some regions. Cf. the Rayleigh distribution of Sec. 8.)

As a concrete illustration of the above formulas, let us find the d.f. and fr.f. of the variate Z where

$$Z = X + Y \quad.$$

From Equation (12),

$$R(z) = \int\!\!\int_A p(X,\,Y)dX\,dY \quad, \tag{15}$$

where A is the region in the (X, Y)-plane determined by the inequality

$$X + Y \leq z$$

(cf. Fig. 7.4). Consider the transformation T:

$$T: \begin{cases} X' = X \\ Y' = X + Y \end{cases} ,$$

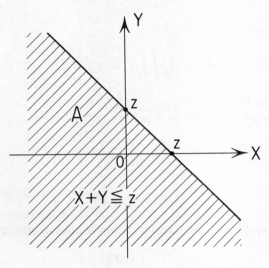

Fig. 7.4

which is made merely for the purpose of evaluating the integral of Equation (15). The Jacobian of T is 1; hence (cf. Fig. 7.5)

$$\iint_A p(X, Y)dX\, dY = \iint_{Y' \leq z} p(X', Y' - X')dS'$$

$$= \int_{-\infty}^{z} dY' \int_{-\infty}^{\infty} p(X', Y' - X')dX' \quad .$$

Therefore, from Equation (13),

$$r(z) = \frac{\partial}{\partial z} \iint_A p(X, Y)dX\, dY = \int_{-\infty}^{\infty} p(X', z - X')dX' \quad ,$$

and, if we drop the primes,

$$r(Z) = \int_{-\infty}^{\infty} p(X, Z - X)dX \quad .$$

If X and Y are independent, $p(X, Y) = p(X)q(Y)$ and

$$r(Z) = \int_{-\infty}^{\infty} p(X)q(Z - X)dX \quad . \tag{16}$$

Utilizing the second method, we introduce the equation

$$U = X$$

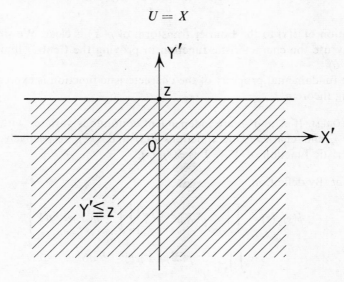

Fig. 7.5

along with

$$Z = X + Y \quad .$$

The Jacobian is unity; hence Equation (14) yields

$$r(Z) = \int_{-\infty}^{\infty} p(X, Y)dU = \int_{-\infty}^{\infty} p(U, Z - U)dU \quad .$$

If X and Y are independent,

$$r(Z) = \int_{-\infty}^{\infty} p(U)q(Z - U)dU \quad .$$

Again, one has to be careful to ascertain the range of integration in this second method.

5. Characteristic Functions

Another important function associated with a distribution is its *characteristic function*. Let X be a variate with fr.f. $p(X)$. Then the characteristic function $\phi(s)$ of the distribution is, by definition,

$$\phi(s) = E[e^{jsX}] = \int_{-\infty}^{\infty} e^{jsX} p(X) dX \quad .$$

The relation of $\phi(s)$ to the Fourier transform of $p(X)$ is clear. We shall advantageously use the characteristic function in proving the Central limit theorem (cf. Sec. 6).

The fundamental property of the characteristic function is expressed in the following theorem.

THEOREM. *If X and Y are independent continuous variates with fr.f. $p(X)$ and $q(Y)$, and characteristic functions $\phi(s)$ and $\psi(s)$, respectively, then the characteristic function of $X + Y$ is $\phi(s)\psi(s)$.*

Proof. By definition,

$$\phi(s)\psi(s) = \left[\int_{-\infty}^{\infty} p(X)e^{jsX}dX\right]\left[\int_{-\infty}^{\infty} q(Y)e^{jsY}dY\right]$$

$$= \int\int_{XY-\text{pl.}} p(X)q(Y)e^{js(X+Y)}dS \quad .$$

Now let $\chi(s)$ be the characteristic function of $Z = X + Y$.

$$\chi(s) = \int_{-\infty}^{\infty} r(Z)e^{jsZ}dZ = \int_{-\infty}^{\infty} e^{jsZ}dZ \int_{-\infty}^{\infty} p(X)q(Z - X)dX$$

$$= \int\int_{XZ-\text{pl.}} p(X)q(Z - X)e^{jsZ}dS \quad .$$

In the above formula $r(Z)$ is the fr.f. of Z, and we have used Equation (16).

Consider the transformation

$$X = u$$

$$Z = u + v$$

with Jacobian unity. Then $\chi(s)$ becomes

$$\chi(s) = \int\int_{uv-\text{pl.}} p(u)q(v)e^{js(u+v)}dS = \phi(s)\psi(s) \quad .$$

This formula can be used, for example, to find the d.f. of the sum of any finite number of independent variates with arbitrary distributions.

EXERCISES

1. In a series of N observations (where we assume N very large), three events A, B, and C can occur or not occur. Define $p(A)$, $p(B)$, $p(C)$, $p(A, B)$, $p(A, C)$, $p(B, C)$, $p(A, B, C)$, $p(A + B)$, $p(A + C)$, $p(B + C)$, $p(A + B + C)$, $p_A(B, C)$, $p_B(A, C)$, $p_C(A, B)$, $p_{AB}(C)$, $p_{AC}(B)$, $p_{BC}(A)$. Express $p(A + B + C)$ in terms of absolute and joint probabilities. Consider the relations that may exist among the various probabilities defined above. Extend the results to more than three events, A, B, C.

2. Let X be a discrete variate which takes on the values $x_1, x_2, \cdots, x_n$ with respective probabilities of assuming these values of $p(x_1), p(x_2)$, $\cdots, p(x_n)$. Interpret the d.f. $P(x)$ of X,

$$P(x) = \sum_{x_i \leq x} p(x_i) \quad ,$$

as a Stieltjes integral.

3. If X and Y are random variables, show that their conditional probabilities satisfy the equations

$$\sum_{i=1}^{n} p_{y_j}(x_i) = 1 = \sum_{j=1}^{m} q_{x_i}(y_j)$$

in the discrete case and

$$\int_{-\infty}^{\infty} p_Y(X) dX = 1 = \int_{-\infty}^{\infty} q_X(Y) dY$$

in the continuous case.

4. If X and Y are independent discrete random variables, prove that

$$E[XY] = E[X] \cdot E[Y] \quad .$$

5. Let the fr.f. $p(X)$ of a random variable X be as indicated in Figure 7.6.

   (i) What is $p(0)$?

   (ii) What is the expected value of X?

   (iii) What is the variance of X?

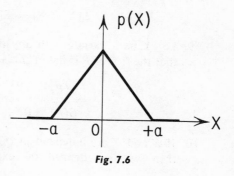

Fig. 7.6

6. Repeat Problem 5 for the fr.f. of Figure 7.7 below.

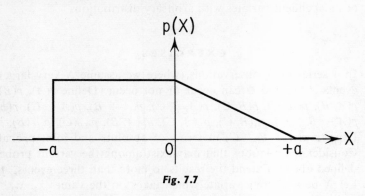

Fig. 7.7

7. Let $0 < p < 1$ and $q = 1 - p$. Then, if X is a random variable assuming the values

$$1, 2, 3, \cdots$$

with probabilities

$$g_1, g_2, g_3, \cdots \quad ,$$

respectively, where

$$g_k = pq^{k-1} \quad , \quad k = 1, 2, \cdots \quad ,$$

then we say X has a *geometric distribution*. Prove that

$$\sum_{k=1}^{\infty} g_k = 1 \quad , \quad E[X] = \frac{1}{p} \quad ,$$

and show that the variance of X is q/p^2.

8. If X and Y are continuous stochastic variables, prove that

$$E[X + Y] = E[X] + E[Y] \quad .$$

9. Let X be a variate with any distribution. Let $P(x)$ be its d.f. Prove that the fr.f. of P is flat. That is, if $G(P)$ is the fr.f. of P, then

$$G(P) = 1 \quad , \quad 0 \leqq P \leqq 1$$
$$G(P) = 0 \quad , \quad \text{otherwise} \quad .$$

10. If X and Y are independent random variables with joint fr.f. $p(X, Y)$, then we have defined the expected value of $Z = XY$ as $E[Z] =$

$\int_{-\infty}^{\infty} \int_{-\infty}^{\infty} XYp(X, Y)dX \, dY$. Compute the fr.f. $r(Z)$ of Z, and show that $E[Z]$ could equally as well have been defined by

$$E[Z] = \int_{-\infty}^{\infty} Zr(Z)dZ \quad .$$

11. If X is a variate with d.f. $P(x)$, find the d.f. $Q(y)$ of Y where

$$Y = -\alpha^2 X + \beta \quad .$$

12. The variate X is said to have a *Cauchy distribution* if its fr.f. $p(X)$ is of the form

$$p(X) = \frac{a}{\pi} \frac{1}{a^2 + X^2} \quad .$$

Find the mean and variance of X. If Y is another random variable, Cauchy distributed with constant b, prove, using the characteristic function method, that

$$\frac{c}{\pi} \frac{1}{c^2 + Z^2}$$

is the fr.f. of $Z = X + Y$, where X and Y are assumed independent and $c = a + b$.

13. Let X be a continuous random variable with mean zero and variance Σ. If A is any positive constant, prove that

$$\text{Prob. } [|X| \geq A] \leq \frac{\Sigma^2}{A^2} \quad .$$

(This is the Bienaymé-Tschebyscheff theorem for the continuous case.)

6. The Normal Distribution

We shall now consider some special distributions of great interest. The most important, from both the theoretical and practical viewpoint, is the *normal distribution* whose d.f. is given by the formula

$$P(x) = \frac{1}{\sqrt{2\pi}} \int_{-\infty}^{x} e^{-X^2/2}dX \quad .$$

We shall derive this distribution from basic principles, investigate some of its many interesting properties, and then consider some other distributions associated with it.

Suppose, then, we are conducting an experiment which consists of a sequence of independent trials (for example, the tossing of a coin) such that there are only two possible outcomes for each trial, and the probability does not change throughout the sequence of trials. We shall call such trials *Bernoulli trials*. Then we have the following theorem.

THEOREM. Let $B_{n,r}$ be the probability that in n Bernoulli trials with probability p for "success" r successes occur. Then

$$B_{n,r} = \binom{n}{r} p^r (1 - p)^{n-r} \quad .$$

Proof. The number of ways of choosing r distinct objects from a set of n objects is precisely $\binom{n}{r}$. Now, the probability of r successes (and correspondingly $n - r$ failures) is simply the product of the probabilities, since they are independent. The probability of r successes is p^r, and the probability of $n - r$ failures is $(1 - p)^{n-r}$. Hence

$$B_{n,r} = \binom{n}{r} p^r (1 - p)^{n-r} \quad .$$

Now, if R is a random variable which can assume the $n + 1$ integral values $0, 1, \cdots, n$ with probability $B_{n,r}$ of assuming the value r, then R is a discrete variate which is binomially distributed. In Section 2 we have shown that

$$E[R] = np$$

$$E[(R - np)^2] = npq \quad ,$$

where $q = 1 - p$. Now we wish to consider the distribution of R as n approaches infinity in such a manner that both r and $n - r$ tend to infinity while p remains fixed. The resulting distribution is called the *normal distribution*.

Let us introduce the normalized variate X defined by the equation

$$X = \frac{R - np}{\sqrt{npq}} \quad .$$

Clearly, X has mean zero and variance one. Now, if x and a are any two fixed numbers,

$$\text{Prob. } [a \leq X \leq x] = \Sigma B_{n,r} \quad ,$$

where the summation is extended over all values of r which satisfy the inequalities,

$$np + a\sqrt{npq} \leqq r \leqq np + x\sqrt{npq} \quad .$$

Using Stirling's formula for the factorial (cf. Chap. 2),

$$n! = n^n e^{-n} \sqrt{2\pi n}(1 + \theta_n) \quad ,$$

where $\lim_{n \to \infty} \theta_n = 0$, we may write, after some algebraic manipulations, that

$$\begin{aligned}
\log B_{n,r} = {} & (np + d + \tfrac{1}{2}) \log n + (nq - d + \tfrac{1}{2}) \log n \\
& - (np + d + \tfrac{1}{2}) \log (np + d) - (nq - d + \tfrac{1}{2}) \log (nq - d) \\
& + (np + d + \tfrac{1}{2}) \log p + (nq - d + \tfrac{1}{2}) \log q \\
& - \log \sqrt{2\pi npq} + \theta_n' \quad ,
\end{aligned}$$

where

$$d = r - np \quad .$$

This expression reduces to

$$\begin{aligned}
\log B_{n,r} = {} & - \left(np + d + \frac{1}{2}\right) \log \left(1 + \frac{d}{np}\right) \\
& - \left(nq - d + \frac{1}{2}\right) \log \left(1 - \frac{d}{nq}\right) \\
& - \log \sqrt{2\pi npq} + \theta_n' \quad .
\end{aligned}$$

Now,

$$\frac{d}{np} = \frac{r - np}{np} = \frac{\xi\sqrt{npq}}{np} \quad ,$$

where ξ is some number between a and x, $a \leqq \xi \leqq x$. Hence

$$\left|\frac{d}{np}\right| \leqq \frac{M}{\sqrt{n}} \sqrt{\frac{q}{p}} \quad , \quad M = \max (|a|, |x|) \quad ,$$

which, with p and x fixed, approaches zero as $n \to \infty$. Similarly for $\left|\dfrac{d}{nq}\right|$. We may therefore use the Maclaurin expansion

$$\log (1 + z) = z - \frac{z^2}{2} + \cdots \qquad |z| < 1$$

for the logarithm to write

$$\log B_{n,r} = -\frac{1}{2}\frac{d^2}{npq} - \log\sqrt{2\pi npq} + \theta_n''$$

or

$$\text{Prob. } [a \leq X \leq x] = \sum_r \frac{1}{\sqrt{2\pi npq}} \exp\left[-\frac{1}{2}\frac{(r-np)^2}{npq}\right](1+\theta_n''') \quad .$$

Now,

$$X = \frac{R-np}{\sqrt{npq}} \quad ,$$

and, if we let

$$x_r = \frac{r-np}{\sqrt{npq}} \quad , \quad x_{r+1} = \frac{(r+1)-np}{\sqrt{npq}}$$

and

$$\Delta x_r = x_{r+1} - x_r = \frac{1}{\sqrt{npq}} \quad ,$$

then the above sum becomes

$$\text{Prob. } [a \leq X \leq x] = \frac{1}{\sqrt{2\pi}}\sum e^{-x_r^2/2}\Delta x_r(1+\theta_n''') \quad ,$$

where the summation is extended over all integers r which satisfy the inequalities

$$np + a\sqrt{npq} \leq r \leq np + x\sqrt{npq} \quad .$$

This sum can be regarded as an approximating sum to the integral

$$\frac{1}{\sqrt{2\pi}}\int_a^x e^{-x^2/2}dx \quad .$$

The distribution function

$$P(x) = \text{Prob. } [X \leq x]$$

associated with the limit of the Bernoulli distribution is thus

$$P(x) = \frac{1}{\sqrt{2\pi}} \int_{-\infty}^{x} e^{-X^2/2} dX \quad, \tag{17}$$

and the corresponding fr.f. $p(X)$ is

$$p(X) = \frac{1}{\sqrt{2\pi}} e^{-X^2/2} \quad. \tag{18}$$

Equations (17) and (18) are the famous *normal* or *Gaussian* distribution. We readily verify that (cf. Chap. 2)

$$\int_{-\infty}^{\infty} p(X) dX = 1$$

$$E[X] = \int_{-\infty}^{\infty} X p(X) dX = 0$$

$$D_x = E[X^2] = \int_{-\infty}^{\infty} X^2 p(X) dX = 1 \quad.$$

That is, the distribution has mean zero and variance one.

It is sometimes convenient to consider the Gaussian distribution with mean unequal to zero and variance unequal to one. This form is obtained by a slight change of variable yielding the fr.f.

$$\phi(X) = \frac{1}{\sigma\sqrt{2\pi}} e^{-(X-a)^2/2\sigma^2} \quad.$$

By a direct calculation we find

$$\int_{-\infty}^{\infty} \phi(X) dX = 1$$

and

$$E[X] = a \quad, \quad E[(X-a)^2] = \sigma^2 \quad.$$

Hence $\phi(X)$ has mean a and standard deviation σ. We shall frequently write "X is normally distributed (a, σ)" to mean that "X is a normally distributed random variable with mean a and variance σ^2."

A sketch of $p(X) = \dfrac{1}{\sigma\sqrt{2\pi}}\,e^{-X^2/2\sigma^2}$ appears in Figure 7.8 below. Obvious conclusions can be drawn regarding the shape of the curve for various values of the standard deviation. For example, the smaller σ, the more peaked the curve. We have probability one-half when

$$\frac{1}{2} = \frac{1}{\sigma\sqrt{2\pi}} \int_{-\xi}^{\xi} e^{-X^2/2\sigma^2}\,dX$$

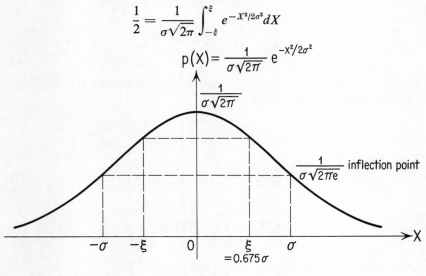

Fig. 7.8

A numerical calculation shows that $\xi = 0.67449\sigma$. Also, the probability that X be less than σ, that is

$$\text{Prob. } [|X| \leqq \sigma] \quad,$$

is approximately 0.6826.

Some idea of the importance of Gaussian distributions can be gained from a survey of the following theorems.

THEOREM. Let X and Y be independent normally distributed random variables. Then $Z = X + Y$ is normally distributed. If X has mean a and variance σ^2, and Y has mean b and variance τ^2, then the mean c and variance v^2 of Z are given by

$$c = a + b$$

and

$$v^2 = \sigma^2 + \tau^2 \quad.$$

Proof. A direct application of Equation (16) yields the desired result. The details may be left to the reader.

One of the most important theorems showing the power of the Gaussian distribution is the so-called Central limit theorem which we now prove.

CENTRAL LIMIT THEOREM. Let $X_1, X_2, \cdots, X_n$ be independent random variables with *arbitrary* distributions. Then the sum

$$X = \frac{X_1 + X_2 + \cdots + X_n}{\sqrt{n}}$$

approaches a normally distributed variable as n approaches infinity. If X_i has mean zero and variance $\sigma_i^2 < \infty$,

$$E[X_i] = 0 \quad , \quad E[X_i^2] = \sigma_i^2 \quad , \quad i = 1, 2, \cdots, n \quad ,$$

then X has mean zero and variance σ^2, where

$$\sigma^2 = \frac{\sigma_1^2 + \sigma_2^2 + \cdots + \sigma_n^2}{n} \quad .$$

Proof. Let

$$E[X_i^3] = \tau_i^3 \quad , \quad E[X_i^4] = v_i^4 \quad , \quad \cdots \quad , \quad i = 1, 2, \cdots, n \quad .$$

The expected value of the powers of X_i are called *moments*. It will be seen that as long as they are uniformly bounded, the exact value of these higher moments is of no concern in our present investigation.

The characteristic function $\phi_n(s)$ of X can be written (cf. Sec. 5)

$$\phi_n(s) = E[e^{jsX}] = \prod_{k=1}^{n} E[e^{jsX_k/\sqrt{n}}] \quad .$$

If we take the logarithm of both sides of the above expression,

$$\log \phi_n(s) = \sum_{k=1}^{n} \log \left(1 - \frac{s^2}{2n} \sigma_k^2 - j \frac{s^3 \tau_k^3}{6n\sqrt{n}} + \frac{s^4 v_k^4}{24n^2} + \cdots \right) \quad .$$

For large values of n the term on the right under the summation sign may be approximated by

$$\log \left(1 - \frac{s^2}{2n} \sigma_k^2 \right) = - \frac{s^2}{2n} \sigma_k^2 \quad .$$

Hence, for large n,

$$\log \phi_n(s) = - \sum_{k=1}^{n} \frac{s^2}{2n} \sigma_k^2 = - \frac{s^2 \sigma^2}{2} \quad,$$

where

$$\sigma^2 = \frac{1}{n} \sum_{k=1}^{n} \sigma_k^2 \quad.$$

Therefore

$$\lim_{n \to \infty} \phi_n(s) = \phi(s) = e^{-s^2 \sigma^2 / 2} \quad,$$

and the fr.f. $p(X)$ of X is given by the inverse Fourier transform

$$p(X) = \frac{1}{2\pi} \int_{-\infty}^{\infty} \phi(s) e^{-jsX} ds = \frac{1}{2\pi} \int_{-\infty}^{\infty} e^{-s^2 \sigma^2 / 2} e^{-jsX} ds \quad.$$

If we make the change of variable $u = s + jX/\sigma^2$,

$$p(X) = \frac{1}{2\pi} e^{-X^2/2\sigma^2} \int_{-\infty}^{\infty} e^{-u^2 \sigma^2 / 2} du = \frac{1}{\sigma \sqrt{2\pi}} e^{-X^2/2\sigma^2} \quad,$$

which is normally distributed $(0, \sigma)$.

7. Multidimensional Normal Distributions

Let $X_1, X_2, \cdots, X_n$ be n (not necessarily independent) random variables with means zero. Let $p(X_1, X_2, \cdots, X_n)$ be their joint fr.f. Then we say $(X_1, X_2, \cdots, X_n)$ are "normally distributed in n dimensions" if their fr.f. is of the form

$$\frac{1}{(2\pi)^{n/2} \sqrt{|M|}} \exp\left[-\tfrac{1}{2}|R'M^{-1}R|\right] \quad, \tag{19}$$

where

$$M = \|\mu_{ij}\|$$

is the matrix of the second moments,

$$\mu_{ij} = E[X_i X_j] \quad, \quad i, j = 1, 2, \cdots, n \quad;$$

M^{-1} is the inverse matrix; $|M|$ is the determinant of the matrix; R is the column vector with components $X_1, X_2, \cdots, X_n$; and R' is the transposed row matrix. More explicitly,

$$|R'M^{-1}R| = \sum_{i=1}^{n} \sum_{j=1}^{n} \frac{M_{ij}}{|M|} X_i X_j \quad,$$

where M_{ij} is the cofactor of μ_{ij} in the matrix M.

The marginal distributions

$$p(X_{i_1}, X_{i_2}, \cdots, X_{i_r})$$

can be determined in the usual fashion,

$$p(X_{i_1}, X_{i_2}, \cdots, X_{i_r}) = \int_{-\infty}^{\infty} \int_{-\infty}^{\infty} \cdots \int_{-\infty}^{\infty} p(X_1, X_2, \cdots, X_n) dX_{i_{r+1}} \cdots dX_{i_n} \quad.$$

They are, of course, r-dimensional normal distributions. If the X_i are independent, then

$$E[X_i X_j] = 0 \quad, \quad i \neq j \quad,$$

and M becomes a pure diagonal matrix. In this case

$$p(X_1, X_2, \cdots, X_n) = p(X_1)p(X_2) \cdots p(X_n) \quad,$$

where each $p(X_i)$ is a one-dimensional normal distribution with mean zero and variance μ_{ii}.

For the two-dimensional case with fr.f. $p(X, Y)$,

$$M = \left\| \begin{matrix} \mu_{11} & \mu_{12} \\ \mu_{12} & \mu_{22} \end{matrix} \right\| ,$$

$$M^{-1} = |M|^{-1} \left\| \begin{matrix} \mu_{22} & -\mu_{12} \\ -\mu_{12} & \mu_{11} \end{matrix} \right\| ,$$

and

$$|M| = \mu_{11}\mu_{22} - \mu_{12}^2 \quad.$$

The vectors R and R' are

$$R = \left\| \begin{matrix} X \\ Y \end{matrix} \right\| \quad, \quad R' = \| \begin{matrix} X & Y \end{matrix} \| \quad,$$

respectively, and

$$|R'M^{-1}R| = |M|^{-1}(\mu_{22}X^2 - 2\mu_{12}XY + \mu_{11}Y^2) \quad .$$

If we introduce the standard notation

$$\mu_{11} = \sigma_x^2 \quad , \quad \mu_{22} = \sigma_y^2 \quad , \quad \mu_{12} = \tau\sigma_x\sigma_y \quad ,$$

where σ_x and σ_y are the standard deviations of X and Y, respectively, and τ is the correlation coefficient, then the probability density function of Equation (19) assumes the standard form

$$p(X, Y) = \frac{1}{2\pi\sqrt{1 - \tau^2}\sigma_x\sigma_y} \exp\left[\frac{-1}{2(1 - \tau^2)}\left(\frac{X^2}{\sigma_x^2} - \frac{2\tau XY}{\sigma_x\sigma_y} + \frac{Y^2}{\sigma_y^2}\right)\right] \quad .$$

If X and Y are independent, then we know that X and Y are uncorrelated cf. Sec. 3). That is $\tau = 0$ and

$$p(X, Y) = \left(\frac{1}{\sigma_x\sqrt{2\pi}} e^{-X^2/2\sigma_x^2}\right)\left(\frac{1}{\sigma_y\sqrt{2\pi}} e^{-Y^2/2\sigma_y^2}\right) \quad .$$

Note that in this case the converse is true. For if X and Y are uncorrelated, $\tau = 0$ by definition. However, if $\tau = 0$, the above formula is valid, that is,

$$p(X, Y) = p(X)p(Y) \quad .$$

But this is precisely the condition that two variates be independent. Hence, in the Gaussian case, zero correlation and statistical independence are coextensive.

Another theorem on joint normal distributions, that will be useful in our discussion of stochastic processes, states that any linear combination of independent normally distributed random variables is also normally distributed. We state the precise theorem in the general case and prove it for the two-dimensional case.

THEOREM. Let $X_1, X_2, \cdots, X_n$ be n normally distributed random variables with means zero and variances σ_i^2, respectively. Let $Y_1, Y_2, \cdots, Y_m, m \le n$ be m linear combinations of the X_i,

$$Y = AX \quad ,$$

where the a_{ij}, $A = \|a_{ij}\|$ are constants and the rank of the matrix A is m. Then the Y_k's have an m-dimensional joint normal distribution

$$p(Y_1, Y_2, \cdots, Y_m) = \frac{1}{(2\pi)^{m/2}\sqrt{|\Delta|}} \exp\left[-\tfrac{1}{2}|Y'\Delta^{-1}Y|\right] \quad ,$$

where

$$\Delta = A\Sigma\Sigma'A' \quad , \quad \Sigma = \| \delta_{ij}\sigma_i \| \quad .$$

Primes denote the transposed matrices and vertical bars, for example, $|\Delta|$ denote the determinant of the matrix; Δ^{-1} is the inverse matrix.

Proof. Consider the case $n = m = 2$, and the variates independent:

$$p(X) = \frac{1}{\sigma\sqrt{2\pi}} e^{-X^2/2\sigma^2} \quad , \quad q(Y) = \frac{1}{\tau\sqrt{2\pi}} e^{-Y^2/2\tau^2} \quad .$$

Let

$$\begin{aligned} U &= a_{11}X + a_{12}Y \\ V &= a_{21}X + a_{22}Y \quad , \end{aligned} \tag{20}$$

where $A = \| a_{ij} \|$ is nonsingular.

Now, by Equation (10)

$$p(U, V) = J\left(\frac{X, Y}{U, V}\right) p(X, Y) \quad ,$$

where $p(U, V)$ is the joint fr.f. of U and V. Also,

$$p(X, Y) = p(X)q(Y) \quad ,$$

since X and Y are independent by hypothesis.

Since A is nonsingular, we can solve Equations (20) for X and Y, namely,

$$\begin{aligned} X &= b_{11}U + b_{12}V \\ Y &= b_{21}U + b_{22}V \quad . \end{aligned}$$

The Jacobian of the transformation is readily seen to be $|A^{-1}|$, where

$$A^{-1} = \begin{Vmatrix} b_{11} & b_{12} \\ b_{21} & b_{22} \end{Vmatrix} = \frac{1}{|A|} \begin{Vmatrix} a_{22} & -a_{12} \\ -a_{21} & a_{11} \end{Vmatrix}$$

and

$$p(U, V) = \frac{1}{2\pi|A|\sigma\tau} \exp\left[-\tfrac{1}{2}(X^2/\sigma^2 + Y^2/\tau^2)\right] \quad .$$

But

$$X^2 = b_{11}^2 U^2 + 2b_{11}b_{12}UV + b_{12}^2 V^2$$

$$Y^2 = b_{21}^2 U^2 + 2b_{21}b_{22}UV + b_{22}^2 V^2 \quad ;$$

hence

$$p(U, V) = \frac{1}{2\pi |A| \sigma\tau} \exp \{- \tfrac{1}{2}[(b_{11}^2/\sigma^2 + b_{21}^2/\tau^2)U^2 + 2(b_{11}b_{12}/\sigma^2 + b_{21}b_{22}/\tau^2)UV$$
$$+ (b_{12}^2/\sigma^2 + b_{22}^2/\tau^2)V^2]\} \quad . \tag{21}$$

Now, in the notation of the theorem,

$$\Sigma = \Sigma' = \left\| \begin{matrix} \sigma & 0 \\ 0 & \tau \end{matrix} \right\| \quad ,$$

and

$$\Delta^{-1} = A'^{-1}\Sigma'^{-1}\Sigma^{-1}A^{-1} = \left\| \begin{matrix} b_{11} & b_{21} \\ b_{12} & b_{22} \end{matrix} \right\| \cdot \left\| \begin{matrix} \sigma^{-2} & 0 \\ 0 & \tau^{-2} \end{matrix} \right\| \cdot \left\| \begin{matrix} b_{11} & b_{12} \\ b_{21} & b_{22} \end{matrix} \right\| \quad ,$$

while

$$Y = \left\| \begin{matrix} U \\ V \end{matrix} \right\| \quad .$$

Thus

$$-\frac{1}{2} |Y'\Delta^{-1}Y| = -\frac{1}{2} \left[\left(\frac{b_{11}^2}{\sigma^2} + \frac{b_{21}^2}{\tau^2} \right) U^2 + 2 \left(\frac{b_{11}b_{12}}{\sigma^2} + \frac{b_{21}b_{22}}{\tau^2} \right) UV \right.$$
$$\left. + \left(\frac{b_{12}^2}{\sigma^2} + \frac{b_{22}^2}{\tau^2} \right) V^2 \right] \quad .$$

Also,

$$|\Delta| = |A|^2 |\Sigma|^2 = |A|^2 \sigma^2 \tau^2 \quad ,$$

and

$$\sqrt{|\Delta|} = |A| \sigma\tau \quad .$$

Therefore Equation (21) assumes the standard form

$$p(U, V) = \frac{1}{2\pi\sqrt{|\Delta|}} \exp\left[-\tfrac{1}{2}|Y'\Delta^{-1}Y|\right] \quad,$$

which is a joint normal distribution. The marginal distributions, of course, are also normal.

8. Other Distributions

Suppose that X and Y are independent random variables normally distributed $(0, \sigma)$. In a practical problem, say, measuring the position of an object in a plane, X and Y could be errors in the x and y coordinates. Frequently it is of interest to determine the range and azimuth, that is, express x and y in polar coordinates. Then the problem arises as to what is the distribution of

$$R = \sqrt{X^2 + Y^2} \quad.$$

We shall determine the distribution of R, which is called a *Rayleigh distribution*.
Since X and Y are independent, their joint fr.f. is simply

$$p(X, Y) = \left(\frac{1}{\sigma\sqrt{2\pi}}\right)^2 e^{-(X^2 + Y^2)/2\sigma^2} \quad.$$

Now, let

$$\begin{aligned} X &= R \cos \Theta \\ Y &= R \sin \Theta \quad, \end{aligned} \tag{22}$$

and let $q(R, \Theta)$ be their joint fr.f. We see from the above equations that

$$R = \sqrt{X^2 + Y^2}$$

and hence that the marginal fr.f. of $q(R, \Theta)$ will give us the desired distribution of R. From Equation (10)

$$q(R, \Theta) = Jp(X, Y) \quad, \quad -\infty < X < \infty \quad, \quad -\infty < Y < \infty$$
$$0 \leq R < \infty \quad, \qquad 0 \leq \Theta \leq 2\pi \quad,$$

where $J = R$ is the Jacobian of the transformation of Equation (22). Hence

$$q(R, \Theta) = \frac{1}{2\pi\sigma^2} R e^{-R^2/2\sigma^2} \quad.$$

The marginal distributions yield $p(R)$ as the fr.f. of R,

$$p(R) = \frac{R}{\sigma^2} e^{-R^2/2\sigma^2} \quad , \quad 0 \leq R < \infty$$

$$= 0 \qquad , \qquad R < 0 \quad ,$$

while the fr.f. of Θ is given by

$$q(\Theta) = \frac{1}{2\pi} \quad , \quad 0 \leq \Theta \leq 2\pi$$

$$= 0 \quad , \quad \text{otherwise} \quad .$$

The fr.f. $p(R)$ of R, as mentioned above, is called a *Rayleigh distribution*. We note in passing that Θ has a *flat* or *uniform* distribution. One also says that Θ is *rectangularly* distributed.

Another important distribution is the *chi squared distribution*. Suppose X is normal $(0, \sigma)$. Then the fr.f. of $Y = X^2$ is $q(Y)$

$$q(Y) = \frac{1}{2\sqrt{Y}} [p(\sqrt{Y}) + p(-\sqrt{Y})]$$

$$= \frac{1}{\sigma\sqrt{2\pi Y}} e^{-Y/2\sigma^2} \quad , \quad Y > 0$$

$$= 0 \qquad \qquad , \quad Y < 0 \quad ,$$

where

$$p(X) = \frac{1}{\sigma\sqrt{2\pi}} e^{-X^2/2\sigma^2}$$

[cf. Equation (11)] is the fr.f. of X.

If X_1 and X_2 are independent normally distributed random variables with means zero and variances one, then the distribution of Y,

$$Y = X_1^2 + X_2^2 \quad ,$$

can be determined by a variety of methods. [(i) Equation (13); (ii) Equation (14); (iii) Characteristic function method; (iv) Square of the Rayleigh distribution.] It turns out to be

$$q(Y) = \tfrac{1}{2} e^{-Y/2} \quad , \quad Y \geq 0$$

$$= 0 \qquad , \quad Y < 0 \quad .$$

The above distributions are special cases of the χ^2-*distribution*. In general, if $X_1, X_2, \cdots, X_n$ are n independent random variables, normal $(0, 1)$, and if

$$Y = \sum_{k=1}^{n} X_k^2 \quad,$$

then Y is said to have a χ^2-distribution with n degrees of freedom. The fr.f. is

$$p(Y) = \frac{1}{2^{n/2}\Gamma\left(\dfrac{n}{2}\right)} Y^{\frac{n}{2}-1} e^{-Y/2}, \quad Y \geqq 0$$

$$= 0 \qquad\qquad , \quad Y < 0 \quad,$$

where $\Gamma\left(\dfrac{n}{2}\right)$ is the Gamma function.

In deducing the normal distribution as the limit of the binomial distribution we assumed that n (the number of trials), r (the number of successes), and $n - r$ (the number of failures) all approached infinity. If we now assume that n is large, p small, and the product $s = np$ is of reasonable size, then we can obtain another limiting form of the binomial distribution called the *Poisson distribution*. It is of the form

$$P_r = e^{-s}\frac{s^r}{r!}$$

and is a discrete distribution. If X is a random variable which assumes the values

$$0, 1, 2, \cdots \quad,$$

with respective probabilities of assuming these values of

$$P_0, P_1, P_2, \cdots \quad,$$

then X is said to be *Poisson distributed*. We readily verify that

$$\sum_{r=0}^{\infty} P_r = 1$$

$$E[X] = s$$

$$\sigma^2 = E[(X - s)^2] = s \quad.$$

The Poisson distribution will be derived in connection with the "random telegraph signal" in Section 15.

We have seen that the normal distribution is, in general, the most convenient distribution with which to deal. If we obtain a fr.f. $p(X)$ in some investigation which is *not* normal, we may be interested in how "close" it is to a Gaussian distribution. For example, if $p(X)$ arises in an experimental problem, we may be willing to assume it is normal for all practical purposes. If we do not wish to be so crude, we can expand the given $p(X)$ in a *Gram-Charlier series*.

By a Gram-Charlier series we mean an expansion in terms of Hermite polynomials. We saw in Chapter 3 that the Hermite polynomials, $H_0(x)$, $H_1(x)$, $H_2(x)$, $\cdots$ were orthogonal in the infinite interval $(-\infty, \infty)$ with respect to the weighting function $e^{-x^2/2}$, and furthermore that

$$\int_{-\infty}^{\infty} e^{-x^2/2} H_n(x) H_m(x) dx = n! \sqrt{2\pi}\, \delta_{nm} \quad . \tag{23}$$

Now, suppose that $f(x)$ is a fr.f. with mean zero and variance 1; that is,

$$\int_{-\infty}^{\infty} f(x)dx = 1 \quad , \quad \int_{-\infty}^{\infty} x f(x)dx = 0 \quad , \quad \int_{-\infty}^{\infty} x^2 f(x)dx = 1 \quad ,$$

whose "closeness" to the normal distribution we wish to investigate. Then, if we write

$$f(x) = e^{-x^2/2} \sum_{n=0}^{\infty} a_n H_n(x) \quad , \tag{24}$$

the coefficients a_n can be determined from the orthogonality conditions of Equation (23). Namely, multiply Equation (24) by $H_m(x)$ and integrate from $-\infty$ to $+\infty$:

$$\int_{-\infty}^{\infty} H_m(x) f(x)dx = \sum_{n=0}^{\infty} a_n \int_{-\infty}^{\infty} e^{-x^2/2} H_m(x) H_n(x) dx = \sum_{n=0}^{\infty} a_n n! \sqrt{2\pi}\, \delta_{nm}$$

$$= a_m m! \sqrt{2\pi} \quad ,$$

and

$$a_m = \frac{1}{m! \sqrt{2\pi}} \int_{-\infty}^{\infty} H_m(x) f(x)dx \quad .$$

Now,

$$a_0 = \frac{1}{\sqrt{2\pi}} \int_{-\infty}^{\infty} f(x) H_0(x)dx = \frac{1}{\sqrt{2\pi}} \int_{-\infty}^{\infty} f(x)dx = \frac{1}{\sqrt{2\pi}}$$

$$a_1 = \frac{1}{\sqrt{2\pi}} \int_{-\infty}^{\infty} f(x) H_1(x)dx = \frac{1}{\sqrt{2\pi}} \int_{-\infty}^{\infty} f(x)(-x)dx = 0$$

$$a_2 = \frac{1}{2! \sqrt{2\pi}} \int_{-\infty}^{\infty} f(x) H_2(x)dx = \frac{1}{2\sqrt{2\pi}} \int_{-\infty}^{\infty} f(x)(x^2 - 1)dx = 0 \quad ;$$

hence

$$f(x) = e^{-x^2/2} \left[\frac{1}{\sqrt{2\pi}} + \sum_{n=3}^{\infty} a_n H_n(x) \right] \quad . \tag{25}$$

Equation (25) is called a *Gram-Charlier* series. Note that the first term is just the normal distribution. If the remaining terms are small, $f(x)$ is a good approximation to the normal distribution. Unfortunately, the expansion of Equation (25) is valid for only a relatively small class of functions. However, these orthogonal representations have other uses. For instance, consider the problem of finding the d.f. of Y where

$$Y = X_1 + X_2 + \cdots + X_n$$

and $X_1, X_2, \cdots, X_n$ are independent random variables. Then we know that for large n, the fr.f. of Y is asymptotically normal. Suppose we expand the fr.f. of Y in a Gram-Charlier series (for example, by first finding the characteristic function of Y). Then it is possible to rearrange slightly and combine the terms of the series such that the first term of the new series is the normal distribution, while the kth term is multiplied by the factor $n^{-(k-1)/2}$. Thus, for large n, the terms after the first are small. Such an expansion, which differs from the Gram-Charlier series by the rearrangement of terms, is called an *Edgeworth* series. Of course, it is still a series involving the Hermite polynomials.

9. Random Sine Waves

A problem of considerable practical interest is to find the fr.f. of a sum of random sine waves. Stated mathematically, we suppose that $X_1, X_2, \cdots, X_N$ are N independent stochastic variables and

$$X = \sum_{n=1}^{N} X_n \quad . \tag{26}$$

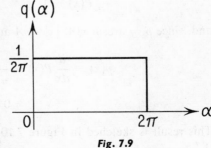

Fig. 7.9

Now, if

$$X_n = A_n \sin \alpha \quad ,$$

where A_n is a constant and α is uniformly distributed between 0 and 2π, we wish to find the fr.f. $p(X)$ of X. (In saying that "α is uniformly distributed between 0 and 2π" we mean that its fr.f. $q(\alpha)$ has the form illustrated in Figure 7.9. (Cf. also the Rayleigh distribution of the previous section where Θ also had a uniform distribution.)

As a first example, let $N = 1$. Then we wish to find the fr.f. $p(X)$ of

$$X = A \sin \alpha \quad .$$

From Equation (8),

$$\text{Prob. } [X \, \varepsilon \, (- A, A)] = \text{Prob. } [\alpha \, \varepsilon \, (0, 2\pi)] \quad .$$

Now, if $- A \leq x \leq 0$ and $x = A \sin \beta$, where β is an angle between $-\dfrac{\pi}{2}$ and $+\dfrac{\pi}{2}$, then

$$P(x) = \text{Prob. } [X \leq x] = \text{Prob. } [\pi - \beta \leq \alpha \leq 2\pi + \beta] = \int_{\pi - \beta}^{2\pi + \beta} q(\alpha) d\alpha$$

$$= \frac{1}{2} + \frac{\beta}{\pi} \quad .$$

On the other hand, if $A \geq x \geq 0$ and $x = A \sin \beta$, where $- \pi/2 \leq \beta \leq \pi/2$, then

$$P(x) = \text{Prob. } [X \leq x] = \text{Prob. } [0 \leq \alpha \leq \beta] + \text{Prob. } [\pi - \beta \leq \alpha \leq 2\pi]$$

$$= \int_{0}^{\beta} q(\alpha) d\alpha + \int_{\pi - \beta}^{2\pi} q(\alpha) d\alpha = \frac{1}{2} + \frac{\beta}{\pi} \quad .$$

Thus

$$P(x) = 0 \quad , \qquad x \leq - A$$

$$P(x) = \frac{1}{2} + \frac{\beta}{\pi} \quad , \quad - A < x < A$$

$$P(x) = 1 \quad , \qquad A \leq x \quad ,$$

and, since $\beta = \arcsin x/A$, $|x| < A$ and $|\beta| < \pi/2$,

$$p(x) = \frac{d}{dx} P(x) = \frac{1}{\pi \sqrt{A^2 - x^2}} \quad , \quad |x| < A \tag{27}$$

$$= 0 \quad , \quad |x| \geq A \quad .$$

This result is sketched in Figure 7.10. We leave it to the reader to verify that $\int_{-\infty}^{\infty} p(X) dX = 1$.

Suppose, now, that

$$X = X_1 + X_2 \quad .$$

Then $p(X)$ can be determined from Equation (16) as

$$p(X) = \int_{-\infty}^{\infty} p_1(X_1)p_2(X - X_1)dX_1 \quad ,$$

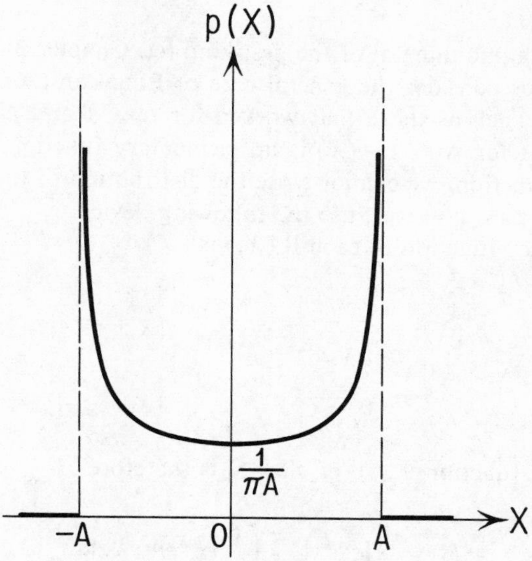

Fig. 7.10

where p_1 is the fr.f. of X_1 and p_2 is the fr.f. of X_2. If we assume without loss of generality that $A_1 \geqq A_2$, then we find† that

$$p(X) = 0 \qquad\qquad\qquad\qquad X < -(A_1 + A_2)$$

$$p(X) = \frac{1}{\pi^2 a} K\left(\frac{z}{2a}\right) \quad , \quad -(A_1 + A_2) < X < -A_1 + A_2$$

$$p(X) = \frac{2}{\pi^2 z} K\left(\frac{2a}{z}\right) \quad , \quad -A_1 + A_2 < X < A_1 - A_2 \qquad (28)$$

$$p(X) = \frac{1}{\pi^2 a} K\left(\frac{z}{2a}\right) \quad , \quad A_1 - A_2 < X < A_1 + A_2$$

$$p(X) = 0 \qquad\qquad , \qquad A_1 + A_2 < X \quad ,$$

where

$$z = \sqrt{(A_1 + A_2)^2 - X^2} \quad ,$$

$$a = \sqrt{A_1 A_2} \quad ,$$

---

† Peirce, *A Short Table of Integrals*, p. 70.

and

$$K(k) = \int_0^{\pi/2} \frac{d\theta}{\sqrt{1 - k^2 \sin^2 \theta}} \quad , \quad k^2 < 1$$

is the complete elliptic integral of the first kind (cf. Chapter 2).

Finally, let us consider the general case of Equation (26). Unfortunately, no special tricks such as those that worked for $N = 1$ and $N = 2$ apply. So, while we see that for $N = 1$, $p(X)$ is an elementary function and for $N = 2$, it is an elliptic function, we cannot write the distribution of the general case in closed form. We can, however, use the following device.

The frequency function of each $p_n(X_n)$ is

$$p_n(X_n) = \frac{1}{\pi \sqrt{A_n^2 - X_n^2}} \quad , \quad |X_n| < A_n$$

$$= 0 \quad , \quad |X_n| \geqq A_n \quad .$$

Its characteristic function $\psi_n(s)$ (cf. Sec. 5) is therefore

$$\psi_n(s) = E[e^{jsX_n}] = \int_{-\infty}^{\infty} e^{jsX_n} p_n(X_n) dX_n$$

$$= \frac{1}{\pi} \int_{-A_n}^{A_n} \frac{e^{jsX_n}}{\sqrt{A_n^2 - X_n^2}} dX_n \quad , \tag{29}$$

since $p_n(X_n)$ vanishes for $|X_n| > A_n$. If we write

$$e^{jsX_n} = \cos sX_n + j \sin sX_n \quad ,$$

we see that the integral of Equation (29) reduces to

$$\psi_n(s) = \frac{2}{\pi} \int_0^{A_n} \frac{\cos sX_n}{\sqrt{A_n^2 - X_n^2}} dX_n \quad .$$

Making the change of variable $X_n = A_n \cos \theta$, in the above integral, we have

$$\psi_n(s) = \frac{2}{\pi} \int_0^{\pi/2} \cos (sA_n \cos \theta) d\theta$$

$$= \frac{1}{\pi} \int_0^{\pi} \cos (sA_n \cos \theta) d\theta = J_0(sA_n) \quad ,$$

where J_0 is the Bessel function of the first kind and order zero [cf. Chap. 3, Equation (105)]. Thus the characteristic function of X is

$$\psi(s) = \prod_{n=1}^{N} \psi_n(s) = \prod_{n=1}^{N} J_0(sA_n) \quad ,$$

and the fr.f. $p(X)$ of X may be written as

$$p(X) = \frac{1}{2\pi} \int_{-\infty}^{\infty} e^{-jsX} \psi(s)\,ds = \frac{1}{2\pi} \int_{-\infty}^{\infty} e^{-jsX} \prod_{n=1}^{N} J_0(sA_n)\,ds \qquad (30)$$

in terms of known functions.

However, we can go one step further in reducing Equation (30) to a form amenable to practical calculations. We recall that each $p_n(X_n)$ vanishes for $|X_n| \geqq A_n$ and hence $p(X)$ vanishes for $|X| \geqq A$ where

$$A = \sum_{n=1}^{N} A_n \quad .$$

Now, let us define a periodic function $r(X)$ by the equations

$$r(X) = p(X) \quad , \quad -A < X < A$$

$$r(X + 2A) = r(X) \quad .$$

Then, since $r(X)$ is an even function, its Fourier series expansion is given by

$$r(X) = \frac{a_0}{2} + \sum_{k=1}^{\infty} a_k \cos \frac{k\pi X}{A} \quad ,$$

where

$$a_k = \frac{2}{A} \int_0^A p(X) \cos \frac{k\pi X}{A}\,dX \quad .$$

But

$$\prod_{n=1}^{N} J_0(sA_n) = \psi(s) = \int_{-\infty}^{\infty} p(X)e^{jsX}\,dX = \int_{-A}^{A} p(X)e^{jsX}\,dX$$

$$= 2 \int_0^A p(X) \cos sX\,dX \quad ,$$

and thus

$$a_k = \frac{1}{A} \prod_{n=1}^{N} J_0\left(\frac{k\pi}{A} A_n\right) \quad .$$

The Fourier series expansion of $r(X)$ is thus given by

$$r(X) = \frac{1}{2A} + \frac{1}{A} \sum_{k=1}^{\infty} \prod_{n=1}^{N} J_0\left(\frac{k\pi}{A} A_n\right) \cos \frac{k\pi X}{A} \quad . \tag{31}$$

EXERCISES

1. If X and Y are independent random variables normally distributed (a, σ) and (b, τ), respectively, prove that Z,

$$Z = X + Y$$

is normally distributed $(a + b, \sqrt{\sigma^2 + \tau^2})$.

2. If X and Y are independent random variables normally distributed $(0, \sigma)$, find the d.f. $S(z)$ and the fr.f. $s(Z)$ of Z where

$$Z = \sqrt{X^2 + Y^2}$$

by using Equation (8).

3. If X has a Poisson distribution

$$P_r = e^{-s} \frac{s^r}{r!} \quad ,$$

prove that

(i) $\sum_{r=0}^{\infty} P_r = 1$

(ii) $E[X] = s$

(iii) $\sigma^2 = s$.

4. Generalize the χ^2-distribution of Y to the case where $X_1, X_2, \cdots, X_n$ are n independent random variables normally distributed $(0, \sigma)$ and

$$Y = \sum_{k=1}^{n} X_k^2 \quad .$$

5. If X, Y, U, V are four independent random variables each normally distributed $(0, \sigma)$ and if

$$X = R \cos \Theta$$

$$Y = R \sin \Theta$$

$$U = S \cos \Phi$$

$$V = S \sin \Phi \quad ,$$

find the distributions of

(i) $T = R + S$

(ii) $\Psi = \Theta + \Phi$.

6. If X, Y, Z are three independent variables with uniform distributions,

$$p(X) = q(Y) = r(Z) = \frac{1}{2a} \quad , \quad -a < X, Y, Z < a$$

$$= 0 \quad , \quad \text{otherwise} \quad ,$$

find the fr.f. $s(U)$ and $t(V)$ of

$$U = X + Y$$

and

$$V = X + Y + Z \quad .$$

Normalize $t(V)$ to variance one and expand it in a Gram-Charlier series. Investigate the sum of n independent variables with the same uniform fr.f. as given above.

7. Let X and Y be independent discrete random variables where X assumes the values 0, 1, 2, $\cdots$ with respective probabilities p_0, p_1, p_2, $\cdots$, and Y assumes these same values with respective probabilities $q_0, q_1, q_2, \cdots$. Prove that if $Z = X + Y$, then Z assumes the values 0, 1, 2, $\cdots$ with respective probabilities $r_0, r_1, r_2, \cdots$, where

$$r_n = \sum_{\alpha=0}^{n} p_\alpha q_{n-\alpha} \quad .$$

[This is the discrete analog of $r(Z) = \int_{-\infty}^{\infty} p(X)q(Z - X)dX$.] If X and Y both have a Poisson distribution, that is,

$$p_\alpha = \frac{\lambda^\alpha}{\alpha!} e^{-\lambda} \quad , \quad q_\beta = \frac{\xi^\beta}{\beta!} e^{-\xi} \quad ,$$

show that Z also has a Poisson distribution,

$$r_n = \frac{(\lambda + \xi)^n}{n!} e^{-(\lambda+\xi)}$$

8. Let

$$X = \sum_{n=1}^{N} X_n \quad ,$$

where X_1, X_2, $\cdots$, X_N are independent random variables. Let $X_n = \sin \alpha$ where α has a flat distribution between 0 and 2π. By the Central limit theorem we know that $X/\sqrt{N}$ is asymptotically normal as N approaches infinity. Normalizing to variance 1, plot the d.f. $P(x)$ versus x for

   (i) $N = 1$, using Equation (27)
   (ii) $N = 2$, using Equation (28)
   (iii) $N = 10$, using Equation (31)
   (iv) $N = \infty$, using the normal distribution,

and compare the results.

9. If X is normally distributed $(0, s)$ and Y has a Rayleigh distribution

$$q(Y) = \frac{Y}{t^2} e^{-Y^2/2t^2} \quad , \quad Y > 0$$

$$= 0 \quad , \quad Y < 0 \quad ,$$

show that if X and Y are independent then their sum $Z = X + Y$ has the fr.f. $r(Z)$,

$$r(Z) = \frac{s}{\sqrt{2\pi}(s^2 + t^2)} e^{-Z^2/2s^2} + \frac{tZ}{2(s^2 + t^2)^{3/2}} e^{-Z^2/2(s^2 + t^2)} \left[1 + \operatorname{erf} \frac{Zt}{s\sqrt{2(s^2 + t^2)}} \right] .$$

10. Let

$$x(t) = a \cos \omega t + b \sin \omega t \quad ,$$

where a and b are independent random variables normally distributed $(0, \sigma)$. Prove that $X = x(t)$ and $Y = dx/dt$ are *independent* random variables, and find their distributions.

11. Let X be a random variable normal (a, σ), and let Y be a random variable normal $(0, \sigma)$. If X and Y are independent and

$$R^2 = X^2 + Y^2 \quad ,$$

show that the fr.f. of R is

$$q(R) = \frac{R}{\sigma^2} e^{-(R^2 + a^2)/2\sigma^2} I_0\left(\frac{aR}{\sigma^2}\right) \quad , \quad R > 0 \quad ,$$

where I_0 is a Bessel function. (This probability function frequently occurs in the study of sinusoidal signals in Gaussian noise.)

12. If X and Y are independent random variables both of which have the same Rayleigh distribution

$$p(X) = Xe^{-X^2/2} \quad , \quad X > 0 \quad ; \quad p(Y) = Ye^{-Y^2/2} \quad , \quad Y > 0$$
$$= 0 \qquad , \quad X < 0 \qquad\qquad = 0 \qquad , \quad Y < 0$$

find the fr.f. $q(Z)$ of $Z = X + Y$. (Cf. Prob. 5). If

$$\psi(z) = \int_0^{\frac{1}{2}z} e^{-Z^2/2} dZ$$

show that the cumulative distribution

$$Q(z) = \int_0^z q(Z) dZ$$

is given by

$$Q(z) = 1 + 4\{\psi(z)\psi''(z) - [\psi'(z)]^2\} \quad .$$

10. Temporal Probability Densities

In Sections 8 and 9 of Chapter 4, and Sections 10 and 11 of Chapter 6 we discussed in some detail the *frequency distribution* of a time function $x(t)$ as well as various properties and applications of the spectral density. The *probability distribution* gives us another important statistical parameter—namely, the *amplitude distribution*. Consider, then, a time function $x(t)$, and let T be a long period of time. Define $x_T(t)$ in the usual fashion as

$$x_T(t) = x(t) \quad , \quad |t| \leqq \frac{T}{2}$$

$$x_T(t) = 0 \quad , \quad |t| > \frac{T}{2} \quad .$$

Then, since time is assumed to be uniformly distributed, the probability density function $r_T(X)$ of $x_T(t)$ may be defined as

$$r_T(x)dx = \text{Prob. } [x_T \leqq X \leqq x_T + dx] \quad ,$$

or, in the case of Figure 7.11 below,

$$r_T(x)dx = \frac{\Delta t_1 + \Delta t_2 + \Delta t_3 + \Delta t_4 + \Delta t_5}{T} \quad .$$

That is, $r_T(X)dX$ represents the amplitude distribution of the signal $x_T(t)$. Since

$$\lim_{T \to \infty} x_T(t) = x(t) \quad ,$$

we may define the probability density function $r(X)$ of $x(t)$ by

$$r(X) = \lim_{T \to \infty} r_T(X) \quad .$$

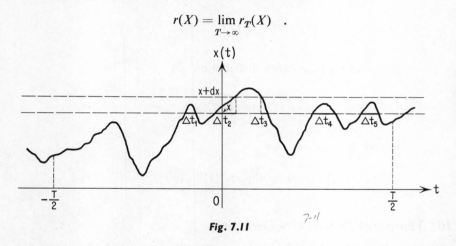

Fig. 7.11

The Gaussian distribution of Figure 7.8 is such an amplitude distribution curve. The probability density function of $x(t) = e^{-|t|}$ is the delta function $\delta(X)$; that of $x(t) = \sin t$ is $\pi^{-1}(1 - X^2)^{-\frac{1}{2}}$, $|X| < 1$. We see, therefore, that amplitude distributions (or probability density functions) can be defined for arbitrary functions, that is, for deterministic functions (such as $e^{-|t|}$ and $\sin t$) as well as "random functions" such as gave rise to the Gaussian distribution. Since, as we have indicated before, our main interest lies in "random functions" (which we have not as yet precisely defined) we must soon embark upon an exact description of their properties. However, in keeping with our previous development, we shall first present those results that apply to *any* function (that is, to deterministic functions) as well as to random functions.

The example illustrated in Figure 7.11 gives us a practical method for evaluating the amplitude distribution of a given function; namely, take a long interval of time $(-T/2, T/2)$ and compute the length of time that $x(t)$ remains between x_0 and $x_0 + h$ where h is small. Then, if we plot these results as indicated in Figure 7.12, the fr.f. $r(X)$ is obtained.

Let us apply this method to the two functions $e^{-|t|}$ and $\sin t$. If we let

$X = x(t) = e^{-|t|}$, then in a long period of time T, the fraction of time that the variate X lies between x_0 and $x_0 + h$ is

$$r_T(x_0)h = \frac{2[\log (x_0 + h) - \log x_0]}{T} \quad,$$

which for $x_0 \neq 0$ approaches zero as T approaches infinity. If, however, $x_0 = 0$, then the fraction of time that X lies between 0 and $h > 0$ is

$$r_T(0)h = \frac{T + 2 \log h}{T} \quad,$$

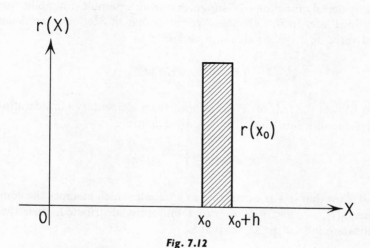

Fig. 7.12

which approaches one as T approaches infinity. Hence we conclude that $r(X)$ is the delta function $\delta(X)$.

Similarly, if $X = \sin t$, then

$$r(x)h = \frac{2|\arcsin (x + h) - \arcsin x|}{2\pi} \quad.$$

(It suffices to consider $T = 2\pi$ because of the periodicity of the function.) Clearly,

$$r(x) = \frac{1}{\pi} \frac{d}{dx} \arcsin x = \frac{1}{\pi\sqrt{1 - x^2}} \quad, \quad |x| < 1$$

$$= 0 \quad\quad\quad\quad, \quad |x| > 1 \quad,$$

a result we have seen before in Section 9.

We can now, in a practical fashion, compute both the amplitude and frequency distribution of a time function. Previously we showed that the auto-correlation function could be practically calculated from a given time function; and, by using the Wiener-Khintchine relations, its power spectrum could be determined. In the previous paragraph we indicated how the amplitude distribution could be calculated. Fortunately, or unfortunately, there is, in general, no relation between the two; that is, a knowledge of the frequency distribution tells us nothing about the amplitude distribution, and conversely. However, in a certain class of time functions (those generated by a Gaussian process—to be defined later) there is a relation.

The fr.f. $r(X)$ used in the previous discussion may be termed a *temporal* probability density function to distinguish it from ensemble probability densities to be defined later in this chapter. We recall that in Section 3 we defined the expected value or average value of a variate X as

$$E[X] = \int_{-\infty}^{\infty} Xr(X)dX \quad ,$$

where $r(X)$ was the fr.f. of X. Of course, from elementary considerations, the average value of a function of time is, by definition,

$$\bar{x} = \lim_{T \to \infty} \frac{1}{T} \int_{-T/2}^{T/2} x(t)dt \quad .$$

We shall show that if X is considered as a variate which assumes the continuum of values $x(t)$, $-\infty < t < \infty$ with t uniformly distributed, then these two definitions are indeed the same; that is,

$$\int_{-\infty}^{\infty} Xr(X)dX = \lim_{T \to \infty} \frac{1}{T} \int_{-T/2}^{T/2} x(t)dt \quad .$$

Suppose, then, that $x(t)$ is a measurable function defined on the closed interval $[-T/2, T/2]$. Let $M > |x(t)|$ on $[-T/2, T/2]$, and divide the region $[-M, M]$ into n parts by the points of subdivision $x_0, x_1, \cdots, x_n$, where

$$-M = x_0 < x_1 < x_2 < \cdots < x_n = M \quad .$$

Let

$$\Delta x_k = x_k - x_{k-1} \quad , \quad k = 1, 2, \cdots, n \quad ,$$

and let x_k' be a point in the kth interval Δx_k. We may then define a function $r(x)$ by the equation

$$r(x_k')\Delta x_k = \frac{m(I_k)}{T} \quad , \tag{32}$$

where I_k is the Borel set of all t such that $x_{k-1} < x(t) < x_k$ and $m(I_k)$ is the measure of this set. If we multiply both sides of the above equation by x_k' and sum over k,

$$\sum_{k=1}^{n} x_k' r(x_k') \Delta x_k = \sum_{k=1}^{n} x_k' \frac{m(I_k)}{T} \quad .$$

The first sum approaches $\int_{-M}^{M} X r(X) dX$, and the second approaches

$$\frac{1}{T} \int_{-T/2}^{T/2} x(t) dt$$

as the largest of the Δx_k's approaches zero. If we now let T approach infinity, we have

$$\int_{-\infty}^{\infty} X r(X) dX = \lim_{T \to \infty} \frac{1}{T} \int_{-T/2}^{T/2} x(t) dt \quad ,$$

as was desired to be proved. From the definition of $r(X)$, Equation (32), we see that it is a probability density function as defined earlier in this section. Because it is based on a division of the time axis, we use the adjective "temporal" to define $r(X)$. (As discussed above, some modifying word is necessary to distinguish $r(X)$ from *ensemble* probability density functions.)

If $f(x)$ is some deterministic function of $x(t)$, then the above equation can be immediately generalized to

$$E[f(X)] = \int_{-\infty}^{\infty} f(X) r(X) dX = \overline{f(x)} = \lim_{T \to \infty} \frac{1}{T} \int_{-T/2}^{T/2} f(x) dt \quad .$$

We shall consistently use the "bar" over a function to indicate a time average. In this notation the mean square value of $x(t)$ becomes

$$\overline{x^2(t)} = \lim_{T \to \infty} \frac{1}{T} \int_{-T/2}^{T/2} x^2(t) dt = \int_{-\infty}^{\infty} X^2 r(X) dX = E[X^2] \quad .$$

From this particular example we can deduce some relation between $r(X)$ and the power spectrum of $x(t)$. We recall from Section 9 of Chapter 4 that the first integral in the above equation is precisely the autocorrelation function $\psi(\tau)$ evaluated at $\tau = 0$. Hence

$$\overline{x^2} = \psi(0) = \int_{0}^{\infty} w(f) df = \rho \quad ,$$

where $w(f)$ is the power spectrum of $x(t)$. If, in particular, $x(t)$ is normally distributed $(0, \sigma)$, then we may also write

$$\overline{x^2} = \sigma^2 \quad .$$

The above equations are not intended to show that the spectrum and amplitude distribution are related. It is true, of course, that certain functionals of $w(f)$ and $r(X)$ *are* related as indicated above. However, we can easily visualize many different time functions which have the same r.m.s. value, yet could have different amplitude and frequency distributions; hence, neither $w(f)$ nor $r(X)$ is uniquely specified by the above equations.

11. Stochastic Processes

Let $x(t)$ be a function of time, defined on the whole t-axis, which has a finite mean square value. That is,

$$\lim_{T \to \infty} \frac{1}{T} \int_{-T/2}^{T/2} x^2(t)dt < \infty \quad .$$

If we think of $x(t)$ as the outcome of an experiment, then if we repeat this experiment a large number of times, say, N, we obtain a set of functions $\{x(t, \alpha)\}$, $\alpha = 1, 2, \cdot \cdot \cdot, N$. The idealization of this situation is to consider a family of functions of time $\{x(t, \alpha)\}$ depending on a parameter α where α varies in some Borel set A. If A is the set of positive integers $\{1, 2, \cdot \cdot \cdot, n, \cdot \cdot \cdot\}$, then $\{x(t, \alpha)\}$ may be written in the more familiar form

$$\{x_\alpha(t)\} \quad , \quad \alpha = 1, 2, \cdot \cdot \cdot$$

and becomes a *sequence* of functions. For example,

$$\sin t, \quad \sin 2t, \quad \cdot \cdot \cdot, \quad \sin nt, \quad \cdot \cdot \cdot$$

is such a family. On the other hand, if A is the set of real numbers $\{0 \leq \alpha \leq 1\}$, then $\{x(t, \alpha)\}$ depends on the continuous parameter α. The set of functions $\{e^{\alpha t}\}$ defined for every real value of α between 0 and 1 is an example of this situation.

If we associate a d.f. $P(\alpha)$ [or a fr.f. $p(\alpha)$] with the parameter α, then we shall call the set of functions $\mathfrak{X} = \{x(t, \alpha)\}$ a *stochastic process*. This is equivalent to defining a stochastic process as a family of random variables.† Occasionally we refer to $\mathfrak{X}$ as an *ensemble of functions*.‡

---

† Cf. Doob, *Stochastic Processes*, and Grenander, "Stochastic Processes and Statistical Inference."

‡ Cf. Shannon, "A Mathematical Theory of Communication."

Associating a d.f. $P(\alpha)$ with $\mathfrak{X}$ is equivalent to defining an α-measure on A where the total measure of the space is unity (cf. Appendix 1). Suppose $\mathfrak{X}' \subseteq \mathfrak{X}$ is a subset† of the functions $\{x(t, \alpha)\}$. Let A' be the set of all $\alpha \, \varepsilon \, A$ such that $x(t, \alpha) \, \varepsilon \, \mathfrak{X}'$. Then we define Prob. $[\mathfrak{X}']$ as

$$\text{Prob. } [\mathfrak{X}'] = \text{Prob. } [x \, \varepsilon \, \mathfrak{X}'] = \text{Prob. } [\alpha \, \varepsilon \, A'] = \int_{A'} dP(\alpha) \quad ,$$

where $P(\alpha)$ is the d.f. (α-measure) defined on A. Clearly,

$$\text{Prob. } [\mathfrak{X}] = \int_A dP(\alpha) = 1 \quad .$$

Examples of stochastic processes abound. Two of considerable practical importance are

(i)
$$\mathfrak{X} = \{\sin{(t + \alpha)}\} \tag{33}$$

where α is uniformly distributed between 0 and 2π. That is, the fr.f. $p(\alpha)$ of α is

$$p(\alpha) = \frac{1}{2\pi} \quad , \quad 0 < \alpha < 2\pi$$

$$= 0 \quad , \quad \text{otherwise} \quad .$$

Here the set A is the whole α-axis.

(ii)
$$\mathfrak{X} = \{x(t, a_1, \cdots, a_N, b_1, \cdots, b_N)\}$$

$$= \{\sum_{n=1}^{N} (a_n \cos \omega_n t + b_n \sin \omega_n t)\} \quad , \tag{34}$$

where the a_n and b_n are independent variates normally distributed $(0, \sigma_n)$.

Notice that in Case (i), α is one dimensional, while in Case (ii) we have $2N$ parameters $a_1, \cdots, a_N, b_1, \cdots, b_N$. That is, α is a $2N$ dimensional parameter.

We have seen that with every function of time $X = x(t)$ we could associate a temporal probability density function $r(X)$. If $x(t)$ is a member of a stochastic process $\mathfrak{X}$, then in general $r(X)$ will depend on the parameter α. We write this as $r_\alpha(X)$. That is, $r_\alpha(X)$ is the temporal probability density function associated with $x(t, \alpha') \, \varepsilon \, \mathfrak{X}$. Again, if we consider $\mathfrak{X} = \{x(t, \alpha)\}$ and fix t, say, $t = t'$, we obtain a random variable X which assumes the values $x(t', \alpha)$ as α ranges in A. The probability density function associated with $x(t', \alpha)$ will be called $p(X)$.

---

† By $\mathfrak{X}' \subseteq \mathfrak{X}$ we mean $\mathfrak{X}'$ is a subset of $\mathfrak{X}$, equality not excluded. In other words, every function in $\mathfrak{X}'$ is also in $\mathfrak{X}$.

Of course, in general, $p(X)$ will depend on t. To exhibit this dependence explicitly we write $p(X, t')$ rather than $p(X)$. In terms of earlier notation,

$$p(x, t')dx = \text{Prob. } [x \leqq x(t, \alpha) \leqq x + dx; t = t'] \quad .$$

To distinguish $p(X, t')$ from the temporal fr.f. $r_\alpha(X)$, we call $p(X, t')$ an *ensemble* probability density function. If, for example, α is discrete, say $A = \{1, 2, \cdots, n\}$, then the members of the stochastic process may be explicitly written down as

$$x(t, 1), x(t, 2), \cdots, x(t, n) \quad .$$

If m of these functions lie between x' and $x' + dx'$ at the time $t = t'$ and if the parameter α has a uniform distribution, then the ensemble fr.f. $p(X, t)$ may be interpreted as

$$p(x', t')dx' = \frac{m}{n} \quad .$$

12. Stationary Processes

Let μ and ν be any real numbers. We define a *translation operator* T^μ operating on a function of time $x(t)$ as

$$T^\mu x(t) = x(t + \mu) \quad .$$

If T^ν is another translation operator, then we define the composition of T^μ and T^ν as $T^\mu T^\nu = T^{\mu+\nu}$. Under this binary operation the translation operators form a *group*† G.

Consider now a stochastic process $\mathfrak{X} = \{x(t, \alpha)\}$ depending on a continuous parameter α. If T is an element of the translation group G, then

$$T^\mu x(t, \alpha) = x(t + \mu, \alpha)$$

is well defined where $x(t, \alpha)$ is an element of $\mathfrak{X}$. However, $x(t + \mu, \alpha)$ may fail to belong to $\mathfrak{X}$. We proceed to remedy this defect. Let $\mathfrak{X}'$ be a maximal subset‡ of $\mathfrak{X}$ which has the property that

$$T^\mu \mathfrak{X}' \subseteq \mathfrak{X} \quad , \quad T^\mu \varepsilon G \quad .$$

---

† We say $G = \{T^\mu\}$ is a *group* under the binary operation $T^\mu T^\nu = T^{\mu+\nu}$ if (i) Whenever T^μ and T^ν are in G, then $T^{\mu+\nu}$ is also in G. That is, G is *closed* with respect to the binary operation. (ii) $(T^\mu T^\nu)T^\rho = T^\mu(T^\nu T^\rho)$; that is, G is *associative*. (iii) $I = T^\circ$, $(IT^\mu = T^\mu I = T^\mu)$, is in G; that is, G has an *identity* operator. (iv) For every T^μ in G there exists a T^σ in G such that $T^\mu T^\sigma = I = T^\sigma T^\mu$; that is, *inverses* exist. We shall write $T^\sigma \equiv T^{-\mu}$.

‡ $\mathfrak{X}'$ is said to be a maximal set with a certain property if there exists no set of larger α-measure with this property.

In this way we construct a set $\mathfrak{X}' \subseteq \mathfrak{X}$ which has the property that if $x \, \varepsilon \, \mathfrak{X}'$ then $T^{\mu} x \, \varepsilon \, \mathfrak{X}$ for all $T^{\mu} \, \varepsilon \, G$.

Suppose, using the notation of the previous paragraph, that

$$\text{Prob. } [\mathfrak{X}'] = 1 \quad .$$

Then we shall say that the process is *stationary*. (Note that this statement implies that $\mathfrak{X}'$ is measurable and differs from the whole set only by a set of α-measure zero.) Roughly speaking, this means that the ensemble of functions $\mathfrak{X}$ is invariant under translations in time.

Let $\mathfrak{X}$ be a stationary stochastic process and let $\mathfrak{X}'$ be a maximal subset of $\mathfrak{X}$ with the property that $T^{\mu}\mathfrak{X}' \subseteq \mathfrak{X}$ for all $T^{\mu} \, \varepsilon \, G$. If for every measurable subset S of $\mathfrak{X}'$ we have

$$\text{Prob. } [T^{\mu}S] = \text{Prob. } [S] \tag{35}$$

for all T^{μ} in G, then we shall say that the stochastic process $\mathfrak{X} = \{x(t, \alpha)\}$ is *stationary in the strict sense*. Note that Equation (35) implies that $T^{\mu}S$ is measurable.

It is an important property of stationary stochastic processes that the ensemble probability density functions $p(X, t)$ are independent of time. That is,

$$p(X, t') = p(X, t'')$$

for any two values of t' and t''. We proceed to prove this result.

Let $\mathfrak{X} = \{x(t, \alpha)\}$ be a stochastic process stationary in the strict sense. Let $\mathfrak{X}'$ be a maximal subset of $\mathfrak{X}$ with the property that if $x \, \varepsilon \, \mathfrak{X}'$ then $T^{\mu} x \, \varepsilon \, \mathfrak{X}$ for all T^{μ} in G. Now, let t' and t'' be any two values of time. By definition,

$$\text{Prob. } [X < x(t, \alpha) < X + dX; t = t'] = p(X, t')dX \tag{36}$$

$$\text{Prob. } [X < x(t, \alpha) < X + dX; t = t''] = p(X, t'')dX \quad . \tag{37}$$

Let $\mathfrak{X}_{t'}$ be the subset of $\mathfrak{X}'$ such that the inequalities in Equation (36) are true for all $x \, \varepsilon \, \mathfrak{X}_{t'}$ and let $\mathfrak{X}_{t''}$ be the corresponding ensemble for Equation (37). Then for every α such that $x(t', \alpha)$ is in $\mathfrak{X}_{t'}$,

$$T^{t'-t''}x(t'', \alpha) = x(t', \alpha) = x(t'', \alpha')$$

for some α'. Therefore $x(t'', \alpha')$ is an element of $\mathfrak{X}_{t''}$ and

$$T^{t'-t''} \, \mathfrak{X}_{t'} \subseteq \mathfrak{X}_{t''} \quad .$$

But, in general, if A and B are two sets and $A \subseteq B$, then

$$\text{Prob. } [A] \leq \text{Prob. } [B] \quad .$$

Therefore,

$$\text{Prob. } [\mathfrak{X}_{t'}] = \text{Prob. } [T^{t'-t''} \mathfrak{X}_{t'}] \leq \text{Prob. } [\mathfrak{X}_{t''}] \quad . \tag{38}$$

Similarly, interchanging the rôles of t' and t'', we have

$$\text{Prob. } [\mathfrak{X}_{t''}] \leq \text{Prob. } [\mathfrak{X}_{t'}] \quad . \tag{39}$$

Equations (38) and (39) imply

$$\text{Prob. } [\mathfrak{X}_{t'}] = \text{Prob. } [\mathfrak{X}_{t''}]$$

or $p(X, t') = p(X, t'')$, which completes our proof.

We shall now prove that the two examples noted earlier [Equations (33) and (34)] are both examples of stationary stochastic processes.

(i) Consider the ensemble $\mathfrak{X} = \{\sin (t + \alpha)\}$ where α has a uniform distribution. If $\sin (t + \alpha')$ is any member of $\mathfrak{X}$ and T^μ is any element of G, then

$$T^\mu \sin (t + \alpha') = \sin [(t + \mu) + \alpha'] = \sin [t + (\mu + \alpha')]$$
$$= \sin (t + \beta) \quad ,$$

where β, $0 \leq \beta \leq 2\pi$, differs from $\mu + \alpha'$ only by multiples of 2π (that is, β is congruent to $\mu + \alpha'$ modulo 2π). Since $\sin (t + \beta) \, \varepsilon \, \mathfrak{X}$, we conclude that $\mathfrak{X}$ is stationary.

If S is any measurable subset of $\mathfrak{X}$, then

$$T^\mu S = S_\mu \quad ,$$

where S_μ is again a subset of $\mathfrak{X}$. Furthermore, since α is uniformly distributed,

$$\text{Prob. } [S] = \text{Prob. } [S_\mu] \quad .$$

We conclude, therefore, that $\mathfrak{X}$ is stationary in the strict sense.

(ii) Let

$$\mathfrak{X} = \{\sum_{n=1}^{N} (a_n \cos \omega_n t + b_n \sin \omega_n t)\}$$

where a_n and b_n are independent and normally distributed $(0, \sigma_n)$. We note that the "parameter" $a_1, \cdots, a_N, b_1, \cdots, b_N$ ranges in the $2N$ dimensional space $\mathfrak{A}$ of the a_n and b_n variates where each one dimensional parameter (a_n or b_n) ranges over the whole real axis. If we represent the infinite line $(-\infty, \infty)$ on which a_n ranges by A_n (and similarly for b_n), then the domain of definition $\mathfrak{A}$

of $(a_1, \cdots, a_N, b_1, \cdots, b_N)$ can be represented as the *cartesian product* of the A_n's and B_n's, namely,

$$\mathfrak{A} = A_1 \times A_2 \times \cdots \times A_N \times B_1 \times B_2 \times \cdots \times B_N \ .$$

If $x = \Sigma(a_n' \cos \omega_n t + b_n' \sin \omega_n t)$ is any member of $\mathfrak{X}$ and T^μ is any element of G, then

$$T^\mu x = \Sigma(a_n'' \cos \omega_n t + b_n'' \sin \omega_n t) = y \ ,$$

where

$$
\begin{aligned}
a_n'' &= a_n' \cos \omega_n \mu + b_n' \sin \omega_n \mu \ , \\
b_n'' &= -a_n' \sin \omega_n \mu + b_n' \cos \omega_n \mu \ .
\end{aligned}
\tag{40}
$$

Hence we see that for every $x \, \varepsilon \, \mathfrak{X}$, $T^\mu x = y \, \varepsilon \, \mathfrak{X}$ for all $T^\mu \, \varepsilon \, G$ and therefore $\mathfrak{X}$ is stationary.

Now, let $\mathfrak{X}'$ be any measurable subset of $\mathfrak{X}$. To prove that $\mathfrak{X}$ is stationary in the strict sense we must show that

$$\text{Prob. } [T^\mu \mathfrak{X}'] = \text{Prob. } [\mathfrak{X}']$$

for all $T^\mu \, \varepsilon \, G$. Let $\{x(t, a_1', \cdots, a_N', b_1', \cdots, b_N')\} = \mathfrak{X}'$. Then

$$(a_1', \cdots, a_N', b_1', \cdots, b_N') \, \varepsilon \, \mathfrak{A}' \ ,$$

where $\mathfrak{A}'$ is a subset of $\mathfrak{A}$, $\mathfrak{A}' \subseteq \mathfrak{A}$ and we assume

$$\mathfrak{A}' = A_1' \times \cdots \times A_N' \times B_1' \times \cdots \times B_N' \ ,$$

where a_n' ranges in $A_n' \subseteq A_n$ and b_n' ranges in $B_n' \subseteq B_n$. If T^μ is any element of G, then

$$T^\mu \mathfrak{X}' = \mathfrak{X}'' \ ,$$

where

$$\mathfrak{X}'' = \{x(t, a_1'', \cdots, a_N'', b_1'', \cdots, b_N'')\} \ ,$$

$$(a_1'', \cdots, a_N'', b_1'', \cdots, b_N'') \, \varepsilon \, \mathfrak{A}'' = A_1'' \times \cdots \times A_N'' \times B_1'' \times \cdots \times B_N'' \ .$$

Hence, proving that $\mathfrak{X}$ is strictly stationary, that is, Prob. $[\mathfrak{X}'] = $ Prob. $[\mathfrak{X}'']$, is equivalent to proving that

$$\text{Prob. } [\mathfrak{A}'] = \text{Prob. } [\mathfrak{A}''] \ .$$

The first step in our proof will be to show that the a_n'' and b_n'' are independent random variables normally distributed $(0, \sigma_n)$. [The a_n'' and b_n'' are related to the a_n' and b_n' by Equation (40).] From Section 7, we conclude that the a_n'' and b_n''

are normally distributed. Clearly, a_n'' and a_m'' are independent with $n \neq m$ as well as b_n'' and b_m'', $n \neq m$; and a_n'' and b_m'', $n \neq m$. It remains but to show that a_n'' and b_n'' are independent with means zero and variances σ_n. The determinant of the matrix of Equations (40) is

$$
\begin{vmatrix}
\cos \omega_n \mu & \sin \omega_n \mu \\
- \sin \omega_n \mu & \cos \omega_n \mu
\end{vmatrix} = 1 \quad ,
$$

and, using the notation of Equation (20) et seq., we have

$$
b_{11} = \cos \omega_n \mu \; , \; b_{12} = - \sin \omega_n \mu \; , \; b_{21} = \sin \omega_n \mu \; , \; b_{22} = \cos \omega_n \mu \quad ,
$$

$$
\tau = \sigma = \sigma_n
$$

and

$$
p(a_n'', b_n'') = \frac{1}{2\pi\sigma_n^2} \exp \left[- \frac{1}{2\sigma_n^2} (a_n''^2 + 0 \cdot a_n'' b_n'' + b_n''^2) \right]
$$

$$
= \left(\frac{1}{\sigma_n \sqrt{2\pi}} e^{-a_n''^2/2\sigma_n^2} \right) \left(\frac{1}{\sigma_n \sqrt{2\pi}} e^{-b_n''^2/2\sigma_n^2} \right) = p(a_n'')p(b_n'') \quad . \tag{41}
$$

Since we have shown that the a_n'' and b_n'' are independent, we may write

$$
\text{Prob. } [\mathfrak{A}''] = \prod_{n=1}^{N} \text{Prob. } [A_n''] \prod_{n=1}^{N} \text{Prob. } [B_n''] = \int_{\mathfrak{A}''} \prod_{n=1}^{N} p(a_n'')p(b_n'') da_n'' db_n'' \quad . \tag{42}
$$

If we make the change of variables in Equation (42) indicated by Equation (40), then

$$
\text{Prob. } [\mathfrak{A}''] = \int_{\mathfrak{A}'} \prod_{n=1}^{N} p(a_n' \cos \omega_n \mu + b_n' \sin \omega_n \mu) p(- a_n' \sin \omega_n \mu + b_n' \cos \omega_n \mu)
$$

$$
J \left(\frac{a_n'', b_n''}{a_n', b_n'} \right) da_n' db_n' \quad ,
$$

where J is the Jacobian of the transformation from the a_n'', b_n'' variables to the a_n', b_n' variables. But $J \equiv 1$, and, furthermore,

$$
p(a_n'')p(b_n'')
$$

$$
= p(a_n' \cos \omega_n \mu + b_n' \sin \omega_n \mu) p(- a_n' \sin \omega_n \mu + b_n' \cos \omega_n \mu)
$$

$$
= \left(\frac{1}{\sigma_n \sqrt{2\pi}} e^{-(a_n' \cos \omega_n \mu + b_n' \sin \omega_n \mu)^2/2\sigma_n^2} \right) \left(\frac{1}{\sigma_n \sqrt{2\pi}} e^{-(-a_n' \sin \omega_n \mu + b_n' \cos \omega_n \mu)^2/2\sigma_n^2} \right)
$$

$$
= \left(\frac{1}{\sigma_n \sqrt{2\pi}} e^{-a_n'^2/2\sigma_n^2} \right) \left(\frac{1}{\sigma_n \sqrt{2\pi}} e^{-b_n'^2/2\sigma_n^2} \right) = p(a_n')p(b_n') \quad .
$$

Hence

$$\text{Prob. } [\mathfrak{A}''] = \int_{\mathfrak{A}'} \prod_{n=1}^{N} p(a_n')p(b_n')da_n'db_n' \quad . \tag{43}$$

But the a_n' and b_n' are independent by hypothesis. Thus

$$\text{Prob. } [\mathfrak{A}'] = \prod_{n=1}^{N} \text{Prob. } [A_n'] \prod_{n=1}^{N} \text{Prob. } [B_n'] = \int_{\mathfrak{A}'} \prod_{n=1}^{N} p(a_n')p(b_n')da_n'db_n' \quad . \tag{44}$$

Equations (43) and (44) establish our result, that is, $\mathfrak{X}$ is stationary in the strict sense.

13. The Ergodic Hypothesis

It may be that we have a stochastic process in which the functions of the ensemble are "similar in nature"; that is, any one function could be taken as representative of the ensemble. In this case we have a kind of "statistical homogeneity." Such a state of affairs is desirable, since the statistical properties of the stochastic process can be deduced (i) either by considering any *one* function of the ensemble at various times or (ii) considering the various functions at a *single* fixed instant of time.

Let us see what conditions we must impose upon a stochastic process $\mathfrak{X} = \{x(t, \alpha)\}$ to obtain the "statistical homogeneity" mentioned above. First, we would like to have all temporal probability density functions $r_\alpha(X)$ identical, that is, independent of the function $x \, \varepsilon \, \mathfrak{X}$ which was used to compute it. Further, we would like to have all ensemble probability density functions $p(X, t)$ identical, that is, independent of the time at which it was calculated. Finally, we would like to have the temporal probability density function $r_\alpha(X)$ equal to the ensemble probability density function $p(X, t)$. Thus, for a stochastic process, we would like to have

$$r_\alpha(X) = r(X) \quad , \quad \text{independent of } \alpha \quad ,$$
$$p(X, t) = p(X) \quad , \quad \text{independent of } t \quad , \tag{45}$$

and

$$r(X) \equiv p(X) \quad . \tag{46}$$

If the last equation be true, then the *ensemble average* $\widetilde{\widetilde{x}}$,

$$\widetilde{\widetilde{x}} = \int_{-\infty}^{\infty} Xp(X)dX$$

becomes identical with the time average

$$\bar{x} = \int_{-\infty}^{\infty} Xr(X)dX = \lim_{T \to \infty} \frac{1}{T} \int_{-T/2}^{T/2} x(t)dt \quad ,$$

and in general

$$\overline{F(x)} = \lim_{T \to \infty} \frac{1}{T} \int_{-T/2}^{T/2} F(x(t))dt = \int_{-\infty}^{\infty} F(X)p(X)dX = \widetilde{F(x)} \quad . \tag{47}$$

In other words, the statistical properties of the stochastic process, whether determined from a time average or an ensemble average, are identical. Such results as these, exemplified in Equation (47), are contained in the so-called *ergodic* hypothesis. Roughly speaking, we say a stochastic process has the ergodic property if time averages are equivalent to ensemble averages.

Consider then a stochastic process $\mathfrak{X}$, and let S be a measurable subset of $\mathfrak{X}$. If $T^\mu S = S$ for all $T^\mu \varepsilon G$, then we shall say that S is *invariant* with respect to the translation operator. If the only subsets of $\mathfrak{X}$ which are invariant have α-measure zero or one, then we shall say that the process is *metrically transitive* or *ergodic*.

We shall now show that if $\mathfrak{X}$ is a strictly stationary ergodic process, then the temporal probability density function $r_\alpha(X)$ is independent of α. Previously, we showed that the ensemble probability density function $p(X, t)$ was independent of time for a stochastic process stationary in the strict sense. Hence we shall have established Equations (45) for a strictly stationary ergodic process.

Let, then, $\mathfrak{X} = \{x(t, \alpha)\}$ be a strictly stationary ergodic process where we shall assume for convenience that α varies discretely; and let $\mathfrak{X}'$ be a maximal subset of $\mathfrak{X}$ with the property that $T^\mu x \varepsilon \mathfrak{X}$ for all $x \varepsilon \mathfrak{X}'$ and all $T^\mu \varepsilon G$. Since $\mathfrak{X}$ is stationary, Prob. $[\mathfrak{X}'] = 1$. The set of translates $T^\mu x$ for $x \varepsilon \mathfrak{X}'$ fixed and T^μ arbitrary in G will be called the set generated by x. Let $x^*(t, \alpha)$ be a fixed element in $\mathfrak{X}'$, and let $\mathfrak{X}^*$ be its set of translates. Clearly,

$$T^\mu \mathfrak{X}^* = \mathfrak{X}^*$$

for all T^μ in G, since every member of $\mathfrak{X}^*$ is obtained by a translation of the fixed element $x^*(t, \alpha)$. The set $\mathfrak{X}^*$ is therefore invariant with respect to the translation operator T. Since the process is ergodic,

$$\text{Prob. } [\mathfrak{X}^*] = 0 \text{ or } 1 \quad .$$

Now, not every $x^* \varepsilon \mathfrak{X}'$ can generate a set of α-measure zero, for if this were true,

$$\sum_{x \varepsilon \mathfrak{X}'} \text{Prob. } [\mathfrak{X}^*] = 0 \quad ,$$

since Prob. is a completely additive measure. But

$$\sum_{x \varepsilon \mathfrak{X}'} \text{Prob. } [\mathfrak{X}^*] \geqq \text{Prob. } [\mathfrak{X}'] = 1 \quad ,$$

a contradiction.

We may therefore assume without loss of generality that Prob. $[\mathfrak{X}^*] = 1$.

But any element could have been taken as the generator of $\mathfrak{X}^*$. Hence, except for a set of α-measure zero, every $x \, \varepsilon \, \mathfrak{X}$ generates the same set of translates $\mathfrak{X}^*$ of measure one. Thus, if $r_\alpha(X)$ is the temporal probability density function of $x(t, \alpha)$ and $r_{\alpha'}(X)$ the temporal probability density function of $T^\mu x(t, \alpha) = x(t + \mu, \alpha) = x(t, \alpha')$, we conclude that $r_\alpha(X) = r_{\alpha'}(X)$. This is true, since $x(t + \mu, \alpha)$ and $x(t, \alpha)$ are identical when considered over all time. Hence, except for a set of α-measure zero, every $x(t, \alpha) \, \varepsilon \, \mathfrak{X}$ has the same temporal probability density function.

Another consequence of the ergodic property is that the temporal probability density function $r(X)$ is equal to the ensemble probability density function $p(X)$, and hence, time averages and ensemble averages are identical. To prove this contention let $\mathfrak{X}$ be a strictly stationary ergodic process, and let $x^*(t, \alpha)$ be an element of $\mathfrak{X}$ with the property that the set $\mathfrak{X}^*$ generated by x^* has α-measure unity. Then almost every function in $\mathfrak{X}$ is in $\mathfrak{X}^*$. If we write

$$T^\mu x^*(t, \alpha) = x^*(t + \mu, \alpha) = x(t, \alpha') \quad,$$

then as μ ranges from $-\infty$ to $+\infty$ with t fixed, α' will range in A', a subset of A (the domain of definition of α), and A' will differ from A only by a set of α-measure zero. Since the ensembles $\{x^*(t + \mu, \alpha)\}$ and $\{x(t, \alpha')\}$ are identical, their fr.f. are equal. Further, since both sets include almost every function in $\mathfrak{X}$,

$$r(X) = p(X) \quad.$$

While ergodicity is a very desirable property to have for a set of time functions, it appears to be an extremely difficult problem to determine whether a given ensemble of functions is ergodic or not. Generally, in practise, we assume the process to be ergodic.

14. Stationary Ergodic Processes

In dealing with a single function of time $x(t)$ we considered the temporal probability density function $r(X)$ of $X = x(t)$. If we had two functions of time, $x(t)$ and $y(t)$, we could consider a joint fr.f. $r(X, Y)$ and so on for higher order distributions. If $x(t)$ and $y(t)$ are both members of a stochastic process $\mathfrak{X}$, then $r(X, Y)$ would be a joint temporal probability density function, and, in general, would depend on the parameter values associated with x and y. We have also defined the ensemble probability density function $W_1 = p(X, t)$ of the stochastic process $\mathfrak{X} = \{x(t, \alpha)\}$ as

$$p(x, t')dx = \text{Prob.} \, [x \leqq x(t, \alpha) \leqq x + dx; t = t'] \quad.$$

The second order ensemble probability density function $W_2 = p(x_1, t'|x_2, t'')$ is defined as

$$p(x_1, t'|x_2, t'')dx_1 \, dx_2$$
$$= \text{Prob.} \, [x_1 \leqq x(t, \alpha) \leqq x_1 + dx_1; t = t' \text{ and } x_2 \leqq x(t, \alpha) \leqq x_2 + dx_2; t = t''] \quad.$$

We can, of course, consider higher order probability density functions. For example,

$$p(x_1, t' | x_2, t'' | \cdots | x_n, t^{(n)}) dx_1\, dx_2 \cdots dx_n$$

is the probability that $x(t, \alpha)$ lie between x_i and $x_i + dx_i$ at time $t = t^{(i)}$ for all i, $i = 1, 2, \cdots, n$.

If the stochastic process $\mathfrak{X}$ is strictly stationary, we have seen that the first probability density function W_1 is independent of time. It is not too difficult to show that the second-order probability density function W_2 depends only on the time difference $\tau = t' - t''$. That is, for a stationary ensemble,

$$W_2 = p(x_1, t' | x_2, t'') = p(x_1, x_2; \tau) \quad .$$

In general, the nth-order distribution W_n depends on the n parameters t', t'', $\cdots$, $t^{(n)}$, but in the *stationary* case it depends only on $n - 1$ parameters.

Similarly, if the stochastic process $\mathfrak{X}$ is ergodic as well as strictly stationary, then it can be shown that the joint temporal distributions are equivalent to the joint ensemble distributions. Hence, if x and y are members of the stochastic process and, for example, F is an arbitrary function of two variables, then $\mathfrak{X}$ has the ergodic property

$$\overline{F(x, y)} = \stackrel{\wwwww}{F(x, y)} \quad .$$

In many practical problems the second-order distribution gives an accurate statistical description of the process. In such cases we say we have a *Markoff process*. Even simpler, if all information is contained in the first probability density function, then we say we have a *purely random process*.

Some simple consequences of the stationarity and ergodicity of a stochastic process will now be deduced. Suppose that $\mathfrak{X} = \{x(t, \alpha)\}$ is an ergodic stochastic process which is stationary in the strict sense. Then, from the ergodic property, we have

$$\bar{x} = \stackrel{\wwww}{x}$$

with probability one. Hence, if the first probability density function is known, the mean value $\bar{x}$ of $\mathfrak{X}$ can be computed, since

$$\bar{x} = \lim_{T \to \infty} \frac{1}{T} \int_{-T/2}^{T/2} x(t, \alpha) dt = \int_{-\infty}^{\infty} X p(X) dX = \int_{-\infty}^{\infty} X r(X) dX$$

$$= E[X] = \stackrel{\wwww}{x}$$

for almost every $x(t, \alpha)$ in $\mathfrak{X}$.

Now, suppose that the joint ensemble fr.f. $p(x_1, t' | x_2, t'')$ is known. For a stationary process we have seen that it depends only on the time difference $\tau = t' - t''$; that is,

$$W_2 = p(x_1, t' | x_2, t'') = p(x_1, x_2; \tau) \quad.$$

Now, by definition,

$$\overline{\widetilde{x_1 x_2}} = \int_{-\infty}^{\infty} \int_{-\infty}^{\infty} x_1 x_2 p(x_1, x_2; \tau) dx_1\, dx_2 \quad,$$

which is a function of the time, τ. By the ergodic hypothesis

$$\overline{\widetilde{x_1 x_2}} = \overline{x_1(t, \alpha) x_1(t + \tau, \alpha)}$$

where $x_2(t, \alpha) = x_1(t + \tau, \alpha)$. But, by definition,

$$\overline{x_1(t, \alpha) x_1(t + \tau, \alpha)} = \lim_{T \to \infty} \frac{1}{T} \int_{-T/2}^{T/2} x_1(t, \alpha) x_1(t + \tau, \alpha) dt = \psi(\tau) \quad.$$

Hence, knowing W_2 gives us the autocorrelation function $\psi(\tau)$. With the knowledge of $\psi(\tau)$ the power spectrum $w(f)$ of the ensemble can be found by the Wiener-Khintchine relations.

We now wish to investigate a certain subclass of stationary ergodic processes which we shall call *Gaussian processes*. Let $\mathfrak{X}$ be an ergodic process stationary in the strict sense. Suppose that for every sufficiently large value of T every member of $\mathfrak{X}$ can be developed in the form (cf. the "$x^T(t)$ method" of Sec. 8, Chap. 4),

$$x(t) = \sum_{n=1}^{\infty} (a_n \cos \omega_n t + b_n \sin \omega_n t) \quad, \tag{48}$$

where $\omega_n = 2\pi n / T$ and the a_n and b_n of the ensemble are independent random variables normally distributed $(0, \sigma_n)$. Then we shall say that the process $\mathfrak{X}$ is *Gaussian*.

This type of process is essentially completely determined if its spectral density is known. For, if it is known that the process is Gaussian, then all we need know to specify its amplitude distribution is the variance, since

$$p(X) = \frac{1}{\sigma \sqrt{2\pi}} e^{-X^2 / 2\sigma^2} \quad.$$

But

$$\sigma^2 = \int_{-\infty}^{\infty} X^2 p(X) dX = \overline{\widetilde{X^2}} = \overline{X^2} = \lim_{T \to \infty} \frac{1}{T} \int_{-T/2}^{T/2} x^2(t) dt = \psi(0) \quad.$$

And certainly, if the spectral density is known, the autocorrelation function $\psi(\tau)$ can be determined by the Wiener-Khintchine relations. On the other hand, knowing the spectrum itself gives us the frequency distribution.

Another less trivial property of Gaussian processes is the following:

THEOREM. Let N be a passive linear network. Let the response to the input $x(t)$ be $y(t)$. Then, if $x(t)$ is a member of a Gaussian process $\mathfrak{X} = \{x(t)\}$, the collection of outputs $\mathfrak{Y} = \{y(t)\}$ is also a Gaussian process.

Roughly stated, if the input to a linear system is normal, then the output is also normal.

Proof. Let $\mathfrak{X} = \{x(t)\}$ be a Gaussian process. For every $x \, \varepsilon \, \mathfrak{X}$ and for every sufficiently large value of T there exists a function

$$x^T(t) = \sum_n (a_n \cos \omega_n t + b_n \sin \omega_n t) \quad ,$$

where the a_n and b_n of the ensemble $\mathfrak{X}^T = \{x^T(t)\}$ are independent random variables normally distributed $(0, \sigma_n)$. Now, if $K(j\omega)$ is the transfer function of the network, then

$$\mathfrak{Y}^T = \{y^T(t)\} = K(p)\mathfrak{X}^T = \{\sum_n [a_n K(p) \cos \omega_n t + b_n K(p) \sin \omega_n t]\}$$

$$= \{\sum_n (c_n \cos \omega_n t + d_n \sin \omega_n t)\} \quad .$$

Thus, by the theorem of Section 7, the c_n and d_n of $\mathfrak{Y}^T$ are normally distributed random variables.

If $\mathfrak{X}$ is a stochastic process in which only the *first*-order probability density function is normal, the above theorem is not necessarily true.

Consider again the Gaussian process of Equation (48), which is essentially the second example of Section 11, Equation (34). For fixed t, let

$$X_1 = x_1(t) = x^T(t, a_1, \cdots, b_1, \cdots) = \sum_n (a_n \cos \omega_n t + b_n \sin \omega_n t)$$

and

$$X_2 = x_2(t) = x_1(t + \tau) = x^T(t + \tau, a_1, \cdots, b_1, \cdots)$$

$$= \sum_n [a_n \cos \omega_n(t + \tau) + b_n \sin \omega_n(t + \tau)] \quad ,$$

where the a_n and b_n of the ensemble $\mathfrak{X}^T = \{x^T(t)\}$ are independent and normal $(0, \sigma_n)$. Since the process is Gaussian, the joint fr.f. $p(X_1, X_2)$ is a two-dimensional normal distribution (cf. the theorem of Sec. 7) given by [cf. Equation (19)]

$$p(X_1, X_2) = \frac{1}{2\pi\sqrt{|M|}} \exp\left[-\tfrac{1}{2}|M|^{-1}(\mu_{22}X_1^2 - 2\mu_{12}X_1X_2 + \mu_{11}X_2^2)\right] \quad ,$$

where

$$\mu_{ij} = E[X_i X_j] \quad , \quad i, j = 1, 2 \quad ;$$

are the second moments and $|M|$ is the determinant of the matrix

$$M = \left\| \begin{array}{cc} \mu_{11} & \mu_{12} \\ \mu_{12} & \mu_{22} \end{array} \right\| .$$

Now, by the ergodic property,

$$M = \left\| \begin{array}{cc} E[X_1 X_1] & E[X_1 X_2] \\ E[X_1 X_2] & E[X_2 X_2] \end{array} \right\| = \left\| \begin{array}{cc} \widetilde{X_1^2} & \widetilde{X_1 X_2} \\ \widetilde{X_1 X_2} & \widetilde{X_2^2} \end{array} \right\|$$

$$\left\| \begin{array}{cc} \overline{X_1^2} & \overline{X_1 X_2} \\ \overline{X_1 X_2} & \overline{X_2^2} \end{array} \right\| = \left\| \begin{array}{cc} \psi(0) & \psi(\tau) \\ \psi(\tau) & \psi(0) \end{array} \right\| .$$

The last equation follows from the fact that

$$\overline{X_1 X_2} = \overline{x_1(t) x_1(t + \tau)}$$

$$= \lim_{T \to \infty} \frac{1}{T} \int_{-T/2}^{T/2} x_1(t) x_1(t + \tau) dt = \psi(\tau)$$

by definition of the autocorrelation function. (For this reason M is sometimes spoken of as the "correlation matrix.")

If we write

$$\psi(\tau) = \lambda \, \psi(0) \quad ,$$

then we know that $\lambda \leq 1$; in fact, λ is precisely the *correlation coefficient* defined in Section 3.

Our joint distribution therefore takes on the form

$$p(X_1, X_2) = \frac{1}{2\pi\psi(0)\sqrt{1 - \lambda^2}} \exp\left[\frac{- X_1^2 + 2\lambda X_1 X_2 - X_2^2}{2\psi(0)(1 - \lambda^2)}\right] .$$

If $\psi(\tau) = 0$, then $\lambda = 0$; X_1 and X_2 are uncorrelated, and the above expression reduces to

$$p(X_1, X_2) = p(X_1) p(X_2) .$$

Hence X_1 and X_2 are *statistically independent* (cf. Sec. 7). Similar remarks apply to the higher order distributions W_n.

We recall that if a signal has a white power spectrum then its autocorrelation function is the delta function $\delta(\tau)$. Now, if $\mathfrak{X}$ is a Gaussian process which has a white spectrum, $\psi(\tau) = 0$, $\tau \neq 0$, and we always have

$$p(X_1, X_2) = p(X_1)p(X_2) \quad .$$

In general,

$$p(X_1, X_2, \cdot \cdot \cdot, X_n) = p(X_1)p(X_2) \cdot \cdot \cdot p(X_n) \quad ,$$

since the correlation matrix M of the above discussion is pure diagonal. Therefore, a Gaussian process with a white spectrum is an example of a *purely random process* as defined earlier in this section.

15. Some Applications and Examples

As a final topic, we would like to give some examples and applications of stochastic processes. Our first example will be to the *random telegraph signal*.

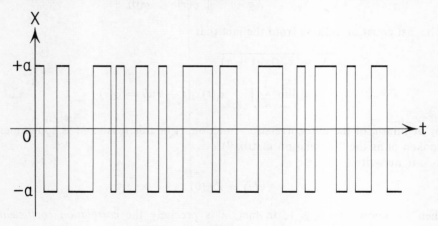

Fig. 7.13

(1) We have seen that in general there is no relation between the frequency distribution and the amplitude distribution. That is, given one, nothing can be said about the other. If, however, we are given the *mechanism* that generates our stationary stochastic process, then both can be determined. In this section we shall give an example of such a phenomenon which we call, by analogy with a physical problem, the "random telegraph signal."

We shall consider a stochastic variable $X = x(t)$ which can take on the values $+a$ and $-a$ only (cf. Fig. 7.13). It will be assumed that

  (i) On the average there are m changes of sign per second.

  (ii) The probability of a change of sign in $(t, t + dt)$ is $m\,dt$ and is independent of what happens outside the interval $(t, t + dt)$.

Consider now a long time interval T, and divide the interval $(0, T)$ into N subintervals, each of length h,

$$h = \frac{T}{N}$$

Let $q = mh$ be the probability of a change in sign in any interval of length h. Let $p(K)$ equal the probability of exactly K sign changes in the interval $(0, T)$.

Now, the probability of *no* sign changes in any interval of length h is $(1 - q)$. Since the N subintervals are all such that the probabilities are independent (Assumption ii),

$$p(0) = (1 - q)^N = (1 - mh)^{T/h} \to e^{-mT}$$

as $h \to 0$.

The probability of one sign change, $p(1)$, is equal to the probability of one sign change in the first interval and no sign changes in the remaining, plus the probability of one sign change in the second interval and none in the remaining $N - 1$, etc. Thus

$$p(1) = q(1 - q)^{N-1} + (1 - q)q(1 - q)^{N-2} + \cdots + (1 - q)^{N-1}q$$

$$= Nq(1 - q)^{N-1} = Nq \frac{(1 - q)^N}{1 - q} = (mT) \frac{(1 - mh)^{T/h}}{(1 - mh)} \quad,$$

which approaches $(mT)e^{-mT}$ as h approaches zero. Similarly, the probability of two sign changes is equal to

$$p(2) = Nq^2(1 - q)^{N-1} + \binom{N}{2} q^2(1 - q)^{N-2} \quad,$$

where $Nq^2(1 - q)^{N-1}$ represents the probability of two sign changes in one interval and none in the remaining $N - 1$ intervals, while the second term $\binom{N}{2} q^2(1 - q)^{N-2}$ represents the probability of one sign change in each of two distinct intervals and none in the remaining $N - 2$ intervals. Thus

$$p(2) = \frac{(Nq)^2 + (Nq)q - 2(Nq)q^2}{2} \frac{(1 - q)^N}{(1 - q)^2}$$

$$\to \frac{(mT)^2}{2!} e^{-mT}$$

as $h \to 0$. (We have assumed that two changes of sign in the same interval are independent.) One can also see that

$$p(3) = \left[N(1-q)^2 + 2 \binom{N}{2}(1-q) + \binom{N}{3} \right] q^3 (1-q)^{N-3} \to \frac{(mT)^3}{3!} e^{-mT}$$

as $h \to 0$ and in general

$$p(K) = \frac{(mT)^K}{K!} e^{-mT} \quad .$$

We have seen earlier that this is the Poisson distribution.

To compute the power spectrum of X we note that the average value of $x(t)x(t + \tau)$ equals a^2 times the probability of an even number of sign changes in the interval $[t, t + \tau]$ minus a^2 times the probability of an odd number of sign changes in this interval. Hence

$$\overline{x(t)x(t + \tau)} = a^2 p(0) + (-a^2)p(1) + a^2 p(2) + (-a^2)p(3) + \cdots \quad .$$

If we assume $\tau > 0$ for the moment,

$$\overline{x(t)x(t + \tau)} = a^2 e^{-m\tau} \left[1 - m\tau + \frac{(m\tau)^2}{2!} - \frac{(m\tau)^3}{3!} + \cdots \right]$$

$$= a^2 e^{-m\tau} e^{-m\tau} = a^2 e^{-2m\tau} \quad .$$

Similarly, letting $\tau < 0$, we arrive at

$$\psi(\tau) = a^2 e^{-2m|\tau|} \quad , \quad \tau \gtrless 0 \quad ,$$

and by the Wiener-Khintchine relations the power spectrum is

$$w(f) = 4 \int_0^\infty \psi(\tau) \cos 2\pi f\tau \, d\tau = \frac{2a^2 m}{\pi^2 f^2 + m^2} \quad .$$

We see, therefore, that the random telegraph signal leads to the Markoffian spectral density,

$$S(\omega) = \frac{4a^2 m}{\omega^2 + (2m)^2} \quad .$$

On the other hand, the amplitude distribution $r(X)$ of $x(t)$ considered over all time is simply the triplet of delta functions $\frac{1}{4}\delta(X - a)$, $\frac{1}{2}\delta(X)$, $\frac{1}{4}\delta(X + a)$, while considered over $t > 0$ it is the pair of delta functions $\frac{1}{2}\delta(X - a)$ and $\frac{1}{2}\delta(X + a)$.

(2) As an example of a stochastic process, let us consider

$$\mathfrak{X} = \{A \sin(\Omega t + \alpha)\} \quad,$$

where α has a uniform distribution between 0 and 2π and is zero elsewhere, while A and Ω are constants. We shall compute the ensemble fr.f., $p(X)$, the d.f. $P(x)$, the autocorrelation function $\psi(\tau)$, the power spectrum $w(f)$, the power ρ, and the joint fr.f. $p(X, Y)$ of $\mathfrak{X}$.

The reader may verify that $\mathfrak{X}$ is strictly stationary, and thus the ensemble fr.f. $p(X)$ is independent of time. Hence we may conveniently let $t = 0$ and write

$$X = A \sin \alpha \quad.$$

We have seen earlier that $p(X)$ is

$$p(X) = \frac{1}{\pi \sqrt{A^2 - X^2}} \quad, \quad |X| < A$$

$$= 0 \qquad\qquad , \quad |X| > A \quad,$$

since $p(\alpha)$ is uniform. We leave it to the reader to show that $\mathfrak{X}$ is also ergodic and hence the temporal and ensemble fr.f. are equal, that is,

$$r(X) = p(X) \quad.$$

[Cf. also Section 10 where $r(X)$ was computed directly and found to be $r(X) = \pi^{-1}(A^2 - X^2)^{-\frac{1}{2}}$, $A > |X|$.]

The d.f. $P(x)$ is therefore

$$P(x) = 0 \qquad\qquad , \qquad x < -A$$

$$P(x) = \frac{1}{2} + \frac{1}{\pi} \arcsin \frac{x}{A} \quad, \quad -A < x < A$$

$$P(x) = 1 \qquad\qquad , \qquad A < x$$

Elementary integrations show that $\int_{-\infty}^{\infty} p(X)dX = 1$ and that $E[X] = 0$, $E[X^2] = \sigma^2 = A^2/2$. Also, we note that

$$\psi(\tau) = \lim_{T \to \infty} \frac{1}{T} \int_{-T/2}^{T/2} A^2 \sin(\Omega t + \alpha) \sin[\Omega(t + \tau) + \alpha] dt$$

$$= \frac{A^2 \cos \Omega \tau}{2}$$

and by the Wiener-Khintchine formula,

$$w(f) = 4 \int_0^\infty \psi(\tau) \cos \omega\tau \, d\tau = 2A^2 \int_0^\infty \cos \Omega\tau \cos \omega\tau \, d\tau = A^2 \pi \delta(\Omega - \omega) \quad.$$

Therefore,

$$\rho = \psi(0) = \sigma^2 = \int_0^\infty w(f)df = \frac{A^2}{2\pi} \int_0^\infty \pi\delta(\Omega - \omega)d\omega = \frac{A^2}{2} \quad.$$

To calculate the joint fr.f. $p(X, Y)$ of $\mathfrak{X}$, let

$$X = A \sin (\Omega t + \alpha)$$
$$Y = A \sin [\Omega(t + \tau) + \alpha] \quad.$$

If we let

$$Y_0 = X \cos \Omega\tau + \sqrt{A^2 - X^2} \sin \Omega\tau \equiv f_0(X)$$
$$Y_1 = X \cos \Omega\tau - \sqrt{A^2 - X^2} \sin \Omega\tau \equiv f_1(X) \quad,$$

then the conditional fr.f. $p_X(Y)$ is

$$p_X(Y) = \tfrac{1}{2}[\delta(Y - Y_0) + \delta(Y - Y_1)] \quad,$$

and the joint fr.f. $p(X, Y)$ is

$$p(X, Y) = p(X)p_X(Y) = \tfrac{1}{2}p(X)[\delta(Y - f_0) + \delta(Y - f_1)] \quad.$$

Since the process $\mathfrak{X}$ is ergodic, we can also calculate the autocorrelation function, using the joint fr.f.:

$$\begin{aligned}
\psi(\tau) &= \int_{-\infty}^\infty \int_{-\infty}^\infty XYp(X, Y)dX \, dY \\
&= \tfrac{1}{2}\int_{-A}^A Xp(X)dX \int_{-A}^A Y[\delta(Y - f_0) + \delta(Y - f_1)]dY \\
&= \tfrac{1}{2}\int_{-A}^A Xp(X)[f_0 + f_1]dX = \tfrac{1}{2}\int_{-A}^A Xp(X)[2X \cos \Omega\tau]dX \\
&= \cos \Omega\tau \int_{-A}^A X^2p(X)dX = \frac{A^2 \cos \Omega\tau}{2} \quad.
\end{aligned}$$

(3) A second example is furnished by the stochastic process

$$\mathfrak{X} = \{a \sin (t + \alpha)\} \quad,$$

where a is normal $(0, \sigma)$ and α has a fr.f. $p(\alpha) = 1/2\pi$ for $|\alpha - \pi| < \pi$, $p(\alpha) = 0$ for $|\alpha - \pi| > \pi$. We shall show that $\mathfrak{X}$ is stationary but not ergodic, discuss some of its properties, and compute its fr.f. $p(X)$.

Let, then, $a \sin (t + \alpha)$ be any element of $\mathfrak{X}$ and T^μ any member of the translation group G. Then

$$T^\mu a \sin (t + \alpha) = a \sin (t + \mu + \alpha) = a \sin (t + \beta) \quad ,$$

where β, $0 \leq \beta \leq 2\pi$, differs from $\mu + \alpha$ only by multiples of 2π. (That is, β is congruent to $\mu + \alpha$ modulo 2π.) Hence

$$T^\mu \mathfrak{X} = \mathfrak{X}$$

identically, and $\mathfrak{X}$ is stationary.

The joint fr.f. $p(a, \alpha)$ of a and α has a nonzero domain of definition in the infinite strip $-\infty < a < \infty$, $0 < \alpha < 2\pi$. Choose a rectangle R: $\{b < a < c,\ 0 < \alpha < 2\pi\}$ where b and c are any two finite numbers ($b < c$). Then, if S is that subset of $\mathfrak{X}$ which has the property that $x(t, a, \alpha) \varepsilon S$ implies $a \varepsilon [b, c]$, $\alpha \varepsilon [0, 2\pi]$, then S has positive (a, α)-measure less than one,

$$0 < \text{Prob.} [S] = \int\int_R dP(a, \alpha) < 1 \quad ,$$

where $P(a, \alpha)$ is the d.f. of a and α. But

$$T^\mu S = S$$

for all $T^\mu \varepsilon G$, and, since $0 < \text{Prob.} [S] < 1$, we conclude that $\mathfrak{X}$ is not ergodic.

If a and α are independent, then we can show that $\mathfrak{X}$ is strictly stationary. In this case we have explicitly

$$p(a, \alpha) = \frac{1}{2\pi\sqrt{2\pi}\,\sigma} e^{-a^2/2\sigma^2} \qquad \begin{array}{c} -\infty < a < \infty \\ 0 < \alpha < 2\pi \end{array} \quad ,$$

where $p(a, \alpha)$ is the joint fr.f. of a and α. Let S be any subset of $\mathfrak{X}$. Then there exist two Borel sets A and B such that $x(t, a, \alpha) \varepsilon S$ implies $a \varepsilon A$ and $\alpha \varepsilon B$. Let $C = A \times B$. Then

$$\text{Prob.} [S] = \text{Prob.} [(a, \alpha) \varepsilon C] = \int\int_C dP(a, \alpha) \quad .$$

If T^μ is any member of G, then

$$T^\mu S = U \subseteq \mathfrak{X} \quad ,$$

and $x(t, a, \alpha) \, \varepsilon \, U$ implies $a \, \varepsilon \, A$, $\alpha \, \varepsilon \, B'$ where B' is not necessarily identical with B. But Prob. $[B'] =$ Prob. $[B]$, since α has a uniform distribution. Hence

$$\text{Prob. } [S] = \text{Prob. } [C] = \text{Prob. } [A \times B] = \text{Prob. } [A] \cdot \text{Prob. } [B]$$

$$= \text{Prob. } [A] \cdot \text{Prob. } [B'] = \text{Prob. } [A \times B'] = \text{Prob. } [U] \quad,$$

and $\mathfrak{X}$ is strictly stationary.

Since $\mathfrak{X}$ is not ergodic, the temporal probability density function $r(X)$ is not necessarily independent of the parameters a and α. In fact, if $a \sin (t + \alpha)$ is any particular element of $\mathfrak{X}$, then the temporal fr.f. for this function is

$$r(X) = \frac{1}{\pi \sqrt{a^2 - X^2}} \quad , \quad |X| < a$$

$$= 0 \qquad\qquad , \quad |X| > a \quad .$$

So we see in this case that while the temporal probability density function is independent of α, it is not independent of a.

We showed earlier that if a and α were independent variates, then $\mathfrak{X}$ was strictly stationary. In this case we know that the ensemble fr.f. $p(X)$ is independent of time. We shall compute this density function.

Since $p(X)$ is independent of time, we may conveniently set $t = 0$ and write

$$X = a \sin \alpha$$

where a is normal $(0, \sigma)$

$$\phi(a) = \frac{1}{\sigma \sqrt{2\pi}} e^{-a^2/2\sigma^2} \quad ;$$

α is uniform

$$p(\alpha) = \frac{1}{2\pi} \quad , \quad 0 < \alpha < 2\pi$$

$$= 0 \quad , \quad \text{otherwise} \quad ;$$

and a and α are independent,

$$p(a, \alpha) = \phi(a)p(\alpha)$$

If, for the moment, we let $x > 0$, then the d.f. $P(x)$ of X is

$$P(x) = \text{Prob. } [X \leqq x] = \text{Prob. } [a \sin \alpha \leqq x] = \text{Prob. } [(a, \alpha) \, \varepsilon \, A] \quad,$$

where A is the shaded region in Figure 7.14 below. Hence

$$P(x) = \int\int_A p(a, \alpha)dA = \int\int_A \phi(a)p(\alpha)da\, d\alpha$$

$$= \int_0^\pi p(\alpha)d\alpha \int_{-\infty}^{\frac{x}{\sin\alpha}} \phi(a)da + \int_\pi^{2\pi} p(\alpha)d\alpha \int_{\frac{x}{\sin\alpha}}^\infty \phi(a)da \quad .$$

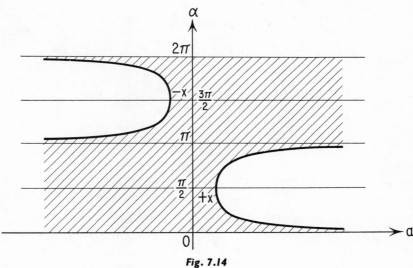

Fig. 7.14

The fr.f. $p(X)$ of the variate X is

$$p(x) = \frac{d}{dx}P(x) = \frac{2}{\pi\sigma\sqrt{2\pi}} \int_0^{\pi/2} \frac{1}{\sin\alpha} e^{\frac{-x^2}{2\sigma^2\sin^2\alpha}} d\alpha \quad ,$$

which is obtained after some trivial manipulations. If we make the change of variable

$$\csc\alpha = \cosh\frac{\theta}{2}$$

in the above integral, then $p(x)$ becomes

$$p(x) = \frac{1}{\pi\sigma\sqrt{2\pi}} e^{-x^2/4\sigma^2} \int_0^\infty e^{-(x^2\cosh\theta)/4\sigma^2} d\theta \quad .$$

Now we have seen in Section 9, Chapter 3, that

$$K_0(z) = \int_0^\infty e^{-z\cosh\theta} d\theta \quad , \quad z > 0 \quad ,$$

where $K_0(z)$ is the Bessel function of the second kind and order zero. Hence

$$p(x) = \frac{1}{\pi\sigma\sqrt{2\pi}} e^{-x^2/4\sigma^2} K_0\left(\frac{x^2}{4\sigma^2}\right) \quad , \quad x > 0 \quad .$$

A similar argument establishes the above formula for $x < 0$. For $x = 0$, $p(x)$ has a singularity, since $K_0(0) = \infty$. However, it is still true that

$$\int_{-\infty}^{\infty} p(x)dx = 1 \quad .$$

To verify this,

$$\int_{-\infty}^{\infty} p(x)dx = \frac{1}{\pi\sigma\sqrt{2\pi}} \int_{-\infty}^{\infty} e^{-x^2/4\sigma^2} K_0\left(\frac{x^2}{4\sigma^2}\right) dx$$

$$= \frac{2}{\pi\sigma\sqrt{2\pi}} \int_{0}^{\infty} e^{-x^2/4\sigma^2} K_0\left(\frac{x^2}{4\sigma^2}\right) dx \quad .$$

Now, let $z = x^2/4\sigma^2$. Then

$$\int_{-\infty}^{\infty} p(x)dx = \frac{1}{\pi}\sqrt{\frac{2}{\pi}} \int_{0}^{\infty} e^{-z} K_0(z) z^{-\frac{1}{2}} dz \quad .$$

But†

$$\int_{0}^{\infty} e^{-t} K_0(t) t^{-\frac{1}{2}} dt = \sqrt{\frac{\pi}{2}} \Gamma\left(\frac{1}{2}\right) \Gamma\left(\frac{1}{2}\right) = \pi\sqrt{\frac{\pi}{2}} \quad .$$

Hence

$$\int_{-\infty}^{\infty} p(X)dX = 1 \quad .$$

An accurate plot of $p(X)$ appears in Figure 7.15.

(4) As a last example, let us consider a Gaussian process $\mathfrak{X}$. If $\mathfrak{X}'$ represents the set of time derivatives of the functions of $\mathfrak{X}$, we shall show that $\mathfrak{X}'$ is Gaussian. Further, we shall prove, by directly computing both ensemble and time averages, that

$$\overline{\mathfrak{X}\mathfrak{X}} = \widetilde{\mathfrak{X}\mathfrak{X}} = \psi(0)$$

and

$$\overline{\mathfrak{X}\mathfrak{X}'} = \widetilde{\mathfrak{X}\mathfrak{X}'} = 0 \quad .$$

---

† Cf. Watson, *A Treatise on the Theory of Bessel Functions*, p. 388.

Every $x \, \varepsilon \, \mathfrak{X}$ can be expressed in the form

$$x = \lim_{T \to \infty} x^T(t) \quad ,$$

where

$$x^T(t) = \sum_n [a_n(x^T) \cos \omega_n t + b_n(x^T) \sin \omega_n t] \quad , \quad \omega_n = \frac{2\pi n}{T}$$

We shall let $\mathfrak{X}^T$ denote the class of all functions x^T such that $x \, \varepsilon \, \mathfrak{X}$.

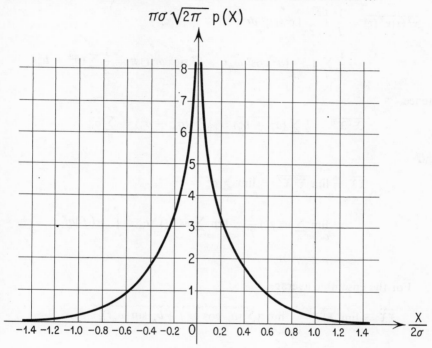

$\pi \sigma \sqrt{2\pi} \; p(X)$

Fig. 7.15

Since $\mathfrak{X}$ is Gaussian

$$\widetilde{a_n(x^T)} = \widetilde{b_n(x^T)} = \widetilde{a_n(x^T)b_m(x^T)} = 0$$

$$\widetilde{a_n(x^T)a_m(x^T)} = \widetilde{b_n(x^T)b_m(x^T)} = \sigma_n^2 \delta_{nm} \quad ,$$

where the ensemble average is taken over all functions $x^T \, \varepsilon \, \mathfrak{X}^T$ with n and m fixed. Furthermore, since $\mathfrak{X}$ is ergodic, we also have

$$\overline{a_n(x^T)} = \overline{b_n(x^T)} = \overline{a_n(x^T)b_m(x^T)} = 0$$

$$\overline{a_n(x^T)a_m(x^T)} = \overline{b_n(x^T)b_m(x^T)} = \sigma_n^2 \delta_{nm} \quad ,$$

where the time average is taken over all a_n and b_n with $x^T \, \varepsilon \, \mathfrak{X}^T$ fixed.

For convenience introduce the following notation

$$\omega_n = 2\pi f_n \quad , \quad \Delta f_n = f_{n+1} - f_n = \frac{1}{T}$$

$$\sigma_n^2 = \frac{1}{T} w(f_n) \quad , \quad \sigma^2 = \lim_{T \to \infty} \sum_n \sigma_n^2 \quad .$$

Now, let x be any element in $\mathfrak{X}$, and consider the corresponding x^T in $\mathfrak{X}^T$:

$$\overline{x^T(t)x^T(t)} = \frac{1}{T} \int_{-T/2}^{T/2} [x^T(t)]^2 \, dt$$

$$= \frac{1}{T} \sum_n \int_{-T/2}^{T/2} (a_n^2 \cos^2 \omega_n t + b_n^2 \sin^2 \omega_n t) dt = \frac{1}{2} \sum_n (a_n^2 + b_n^2) \quad .$$

Hence

$$\overline{\mathfrak{X}^T \mathfrak{X}^T} = \tfrac{1}{2} \sum_n (\overline{a_n^2 + b_n^2}) = \tfrac{1}{2} \sum_n (\sigma_n^2 + \sigma_n^2) = \sum_n \sigma_n^2 \quad ,$$

and

$$\overline{\overline{\mathfrak{X}\mathfrak{X}}} = \lim_{T \to \infty} \overline{\mathfrak{X}^T \mathfrak{X}^T} = \lim_{T \to \infty} \sum_n \sigma_n^2 = \sigma^2$$

$$= \lim_{T \to \infty} \sum_n w(f_n) \frac{1}{T} = \lim_{T \to \infty} \sum_n w(f_n)\Delta f_n = \int_0^\infty w(f) df$$

$$= \rho = \psi(0) \quad .$$

For the ensemble average,

$$\widetilde{\overline{\mathfrak{X}\mathfrak{X}}} = \lim_{T \to \infty} \widetilde{\overline{\mathfrak{X}^T \mathfrak{X}^T}} = \lim_{T \to \infty} \{\widetilde{\sum_n (a_n \cos \omega_n t + b_n \sin \omega_n t)}\}^2 \quad ,$$

$$= \lim_{T \to \infty} \sum_n (\widetilde{a_n^2} \cos^2 \omega_n t + \widetilde{b_n^2} \sin^2 \omega_n t)$$

$$= \lim_{T \to \infty} \sum_n (\cos^2 \omega_n t + \sin^2 \omega_n t)\sigma_n^2 = \lim_{T \to \infty} \sum_n \sigma_n^2 = \sigma^2 = \psi(0) \quad .$$

One can also look at the problem from the following point of view. Since the a_n and b_n of the ensemble are independent and normal $(0, \sigma_n)$, the fr.f. (temporal or ensemble) of $\{x^T(t)\}$ is normal $(0, \sqrt{\sum_n \sigma_n^2})$ (cf. Sec. 6), since

$$E[\{x^T(t)\}] = 0 \quad ,$$

and

$$E[\{x^T(t)\}\{x^T(t)\}] = \sum_n (\sigma_n^2 \cos^2 \omega_n t + \sigma_n^2 \sin^2 \omega_n t) = \sum_n \sigma_n^2 \quad .$$

Hence

$$\overline{\mathfrak{X}\mathfrak{X}} = \widetilde{\widetilde{\mathfrak{X}\mathfrak{X}}} = \lim_{T \to \infty} \frac{1}{\sqrt{2\pi \sum_n \sigma_n^2}} \int_{-\infty}^{\infty} X^2 e^{-X^2/(2\sum_n \sigma_n^2)} dX$$

$$= \lim_{T \to \infty} \sum_n \sigma_n^2 = \sigma^2 \quad .$$

For the time derivatives we have

$$\frac{d}{dt} x^T(t) = \sum_n (-\omega_n a_n \sin \omega_n t + \omega_n b_n \cos \omega_n t) \quad ,$$

and, clearly, $\mathfrak{X}' = \lim_{T \to \infty} [\mathfrak{X}^T]'$ is a Gaussian process. Furthermore,

$$\overline{x^T(t)[x^T(t)]'} = \frac{1}{T} \int_{-T/2}^{T/2} x^T(t)[x^T(t)]' \, dt$$

$$= \frac{1}{T} \sum_n \int_{-T/2}^{T/2} (-\omega_n a_n b_n \sin^2 \omega_n t + \omega_n b_n a_n \cos^2 \omega_n t) dt$$

$$= \frac{1}{T} \sum_n \omega_n a_n b_n \int_{-T/2}^{T/2} (\cos^2 \omega_n t - \sin^2 \omega_n t) dt = 0 \quad .$$

Hence

$$\overline{\mathfrak{X}\mathfrak{X}'} = \lim_{T \to \infty} \overline{\mathfrak{X}^T[\mathfrak{X}^T]'} = \overline{0} = 0 \quad .$$

Also,

$$\widetilde{\widetilde{\mathfrak{X}\mathfrak{X}'}} = \lim_{T \to \infty} \widetilde{\widetilde{\mathfrak{X}^T[\mathfrak{X}^T]'}}$$

$$= \lim_{T \to \infty} \widetilde{\{\sum_n (a_n \cos \omega_n t + b_n \sin \omega_n t)\}\{\sum_m (-\omega_m a_m \sin \omega_m t + \omega_m b_m \cos \omega_m t)\}}$$

$$= \lim_{T \to \infty} \sum_n (-\omega_n \widetilde{a_n^2} \sin \omega_n t \cos \omega_n t + \omega_n \widetilde{b_n^2} \sin \omega_n t \cos \omega_n t)$$

$$= \lim_{T \to \infty} \sum_n \omega_n \sigma_n^2 (-\sin \omega_n t \cos \omega_n t + \sin \omega_n t \cos \omega_n t) = 0 \quad .$$

EXERCISES

1. Let $x(t)$ be a periodic function of period $2a$ where $X = x(t) = At$, $-a < t < a$, and A is a constant. Find the temporal probability density function $r(X)$ of X.

2. Prove that the ensemble $\mathfrak{X} = \{A \sin (\Omega t + \alpha)\}$ (cf. the second example of Sec. 15) is strictly stationary and ergodic.

3. Let $\mathfrak{X} = \{a \sin \Omega t\}$ be a stochastic process where a is normal $(0, \sigma)$ and Ω is a constant. Show that $\mathfrak{X}$ is not stationary.

4. If in the third example of Section 15 a had a *Rayleigh* distribution, prove that $\mathfrak{X}$ is ergodic. Assume that a and α are independent.

5. Let $\mathfrak{X} = \{a \sin t + b \cos t\}$ be a stochastic process where a and b are independent random variables both normally distributed $(0, \sigma)$. Prove that $\mathfrak{X}$ is stationary in the strict sense and ergodic.

6. Show that for a stationary stochastic process which is not *strictly* stationary the ensemble probability density function $p(X, t)$ need not be independent of time.

7. For the random telegraph signal of Section 15, compute the joint fr.f. $r(X, Y)$ where $X = x(t)$ and $Y = x(t + \tau)$.

8. Let $X = A \sin \alpha$ where A and α are independent random variables. If $p(\alpha) = 1/2\pi, 0 < \alpha < 2\pi, p(\alpha) = 0$, otherwise; and $q(A)$ is arbitrary, show that the fr.f. $r(X)$ of X can be written in any one of the three following forms:

$$r(X) = \frac{1}{\pi} \int_0^{\pi/2} \csc \alpha [q(X \csc \alpha) + q(-X \csc \alpha)] d\alpha$$

$$= \frac{1}{\pi} \int_X^\infty \frac{1}{\sqrt{\lambda^2 - X^2}} [q(\lambda) + q(-\lambda)] d\lambda \quad , \quad X > 0$$

$$= \frac{1}{\pi} \int_0^\infty [q(X \cosh z) + q(-X \cosh z)] dz \quad .$$

Show that if

(i) $q(A) = \delta(K - A)$, then $r(X) = \dfrac{1}{\pi} \dfrac{1}{\sqrt{K^2 - X^2}}$, $|X| < K$

$$= 0 \qquad\qquad , \quad |X| > K \quad .$$

(ii) $q(A) = \dfrac{1}{\sigma\sqrt{2\pi}} e^{-A^2/2\sigma^2}$, then $r(X) = \dfrac{1}{\pi\sigma\sqrt{2\pi}} e^{-X^2/4\sigma^2} K_0\left(\dfrac{X^2}{4\sigma^2}\right)$.

(iii) $q(A) = \dfrac{A}{\sigma^2} e^{-A^2/2\sigma^2}$, $A > 0$, then $r(X) = \dfrac{1}{\sigma\sqrt{2\pi}} e^{-X^2/2\sigma^2}$

$$= 0 \qquad\qquad , \quad A < 0 \quad .$$

(iv) $q(A) = \dfrac{2\beta}{\beta^2 + A^2}$,

$$\text{then } r(X) = \frac{2}{\pi\sqrt{X^2 + \beta^2}} \log\left(\frac{\sqrt{X^2 + \beta^2} + \beta}{\sqrt{X^2 + \beta^2} - \beta}\right) \quad .$$

9. Consider a random telegraph signal $x(t)$ generated by the following mechanism: The time interval $[0, T]$ is divided into equal intervals of length h. Let $x(t)$ be either $+a$ or $-a$ with equal probability in any interval of length h and let the value of $x(t)$ in any interval of length h be independent of its value in any other interval. If $\mathfrak{X}$ is a strictly stationary ergodic process for which $x(t)$ is a representative member, show that the power spectrum of $\mathfrak{X}$ is

$$w(f) = 2ha^2 \left(\frac{\sin \omega h/2}{\omega h/2} \right)^2 \quad .$$

10. Let $\mathfrak{X}$ and $\mathfrak{Y}$ be independent Gaussian processes with means zero. Then we define a *Rayleigh process* as $\mathfrak{R} = \sqrt{\mathfrak{X}^2 + \mathfrak{Y}^2}$. If $\mathfrak{X}$ and $\mathfrak{Y}$ both have the same autocorrelation function $\psi(\tau)$ show that the joint distribution $p(R_1, R_2)$ of $\mathfrak{R}$ is given by

$$p(R_1, R_2) = \frac{R_1 R_2}{\psi^2(0)\,(1 - \lambda^2)} \, e^{-\frac{R_1^2 + R_2^2}{2\psi(0)(1 - \lambda^2)}} \, I_0 \left(\frac{\lambda R_1 R_2}{\psi(0)(1 - \lambda^2)} \right)$$

where $\lambda = \psi(\tau)/\psi(0)$ is the normalized autocorrelation function. If K and E are the complete elliptic integrals of the first and second kind respectively, show that the autocorrelation function $C(\tau)$ of $\mathfrak{R}$ is given by

$$C(\tau) = \psi(0)[2E(\lambda) - (1 - \lambda^2)K(\lambda)] \quad .$$

REFERENCES

Arley, Niels, and K. R. Buch, *Introduction to the Theory of Probability and Statistics*. New York: John Wiley & Sons, Inc., 1950.

Cramér, Harald, *Mathematical Methods of Statistics*. Princeton, N.J.: Princeton University Press, 1946.

Doob, J. L., *Stochastic Processes*. New York: John Wiley & Sons, Inc., 1953.

Grenander, Ulf, "Stochastic Processes and Statistical Inference," *Arkiv för Matematik*, 1, No. 17, 195–277 (1950).

James, H. M., N. B. Nichols, and R. S. Phillips, *Theory of Servomechanisms*. New York: McGraw-Hill Book Co., Inc., 1947.

Peirce, B. O., *A Short Table of Integrals*, rev. ed. Boston: Ginn & Co., 1929.

Shannon, C. E., "A Mathematical Theory of Communication," *Bell System Technical Journal*, 27, No. 3, 379–423 (1948); 27, No. 4, 623–656 (1948).

Watson, G. N., *A Treatise on the Theory of Bessel Functions*. New York: The Macmillan Company, 1944.

APPENDICES

Note: The three appendices included here on *Borel Sets, Riemann-Stieltjes Integral,* and *Fourier Series and Integrals* are at a somewhat higher mathematical level than the main text. They are included as reference for the interested, more theoretically inclined reader. It is not necessary to understand all the details of the appendices in order to follow the main thread of development in the text proper.

We shall be working in a space $\mathfrak{S}$ where $\mathfrak{S}$ is either the whole real x-axis R_1 or a closed interval $[a,b]$ in R_1. If $S_1, S_2, \cdots$ are arbitrary point sets in $\mathfrak{S}$, then we denote the *union* of $S_1, S_2, \cdots$ by $\sum_i S_i$, that is, $\sum_i S_i$ is the point set consisting of all points in at least one S_i. We also write $S_1 + S_2 + \cdots$. By $\prod_i S_i$ we mean the *intersection* of $S_1, S_2, \cdots$, that is, $\prod_i S_i$ is the point set consisting of all points in every S_i. We also write $S_1 \cdot S_2 \cdot \cdots$. Of particular interest in our theory is the concept of an *additive* class of sets.

Definition. Let $\mathscr{C}$ be a class of sets in a space $\mathfrak{S}$. We shall say that $\mathscr{C}$ is a completely *additive* class of sets in $\mathfrak{S}$ if

(1) $\mathfrak{S} \, \varepsilon \, \mathscr{C}$.

(2) $\sum_{i=1}^{\infty} S_i$ and $\prod_{i=1}^{\infty} S_i$ are in $\mathscr{C}$ if $S_i \, \varepsilon \, \mathscr{C}$.

(3) $S_1 - S_2 \, \varepsilon \, \mathscr{C}$ if $S_2 \subseteq S_1$ and $S_1, S_2 \, \varepsilon \, \mathscr{C}$.

A natural class of sets to consider is the set of all *intervals*, open, closed, or neither; degenerate or nondegenerate. However, this class is not an additive class, since, in particular, the sum of two disjoint closed intervals is not an interval.

Let us see if we can extend the set of intervals so that it becomes an additive class. We consider the class $\mathfrak{J}$ of all point sets I in $\mathfrak{S}$ such that I is the sum of a finite or an enumerably infinite number of intervals. Of course $\mathfrak{J}$ is a larger class than the set of all intervals; yet it is still not an additive class. Example: Let $I_1 = \mathfrak{S}$, and let I_2 be the set of all rational numbers in $\mathfrak{S}$. Clearly I_1 and I_2

are in $\mathfrak{J}$. Yet their difference $I_1 - I_2$ is not in $\mathfrak{J}$, for $I_1 - I_2$ is the totality of all irrational numbers in $\mathfrak{S}$ and cannot be expressed as the union of an enumerable number of intervals. Now, construct a class of sets consisting of all (finite or denumerable) sums, and products of sets in $\mathfrak{J}$ and all differences of sets (when meaningful). If we continue this process an enumerable number of times, the totality of sets generated by this process will form an additive class. This class is called the class $\mathfrak{B}$ of all *Borel sets* in $\mathfrak{S}$ and is the smallest additive class of sets in $\mathfrak{S}$ that includes all intervals.

The length of an interval is a familiar enough concept. If I is the interval (a, b), open, closed, or neither; then, by the length $\lambda(I)$ of this interval we mean the real number $b - a$. The function "λ" which we have just defined as a "function of intervals" has some interesting properties. Trivially, $\lambda(I) \geqq 0$ for any $I \varepsilon \mathfrak{S}$. Not so trivial is the following theorem.

THEOREM. Let I be an interval in R_1 which is divided into a finite or denumerably infinite number of disjoint intervals I_k,

$$I = \sum_{k=1}^{\infty} I_k \quad .$$

Then

$$\lambda(I) = \sum_{k=1}^{\infty} \lambda(I_k) \quad .$$

Proof. Let a and b be the end points of I and a_k, b_k the endpoints of I_k. Since

$$\sum_{k=1}^{n} I_k \subseteq I$$

for any finite n, we have

$$\sum_{k=1}^{n} \lambda(I_k) \leqq \lambda(I) \quad ,$$

and, because the right-hand side of this equation is independent of n,

$$\sum_{k=1}^{\infty} \lambda(I_k) \leqq \lambda(I) \quad . \tag{1}$$

To prove the inequality in the reverse direction, we use the Heine-Borel theorem. Consider the set S of intervals consisting of the intervals I_k and the intervals

$$\left(a - \frac{\varepsilon}{8}, a + \frac{\varepsilon}{8}\right) \quad , \quad \left(b - \frac{\varepsilon}{8}, b + \frac{\varepsilon}{8}\right)$$

$$\left(a_k - \frac{\varepsilon}{8 \cdot 2^k}, a_k + \frac{\varepsilon}{8 \cdot 2^k}\right) \quad , \quad \left(b_k - \frac{\varepsilon}{8 \cdot 2^k}, b_k + \frac{\varepsilon}{8 \cdot 2^k}\right) \quad ,$$

where ε is any positive number.

Certainly every point of (a, b) is interior to some set of S. Hence, by the Heine-Borel theorem, there exists a finite subset of these intervals with this property. If L is the sum of the lengths of this finite subset, then

$$\sum_{k=1}^{\infty} \lambda(I_k) + 4\left(\frac{\varepsilon}{8}\right) + 4 \sum_{k=1}^{\infty} \frac{\varepsilon}{8 \cdot 2^k} \geqq L \geqq \lambda(I) \quad ,$$

or

$$\sum_{k=1}^{\infty} \lambda(I_k) + \varepsilon \geqq \lambda(I) \quad .$$

But $\varepsilon > 0$ is arbitrary. Hence

$$\sum_{k=1}^{\infty} \lambda(I_k) \geqq \lambda(I) \quad .$$

Together with Equation (1) this establishes the theorem.

We wish now to extend the definition of this "interval" function $\lambda(I)$ to a larger class of sets than intervals. In particular, we should like to define a set function which assigns a nonnegative number $m(B)$ to every Borel set B and which in the particular case in which B is an interval reduces to $\lambda(B)$. Also, we would like m to be additive; that is, we want $m(\Sigma B_i)$ to be equal to $\Sigma m(B_i)$ where the B_i are disjoint Borel sets. Such a set function is called a *measure*. More precisely:

Definition. Let $\mathscr{C}$ be a class of sets, and let m be a set function defined for all sets in $\mathscr{C}$ with the properties:

(i) $m(S) \geqq 0$ for all $S \, \varepsilon \, \mathscr{C}$.

(ii) m is completely additive; that is, if $S = \sum_{i=1}^{\infty} S_i$ and $S_i \cdot S_j = 0$ for $i \neq j$, then $m(S) = \sum_{i=1}^{\infty} m(S_i)$.

(iii) If S is an interval, then $m(S) = \lambda(S)$.

The number $m(S)$ will be called the *measure* of S, and m will be said to be a *measure defined on $\mathscr{C}$*.

If $\mathscr{C}$ is the class $\mathfrak{J}$ considered earlier, then, if $I \varepsilon \mathfrak{J}$, I can be expressed in the form $I = \sum_{k=1}^{\infty} I_k$ where the I_k are disjoint intervals. We define $m(I)$ by

$$m(I) = \sum_{k=1}^{\infty} \lambda(I_k) \quad .$$

It can be shown that this is a unique measure satisfying (i)–(iii) above. Hence we have a measure defined on $\mathfrak{J}$. Suppose, however, we are dealing with more general point sets. It is not possible to define a measure for *every* class of sets. However, we shall show that a measure can be defined for a class of sets which includes all Borel sets, and which reduces to $m(I)$ in the particular case in which $I \, \varepsilon \, \mathfrak{J}$.

Let, then, S be an arbitrary bounded point set in R_1. Let $S \subseteq J$ where J is a bounded *interval*. We define the *outer measure* o.m.(S) by the equation

$$\text{o.m.} (S) = \underset{I \, \supseteq \, S}{\text{g.l.b.}} \; m(I)$$

for all sets $I \, \varepsilon \, \mathfrak{J}$ containing S and the *inner measure* i.m.(S) by

$$\text{i.m.} (S) = m(J) - \text{o.m.} (\bar{S}) \quad,$$

where $\bar{S}$ is the complement of S relative to J.

If a set S has the property that

$$\text{o.m.} (S) = \text{i.m.} (S) \quad,$$

then we shall say S is *Lebesgue measurable* or simply *measurable* and use the symbol $m(S)$ to denote the common value of the inner and outer measures. It is easily shown that m *is* a measure in the sense of (i)–(iii) above. If S is unbounded, we shall call it measurable if $S \cdot [- x, x]$ is measurable for all $x > 0$ and define $m(S)$ as

$$\lim_{x \to \infty} m(S \cdot [- x, x]) \quad.$$

We shall denote the class of all measurable sets in R_1 by $\mathfrak{L}_1$. It can be shown that $\mathfrak{L}_1$ is an additive class in the sense of (1)–(3) above. Since all intervals are measurable, $\mathfrak{L}_1$ contains the class of all intervals. Furthermore, since $\mathfrak{B}$ is the smallest additive class of sets in R_1, $\mathfrak{B} \subseteq \mathfrak{L}_1$; hence all Borel sets are measurable. In fact, if L is a Lebesgue measurable set, then there exists a Borel set $B \, \varepsilon \, \mathfrak{B}$ such that L differs from B only by a set of measure zero. [S is said to be a set of measure zero if $m(S) < \varepsilon$ for any preassigned $\varepsilon > 0$. For example, the rational numbers form a set of measure zero.] Lebesgue measure is the only set function defined for all Borel sets which has properties (i)–(iii) above.

The concept of a measurable set leads us quite naturally into the theory of integration over such sets. We recall that the Riemann integral was defined only on intervals. With the introduction of measurable sets we are invited to define a new integral called the *Lebesgue integral*. Let, then, B be a Borel set of finite measure and let $f(x)$ be a function defined and bounded on B. Then, in analogy with the Riemann integral, we make the following definitions.

Decompose B into a finite number of Borel sets B_k, and let

$$M_k = \text{l.u.b.} \, f(x) \quad \text{on} \quad B_k$$

$$\mu_k = \text{g.l.b.} \, f(x) \quad \text{on} \quad B_k \quad .$$

We define the upper and lower sums by the equations

$$S = \Sigma M_k m(B_k)$$

$$s = \Sigma \mu_k m(B_k) \quad ,$$

respectively. The greatest lower bound of S taken over all partitions of B is called the *upper integral*

$$\overline{\int_B} f(x)dx \quad ,$$

and, similarly, the least upper bound of s taken over all partitions of B is called the *lower integral*

$$\underline{\int_B} f(x)dx$$

of $f(x)$ on B. If $M = \text{l.u.b.} \, f(x)$ on B and $\mu = \text{g.l.b.} \, f(x)$ on B, then

$$\mu \cdot m(B) \leqq s \leqq \underline{\int_B} f(x)dx \leqq \overline{\int_B} f(x)dx \leqq S \leqq M \cdot m(B) \quad .$$

If

$$\underline{\int_B} f(x)dx = \overline{\int_B} f(x)dx \quad ,$$

we say $f(x)$ is *Lebesgue integrable* on B and denote the common value of the upper and lower integrals by

$$\int_B f(x)dx \quad .$$

A *function* $f(x)$ defined for all x in a Borel set B is said to be Borel *measurable* in the set B if the subset of all points $x \, \varepsilon \, B$ such that $f(x) \leqq k$ is a Borel set for all real numbers k. If $f(x)$ is bounded and Borel measurable on a set B of finite measure, then $f(x)$ is integrable over B.

Proof. Let $\varepsilon > 0$ be assigned. Let $|f(x)| < M$ on B, and let ω be a partition of the ordinates $[-M, M]$,

$$-M = y_0 < y_1 < \cdots < y_n = M$$

of norm less than $\dfrac{\varepsilon}{m(B)}$. Let B_k be the set of x points such that

$$y_{k-1} < f(x) \leq y_k \quad , \quad k = 1, \cdots, n \quad .$$

Consider the set

$$B_k = B'_k - B''_k \quad ,$$

where B'_k is the set of all $x \, \varepsilon \, B$ such that $f(x) \leq y_k$, and B''_k is the set of all $x \, \varepsilon \, B$ such that $f(x) \leq y_{k-1}$. Then, since $f(x)$ is measurable, B'_k and B''_k are measurable; hence B_k is a Borel set. Now

$$B = \sum_{k=1}^{n} B_k \quad ,$$

and $B_i \cdot B_j = 0$ for $i \neq j$. Thus

$$m(B) = \sum_{k=1}^{n} m(B_k) \quad .$$

Now let

$$M_k = \text{l.u.b.} f(x) \quad \text{on} \quad B_k$$
$$\mu_k = \text{g.l.b.} f(x) \quad \text{on} \quad B_k \quad ,$$

and consider the upper and lower sums

$$S = \sum_k M_k m(B_k)$$

and

$$s = \sum_k \mu_k m(B_k) \quad ,$$

respectively. We have

$$S - s = \sum_k (M_k - \mu_k) m(B_k) \leq \sum_k \frac{\varepsilon}{m(B)} m(B_k) = \frac{\varepsilon}{m(B)} \sum_k m(B_k) = \varepsilon \quad ,$$

which completes the proof.

Other properties of the integral are: If f and g are Borel measurable, then so are $f \pm g$, fg and $|f|$. If $\{f_n\} \to f$ and every f_n is measurable, then so is f. If the sequence $\{f_n\}$ is uniformly bounded in B and if $\lim_{n \to \infty} f_n = f$ exists almost everywhere (that is, everywhere except on a set of measure zero), then

$$\lim_{n \to \infty} \int_B f_n(x)dx = \int_B f(x)dx \quad .$$

Analogous results hold for Borel sets of nonfinite measure.

A function may be integrable in the Lebesgue sense and yet not be Riemann integrable. For example, consider the function $f(x)$ defined over the unit interval $[0, 1]$ by the equations

$$f(x) = 1 \quad \text{if } x \text{ is irrational}$$

$$f(x) = 0 \quad \text{if } x \text{ is rational.}$$

Clearly $f(x)$ is measurable, and hence $\int_B f(x)dx$ exists in the Lebesgue sense. We can actually evaluate it by a direct application of the above definitions. Decompose B into the two Borel sets B_i and B_r, where B_i is the set of all irrational numbers and B_r the set of all rational numbers. Clearly,

$$B = B_i + B_r \quad .$$

Now the upper sum S is

$$S = M_i \cdot m(B_i) + M_r \cdot m(B_r) = 1 \cdot m(B_i) + 0 \cdot m(B_r) = 1 \quad ,$$

where M_i and M_r are the l.u.b. of $f(x)$ on B_i and B_r, respectively. Also, the lower sum s is given by

$$s = \mu_i \cdot m(B_i) + \mu_r \cdot m(B_r) = 1 \cdot m(B_i) + 0 \cdot m(B_r) = 1 \quad ,$$

where μ_i and μ_r are defined in the expected fashion. Hence

$$1 = s \leqq \underline{\int_B} f(x)dx \leqq \overline{\int_B} f(x)dx \leqq S = 1 \quad ,$$

and $f(x)$ is integrable in the Lebesgue sense,

$$\int_B f(x)dx = 1 \quad .$$

If we use only *intervals* in decomposing $B = [0, 1]$, then we find that

$$\underline{\int_B} f(x)dx = 0 \quad , \quad \overline{\int_B} f(x)dx = 1 \quad ,$$

and $f(x)$ is *not* integrable in the Riemann sense.

We have seen that $m(S)$ is a *set function* which is a measure in the sense of (i)–(iii) above. A set function $p(S)$ which satisfies only the first two conditions defines a *p*-measure on $\mathfrak{B}$ called a *Stieltjes measure*. It is nonnegative and completely additive, but $p(I)$ where I is an interval is not necessarily equal to $\lambda(I)$. Based on this measure we can define a Lebesgue-Stieltjes integral analogous to the Riemann-Stieltjes integral of Appendix 2. However, we shall not go into such a discussion here.

If S is the closed interval $[a, b]$, we frequently write

$$p(S) = p(a \leq X \leq b) \quad .$$

If $p(S)$ is a *set function* and k a constant, we can define a corresponding point function $P_k(x)$ by the equations,

$$P_k(x) = p(k < X \leq x) \quad \text{if} \quad x > k$$
$$P_k(x) = 0 \qquad\qquad \text{if} \quad x = k$$
$$P_k(x) = -p(x < X \leq k) \quad \text{if} \quad x < k \quad .$$

This leads to the following considerations. Let p be a nonnegative additive set function such that $p(R_1) = 1$. Let $P(x)$ be a point function,

$$P(x) = p(X \leq x) \quad ;$$

then

$$0 \leq P(x) \leq 1 \quad ,$$
$$P(-\infty) = 0 \quad , \quad P(+\infty) = 1 \quad .$$

The function $P(x)$ can be identified with the distribution functions of probability theory (cf. Sec. 3 of Chap. 7). Similarly, $p(S)$ can be identified as "Prob.," that is,

$$p(S) = p(a \leq X \leq b) = \text{Prob. } [a \leq X \leq b] \quad .$$

The frequency function of the distribution can be defined as the derivative of $P(x)$, when it exists.

| *Appendix Two* | **RIEMANN-STIELTJES INTEGRAL** |

Let $f(x)$ be continuous on the closed finite interval $[a, b]$. If we subdivide the interval $[a, b]$ into n pieces by the points of subdivision $x_0, x_1, \cdots, x_n$ where

$$a = x_0 < x_1 < \cdots < x_n = b \quad ,$$

then we obtain a *partition* of the interval $[a, b]$. If

$$M_k = \max f(x) \quad \text{on} \quad [x_{k-1}, x_k]$$
$$m_k = \min f(x) \quad \text{on} \quad [x_{k-1}, x_k] \quad ,$$

then we may form the upper and lower Darboux sums S and s, respectively:

$$S = \Sigma M_k(x_k - x_{k-1})$$
$$s = \Sigma m_k(x_k - x_{k-1}) \quad . \tag{1}$$

If ν is the maximum of the lengths $x_k - x_{k-1}$, called the *norm* of the partition, then we know that

$$\lim_{\nu \to 0} S \quad \text{and} \quad \lim_{\nu \to 0} s$$

both exist and are equal. Their common value is denoted by

$$\int_a^b f(x)dx$$

and is called the *Riemann integral* of $f(x)$ over the interval $[a, b]$.

This integral can be generalized to the Riemann-Stieltjes integral, which enjoys most of the properties of the Riemann integral, plus others, which make it a very valuable tool in our investigations. As an example, instead of considering the sums of Equation (1), let us consider

$$S' = \Sigma M_k(x_k^2 - x_{k-1}^2)$$
$$s' = \Sigma m_k(x_k^2 - x_{k-1}^2)$$

on the interval $[a, b]$ where $0 \leqq a < b$. If the limits as v approach zero of S' and s' exist and are equal, we shall denote their common value by

$$\int_a^b f(x)dx^2 \quad , \quad 0 \leqq a < b \quad . \tag{2}$$

Equation (2) is called a *Riemann-Stieltjes* integral.

If we write S' as

$$S' = \Sigma[M_k(x_k + x_{k-1})](x_k - x_{k-1}) \quad ,$$

we easily see that if

$$S'' = \Sigma M_k'(x_k - x_{k-1}) \quad ,$$

where

$$M_k' = \max 2xf(x) \quad \text{on} \quad [x_{k-1}, x_k] \quad ,$$

then

$$\lim_{v \to 0} S' = \lim_{v \to 0} S'' \quad .$$

Similarly, we write

$$s' = \Sigma[m_k(x_k + x_{k-1})](x_k - x_{k-1})$$
$$s'' = \Sigma m_k'(x_k - x_{k-1}) \quad ,$$

where

$$m_k' = \min 2xf(x) \quad \text{on} \quad [x_{k-1}, x_k] \quad ,$$

and we have

$$\lim_{v \to 0} s' = \lim_{v \to 0} s'' \quad .$$

We call the common limit of S'' and s'' as ν approaches zero,

$$\int_a^b 2xf(x)dx \quad ,$$

which is identical with Equation (2). The "dx^2" of Equation (2) can therefore be formally interpreted as the differential $2x\,dx$.

In analogy with the Riemann integral we now define the Riemann-Stieltjes integral.

Definition. Let $F(x)$ be monotonically increasing and let $f(x)$ be any bounded function defined on $[a, b]$. Let $a = x_0, x_1, \cdots, x_n = b$ be a partition of $[a, b]$. Let

$$M_k = \text{l.u.b.}\, f(x) \quad \text{on} \quad [x_{k-1}, x_k]$$
$$m_k = \text{g.l.b.}\, f(x) \quad \text{on} \quad [x_{k-1}, x_k] \quad .$$

Consider the upper and lower sums,

$$S = \sum M_k[F(x_k) - F(x_{k-1})] \quad , \quad s = \sum m_k[F(x_k) - F(x_{k-1})] \quad , \qquad (3)$$

respectively. If the limits of S and s both exist and are equal as the norm of the partition approaches zero, then we say $f(x)$ is *Riemann-Stieltjes integrable* over $[a, b]$ with respect to $F(x)$ and denote the common value of the limits of S and s by

$$\int_a^b f(x)dF(x) \quad . \qquad (4)$$

Certain special cases are of interest. If $f(x)$ is Riemann integrable on $[a, b]$ and $F(x) = x$, then

$$\int_a^b f(x)dF(x) = \int_a^b f(x)dx \quad ,$$

and Equation (4) becomes the ordinary Riemann integral of $f(x)$ over $[a, b]$.

Suppose $f(x)$ is again Riemann integrable on $[a, b]$ and $F(x)$ has a continuous derivative on $[a, b]$. Then, if we write Equations (3) in the form

$$S = \sum M_k \left[\frac{F(x_k) - F(x_{k-1})}{x_k - x_{k-1}} \right] (x_k - x_{k-1})$$

$$s = \sum m_k \left[\frac{F(x_k) - F(x_{k-1})}{x_k - x_{k-1}} \right] (x_k - x_{k-1}) \quad ,$$

we see that the limit of the term in brackets as $x_k - x_{k-1}$ approaches zero (that is, as the norm v of the partition approaches zero) is $F'(x_k)$. Hence

$$\lim_{v \to 0} S' = \lim_{v \to 0} S = \lim_{v \to 0} s = \lim_{v \to 0} s' \quad ,$$

where

$$S' = \Sigma M'_k(x_k - x_{k-1})$$

$$s' = \Sigma m'_k(x_k - x_{k-1})$$

and

$$M'_k = \text{l.u.b.} f(x)F'(x) \quad \text{on} \quad [x_{k-1}, x_k]$$

$$m'_k = \text{g.l.b.} f(x)F'(x) \quad \text{on} \quad [x_{k-1}, x_k] \quad .$$

Equation (4) then becomes

$$\int_a^b f(x)F'(x)dx \quad ,$$

and we see, as in the special case of $F(x) = x^2$, that $dF(x)$ can be formally interpreted as the differential $F'(x)dx$.

Finally, suppose $f(x)$ is continuous and $F(x)$ is a step function with discontinuities $h_1, h_2, \cdots$ at the points $x_1, x_2, \cdots$ in $[a, b]$; that is,

$$F(x_i +) - F(x_i -) = h_i > 0 \quad .$$

Then

$$\int_a^b f(x)dF(x) = \sum_i f(x_i)h_i \quad . \tag{5}$$

If the set of points $\{x_n\}$ is finite, Equation (5) is a finite sum. If the set of points is countably infinite, then

$$\sum_{i=1}^{\infty} f(x_i)h_i$$

is an absolutely convergent infinite series. For, if we set

$$M = \text{l.u.b.} |f(x)| \quad \text{on} \quad [a, b]$$

and note that

$$\Sigma h_i \leqq F(b) - F(a) = K < \infty \quad ,$$

then

$$\sum_{i=1}^{\infty} f(x_i)h_i \leq \sum_i |f(x_i)|h_i \leq M \sum_i h_i \leq MK \quad,$$

which is finite.

Thus, both a sum, finite or infinite, or an ordinary Riemann integral can be interpreted as a Riemann-Stieltjes integral.

The definition of the Riemann-Stieltjes integral does not indicate that any large class of functions is integrable with respect to an arbitrary $F(x)$. In this connection we have the following theorem:

THEOREM. Let $f(x)$ be continuous on $[a, b]$, and let $F(x)$ be a monotonically increasing function defined on $[a, b]$. Then the Riemann-Stieltjes integral of $f(x)$ with respect to $F(x)$,

$$\int_a^b f(x)dF(x) \quad,$$

exists on $[a, b]$.

The theorem is an immediate consequence of the following lemmas. We let π be a partition of $[a, b]$, say,

$$a = x_0 < x_1 < \cdots < x_n = b \quad,$$

let

$$M_k = \max f(x) \quad \text{on} \quad [x_{k-1}, x_k]$$
$$m_k = \min f(x) \quad \text{on} \quad [x_{k-1}, x_k] \quad,$$

and let

$$S = \Sigma M_k[F(x_k) - F(x_{k-1})]$$
$$s = \Sigma m_k[F(x_k) - F(x_{k-1})]$$

be the upper and lower sums, respectively. Since $M_k \geq m_k$ and $F(x_k) \geq F(x_{k-1})$, we have immediately

$$S \geq s \quad.$$

We recall that if π' is a partition which contains all the points of π, then we call π' a *refinement* of π.

LEMMA 1. If π' is a refinement of π, and if S' and s' are the upper and lower sums for this partition, then

$$S' \leq S \quad, \quad s' \geq s \quad.$$

Proof. Let π_1 be a refinement of π which contains one point x^* of π' which is not in π. Let S_1 be the upper sum for π_1. Suppose

$$x_{j-1} < x^* < x_j \quad .$$

Let

$$M'_j = \max f(x) \quad \text{on} \quad [x_{j-1}, x^*]$$
$$M''_j = \max f(x) \quad \text{on} \quad [x^*, x_j] \quad .$$

Clearly,

$$M_j \geq M'_j \quad , \quad M_j \geq M''_j \quad ,$$

and

$$M'_j[F(x^*) - F(x_{j-1})] + M''_j[F(x_j) - F(x^*)]$$
$$\leq M_j[F(x^*) - F(x_{j-1}) + F(x_j) - F(x^*)] = M_j[F(x_j) - F(x_{j-1})] \quad .$$

Thus $S_1 \leq S$. We can construct a chain of subdivisions $S_1, S_2, \cdots, S_m$ each of which contains one more point of π' than its predecessor, and with $S_m = S'$. Thus, by repeated application of the above result,

$$S' = S_m \leq S_{m-1} \leq \cdots \leq S_1 \leq S \quad .$$

In a similar way we may show that

$$s' \geq s \quad .$$

LEMMA 2. If π_1 and π_2 are any two partitions of $[a, b]$, then

$$S_1 \geq s_2 \quad , \quad S_2 \geq s_1 \quad .$$

Proof. Let π' be a refinement of both π_1 and π_2 with upper and lower sums S' and s', respectively. Then

$$S' \geq s' \quad ,$$

and, by Lemma 1,

$$S' \leq S_1 \quad , \quad S' \leq S_2$$
$$s' \geq s_1 \quad , \quad s' \geq s_2 \quad .$$

Thus

$$S_1 \geq S' \geq s' \geq s_2 \quad ,$$

and

$$S_2 \geq S' \geq s' \geq s_1 \quad .$$

LEMMA 3. Let ν be the norm of the partition π of $[a, b]$. Then

$$\lim_{\nu \to 0} S = \lim_{\nu \to 0} s \quad.$$

Proof. The upper sums are bounded from below by any lower sum; hence they have a g.l.b., say, I'. Similarly, the lower sums are bounded from above by any upper sum; hence they have a l.u.b., say, I''. We wish to show that

$$I' = \lim_{\nu \to 0} S = \lim_{\nu \to 0} s = I'' \quad.$$

Let $\varepsilon > 0$ be assigned. We shall first show that there exists a $\delta > 0$ such that

$$S - s < \varepsilon \quad,$$

where S and s are any corresponding upper and lower sums for a partition π of norm less than δ.

Since $f(x)$ is continuous on $[a, b]$, it is uniformly continuous. Let $\delta > 0$ be the uniform δ for $\dfrac{\varepsilon}{F(b) - F(a)}$. Then

$$|f(x') - f(x'')| < \frac{\varepsilon}{F(b) - F(a)}$$

whenever

$$|x' - x''| < \delta \quad.$$

Now let S and s be any two sums of norm less than δ. Then

$$0 \leqq S - s = \Sigma M_k[F(x_k) - F(x_{k-1})] - \Sigma m_k[F(x_k) - F(x_{k-1})]$$
$$= \Sigma(M_k - m_k)[F(x_k) - F(x_{k-1})] \quad.$$

But

$$M_k - m_k < \frac{\varepsilon}{F(b) - F(a)} \quad.$$

(Since a continuous function attains its maximum and minimum on every closed interval, let x' be such that $f(x') = M_k$ and x'' such that $f(x'') = m_k$ on $[x_{k-1}, x_k]$. Then the above inequality is true, since $|x' - x''| \leqq x_k - x_{k-1} < \delta$.) Thus

$$0 \leqq S - s < \frac{\varepsilon}{F(b) - F(a)} \Sigma[F(x_k) - F(x_{k-1})] = \varepsilon \quad.$$

The proof of the lemma is now immediate. For

$$0 \leqq S - s = (S - I') + (I' - I'') + (I'' - s) < \varepsilon \quad .$$

Since each term in parentheses is nonnegative, and $\varepsilon > 0$ is arbitrary,

$$\lim_{\nu \to 0} S = I' \quad , \quad \lim_{\nu \to 0} s = I'' \quad ,$$

and

$$I' = I'' \quad .$$

The common value $I = I' = I''$ is denoted by

$$\int_a^b f(x)dF(x) \quad .$$

The Riemann-Stieltjes integral has all the important properties of the Riemann integral. For example, if $\phi(x)$ and $\psi(x)$ are Riemann-Stieltjes integrable on $[a, b]$ with respect to $F(x)$, then

$$\int_a^b [\phi(x) + \psi(x)]dF = \int_a^b \phi(x)dF + \int_a^b \psi(x)dF \quad .$$

Also, integration by parts,

$$\int_a^b \phi(x)dF = \phi(b)F(b) - \phi(a)F(a) - \int_a^b F(x)d\phi \quad ,$$

is valid, provided the last integral exists either as a Riemann integral or as a Riemann-Stieltjes integral.

One of the advantages of the Riemann-Stieltjes integral is that an expression involving both a Riemann integral *and* a sum can frequently be given by a single expression. More precisely, let $\phi(x)$ be continuous on $[a, b]$, and let $F(x)$ have a piecewise continuous derivative on $[a, b]$ with discontinuities at x_1, x_2, $\cdots$, x_n. If the jumps at the points of discontinuity are h_1, h_2, $\cdots$, h_n, respectively, then

$$\int_a^b \phi(x)dF(x) = \int_a^b \phi(x)F'(x)dx + \sum_{i=1}^n \phi(x_i)h_i \quad .$$

Sometimes we must consider a Riemann-Stieltjes integral when a or b or both are infinite. If

$$\lim_{\substack{a \to -\infty \\ b \to \infty}} \int_a^b \phi(x)dF(x)$$

exists, we call it the infinite Riemann-Stieltjes integral of $\phi(x)$ with respect to $F(x)$ and write

$$\lim_{\substack{a \to -\infty \\ b \to \infty}} \int_a^b \phi(x)dF(x) = \int_{-\infty}^{\infty} \phi(x)dF(x) \quad .$$

We define

$$\int_a^{\infty} \phi(x)dF(x) \quad \text{and} \quad \int_{-\infty}^{b} \phi(x)dF(x)$$

(if they exist) in an analogous fashion.

| # FOURIER SERIES
AND INTEGRALS

1. Fourier Series

We wish to establish some precise conditions under which a Fourier series expansion of a given function actually represents this function. We shall restrict ourselves to Riemann integrals. More general results may be obtained by the use of the Lebesgue integral.

A fundamental formula in our theory is the Riemann-Lebesgue lemma.

RIEMANN-LEBESGUE LEMMA. Let $x(t)$ be integrable on the closed finite interval $[a, b]$. Then

$$\lim_{\alpha \to \infty} \int_a^b x(t) \sin \alpha t \, dt = 0 \quad .$$

Proof. Let $\varepsilon > 0$ be assigned. Divide the interval $[a, b]$ into n pieces by the points of subdivision

$$a = t_0, t_1, \cdots, t_n = b \quad ,$$

where

$$t_0 < t_1 < \cdots < t_n \quad .$$

Let

$$S = \Sigma M_i(t_i - t_{i-1})$$

and

$$s = \Sigma m_i(t_i - t_{i-1})$$

be the upper and lower Darboux sums, respectively, for $x(t)$ on $[a, b]$, where

$$M_i = \text{l.u.b. } x(t) \quad \text{on} \quad [t_{i-1}, t_i]$$

$$m_i = \text{g.l.b. } x(t) \quad \text{on} \quad [t_{i-1}, t_i] \quad .$$

Choose a subdivision of norm sufficiently small such that for all subdivisions of smaller norm

$$S - s < \frac{\varepsilon}{2} \quad .$$

Let $N + 1$ be the number of points in any subdivision such that $S - s < \varepsilon/2$. Hold this partition fixed. We have, identically,

$$\int_a^b x(t) \sin \alpha t \, dt = \sum_{i=1}^N \int_{t_{i-1}}^{t_i} x(t) \sin \alpha t \, dt$$

$$= \sum_{i=1}^N \int_{t_{i-1}}^{t_i} [x(t) - m_i] \sin \alpha t \, dt + \sum_{i=1}^N \int_{t_{i-1}}^{t_i} m_i \sin \alpha t \, dt \quad .$$

Now let $M > |x(t)|$ on $[a, b]$, and choose A so large that for all $\alpha > A$,

$$\frac{2MN}{\alpha} < \frac{\varepsilon}{2} \quad .$$

Then

$$\left| \sum_{i=1}^N \int_{t_{i-1}}^{t_i} m_i \sin \alpha t \, dt \right| = \left| \sum_{i=1}^N m_i \left[\frac{-\cos \alpha t}{\alpha} \right] \Big|_{t_{i-1}}^{t_i} \right|$$

$$\leqq M \sum_{i=1}^N \frac{2}{\alpha} = \frac{2MN}{\alpha} < \frac{\varepsilon}{2}$$

for $\alpha > A$. Also,

$$\sum_{i=1}^N \int_{t_{i-1}}^{t_i} [x(t) - m_i] \sin \alpha t \, dt \leqq \sum_{i=1}^N \int_{t_{i-1}}^{t_i} |x(t) - m_i| dt$$

$$\leqq \sum_{i=1}^N \int_{t_{i-1}}^{t_i} |M_i - m_i| dt = \sum_{i=1}^N (M_i - m_i)(t_i - t_{i-1})$$

$$= S - s < \frac{\varepsilon}{2} \quad .$$

Hence, for $\alpha > A$,

$$\left| \int_a^b x(t) \sin \alpha t \, dt \right| < \varepsilon \quad ,$$

which proves the lemma.

A corollary to the lemma establishes the key result.

COROLLARY. Let $x(t)$ be integrable on $[a, b]$ and let ξ be an *interior* point, $\xi \, \varepsilon \, (a, b)$. Then, if $x(t)$ has a right- and left-hand derivative at $x = \xi$,

$$\lim_{\alpha \to \infty} \int_a^b x(t) \frac{\sin \alpha(t - \xi)}{t - \xi} \, dt = \frac{\pi}{2} \left[x(\xi +) + x(\xi -) \right] \quad .$$

Proof. Write

$$\lim_{\alpha \to \infty} \int_a^b x(t) \frac{\sin \alpha(t - \xi)}{t - \xi} \, dt = \lim_{\alpha \to \infty} \left(\int_a^\xi + \int_\xi^b \right) \quad ,$$

and make the change of variable $u = \xi - t$ in the first integral on the right and $u = t - \xi$ in the second:

$$\lim_{\alpha \to \infty} \int_a^b x(t) \frac{\sin \alpha(t - \xi)}{t - \xi} \, dt$$

$$= \lim_{\alpha \to \infty} \int_0^{\xi - a} x(\xi - u) \frac{\sin \alpha u}{u} \, du + \lim_{\alpha \to \infty} \int_0^{b - \xi} x(\xi + u) \frac{\sin \alpha u}{u} \, du \quad .$$

Now

$$\lim_{\alpha \to \infty} \int_0^{\xi - a} x(\xi - u) \frac{\sin \alpha u}{u} \, du$$

$$= \lim_{\alpha \to \infty} \int_0^{\xi - a} x(\xi -) \frac{\sin \alpha u}{u} \, du + \lim_{\alpha \to \infty} \int_0^{\xi - a} \frac{x(\xi - u) - x(\xi -)}{u} \sin \alpha u \, du \quad .$$

By hypothesis the left-hand derivative

$$\lim_{\substack{h \to 0 \\ h > 0}} \frac{x(\xi - h) - x(\xi -)}{-h}$$

of $x(t)$ exists at $t = \xi$. Hence, by the Riemann-Lebesgue lemma, the second integral on the right is zero. In the first integral, make the change of variables $v = \alpha u$:

$$\lim_{\alpha \to \infty} \int_0^{\xi - a} x(\xi -) \frac{\sin \alpha u}{u} \, du = x(\xi -) \lim_{\alpha \to \infty} \int_0^{\alpha(\xi - a)} \frac{\sin v}{v} \, dv \quad .$$

But

$$\int_0^\infty \frac{\sin v}{v} \, dv = \frac{\pi}{2} \quad .$$

Hence

$$\lim_{\alpha \to \infty} \int_0^{\xi - a} x(\xi - u) \frac{\sin \alpha u}{u} \, du = \frac{\pi}{2} x(\xi -) \quad .$$

Similarly, since $x(t)$ has a right-hand derivative at $t = \xi$,

$$\lim_{\alpha \to \infty} \int_0^{b - \xi} x(\xi + u) \frac{\sin \alpha u}{u} \, du = \frac{\pi}{2} x(\xi +) \quad ,$$

and the corollary is established.

We are now in a position to prove the main theorem. If $x(t)$ is a periodic function of period T, we recall that the usual formal manipulations yield the Fourier series representation

$$x(t) = \frac{1}{T} \sum_{n=-\infty}^{\infty} X(\omega_n) e^{j\omega_n t} \quad ,$$

where the Fourier coefficients are given by

$$X(\omega_n) = \int_{-T/2}^{T/2} x(t) e^{-j\omega_n t} \, dt$$

and

$$\omega_n = \frac{2\pi n}{T} \quad .$$

These formulas are rigorously established in the following theorem.

THEOREM. Let $x(t)$ be a periodic function of period T which is Riemann integrable in $[0, T]$. Then at every point $t = \xi$ where $x(t)$ has a right- and left-hand derivative, the Fourier series

$$\frac{1}{T} \sum_{n=-\infty}^{\infty} X(\omega_n) e^{j\omega_n \xi}$$

converges to

$$\tfrac{1}{2}[x(\xi +) + x(\xi -)] \quad ,$$

where

$$X(\omega_n) = \int_{-T/2}^{T/2} x(t) e^{-j\omega_n t} \, dt \quad .$$

Proof. Consider the partial sum $S_N(\xi)$,

$$S_N(\xi) = \frac{1}{T} \sum_{n=-N}^{N} X(\omega_n) e^{j\omega_n \xi} \quad .$$

We shall show that

$$\lim_{N \to \infty} S_N(\xi) = \tfrac{1}{2}[x(\xi +) + x(\xi -)] \quad .$$

On replacing $X(\omega_n)$ by its integral representation, we have

$$S_N(\xi) = \frac{1}{T} \sum_{n=-N}^{N} \int_{-T/2}^{T/2} x(t) e^{-j\omega_n t} dt \, e^{j\omega_n \xi}$$

$$= \frac{1}{T} \int_{-T/2}^{T/2} x(t) \sum_{n=-N}^{N} e^{-j\omega_n(t-\xi)} dt \quad .$$

The summation represents a finite geometric series whose sum in closed form is

$$\sum_{n=-N}^{N} e^{-j\omega_n(t-\xi)} = \frac{\sin \dfrac{2\pi}{T}(N+\tfrac{1}{2})(t-\xi)}{\sin \dfrac{\pi}{T}(t-\xi)} \quad .$$

(We easily see how to handle the case $t = \xi$.) Hence

$$S_N(\xi) = \frac{1}{T} \int_{-T/2}^{T/2} x(t) \frac{\sin \dfrac{2\pi}{T}(N+\tfrac{1}{2})(t-\xi)}{\sin \dfrac{\pi}{T}(t-\xi)} dt \quad .$$

Now choose a constant a such that ξ is interior to the interval $[a, a+T]$. By the periodicity of the integrand we may write

$$S_N(\xi) = \frac{1}{T} \int_{a}^{a+T} x(t) \frac{\sin \dfrac{2\pi}{T}(N+\tfrac{1}{2})(t-\xi)}{\sin \dfrac{\pi}{T}(t-\xi)} dt \quad .$$

Let

$$y(t) = (t - \xi)x(t) \csc \frac{\pi}{T}(t - \xi) \quad .$$

Since $y(t)$ is integrable on $[a, a + T]$,

$$\lim_{N \to \infty} S_N(\xi) = \lim_{N \to \infty} \frac{1}{T} \int_a^{a+T} y(t) \frac{\sin \frac{2\pi}{T}(N + \frac{1}{2})(t - \xi)}{t - \xi} dt$$

$$= \frac{1}{T} \frac{\pi}{2} [y(\xi +) + y(\xi -)]$$

by the corollary to the Riemann-Lebesgue lemma. But

$$\lim_{t \to \xi+} y(t) = \frac{T}{\pi} x(\xi +) \quad ,$$

and

$$\lim_{t \to \xi-} y(t) = \frac{T}{\pi} x(\xi -) \quad .$$

Hence

$$\lim_{N \to \infty} S_N(\xi) = \tfrac{1}{2} [x(\xi +) + x(\xi -)] \quad ,$$

as was desired to be proved.

2. Fourier Integrals

Starting with the Fourier series representation

$$x(t) = \frac{1}{T} \sum_{n=-\infty}^{\infty} X(\omega_n) e^{j\omega_n t}$$

of a periodic function $x(t)$ of period T where the Fourier coefficients $X(\omega_n)$ are given by

$$X(\omega_n) = \int_{-T/2}^{T/2} x(t) e^{-j\omega_n t} dt$$

and

$$\omega_n = \frac{2\pi n}{T} \quad ,$$

we can deduce the Fourier integral by a formal manipulation. For, let

$$\Delta\omega_n = \omega_{n+1} - \omega_n = \frac{2\pi(n + 1)}{T} - \frac{2\pi n}{T} = \frac{2\pi}{T} \quad .$$

Then

$$x(t) = \frac{1}{2\pi} \sum_{n=-\infty}^{\infty} X(\omega_n)e^{j\omega_n t}\Delta\omega_n \quad.$$

If we let T approach infinity, ω_n approaches a continuous variable, say, ω, and the infinite sum approaches an integral

$$x(t) = \frac{1}{2\pi} \int_{-\infty}^{\infty} X(\omega)e^{j\omega t}d\omega \quad,$$

while the spectrum approaches

$$X(\omega) = \int_{-\infty}^{\infty} x(t)e^{-j\omega t}dt \quad.$$

This analysis, of course, does not constitute a proof of the above formulas; however, it does indicate in what direction our results will lie. Our present task is to establish rigorously the above equations. As in the case of Fourier series, we shall restrict ourselves to the Riemann integral. More general results are of course obtainable by the use of a more general integral.

THEOREM. Let $x(t)$ be integrable in any finite subinterval of the infinite interval $(-\infty, \infty)$. Let $\int_{-\infty}^{\infty} |x(t)| dt$ converge. [That is, $x(t)$ is absolutely integrable on $(-\infty, \infty)$. We write $\|x\| = \int_{-\infty}^{\infty} |x(t)| dt$.] Then $X(\omega)$,

$$X(\omega) = \int_{-\infty}^{\infty} x(t)e^{-j\omega t}dt$$

exists and is a uniformly continuous function of ω. If $x(t)$ has a right- and left-hand derivative at $t = \xi$, then

$$\tfrac{1}{2}[x(\xi +) + x(\xi -)] = \frac{1}{2\pi} \int_{-\infty}^{\infty} X(\omega)e^{j\omega\xi}d\omega \quad. \tag{1}$$

Proof. Since

$$|X(\omega)| \leq \int_{-\infty}^{\infty} |x(t)| \, |e^{-j\omega t}| \, dt = \int_{-\infty}^{\infty} |x(t)| \, dt = \|x\| \quad,$$

we conclude that $X(\omega)$ exists. To prove that it is a uniformly continuous function of ω on $(-\infty, \infty)$:

$$|X(\omega + h) - X(\omega)| = \left| \int_{-\infty}^{\infty} x(t) e^{-j\omega t} (e^{-jht} - 1) dt \right|$$

$$\leqq 2 \int_{-\infty}^{\infty} |x(t)| \left| \sin \frac{ht}{2} \right| dt \quad .$$

Let $\varepsilon > 0$ be assigned. Choose $R > 0$ so large that

$$\int_{-\infty}^{-R} |x(t)| \, dt < \frac{\varepsilon}{6} \quad , \quad \int_{R}^{\infty} |x(t)| \, dt < \frac{\varepsilon}{6} \quad .$$

Let

$$\delta = \frac{\varepsilon}{3R \, \|x\|} \quad .$$

Then, for all h, $|h| < \delta$,

$$|X(\omega + h) - X(\omega)| \leqq 2 \int_{-\infty}^{-R} |x(t)| \left| \sin \frac{ht}{2} \right| dt$$

$$+ 2 \int_{-R}^{R} |x(t)| \left| \sin \frac{ht}{2} \right| dt + 2 \int_{R}^{\infty} |x(t)| \left| \sin \frac{ht}{2} \right| dt$$

$$< 2 \int_{-\infty}^{-R} |x(t)| \, dt + \int_{-R}^{R} |x(t)| \, |ht| \, dt + 2 \int_{R}^{\infty} |x(t)| \, dt$$

$$\leqq 2 \left(\frac{\varepsilon}{6} \right) + R |h| \int_{-R}^{R} |x(t)| \, dt + 2 \left(\frac{\varepsilon}{6} \right)$$

$$\leqq \frac{\varepsilon}{3} + R |h| \cdot \|x\| + \frac{\varepsilon}{3} < \varepsilon \quad .$$

We now establish Equation (1). Let $t = \xi$ be a point at which $x(t)$ has a right- and left-hand derivative. Let $[a, b]$ be any finite interval which contains ξ as an interior point. Then, by the corollary to the Riemann-Lebesgue lemma,

$$\lim_{\alpha \to \infty} \int_{a}^{b} x(t) \frac{\sin \alpha(t - \xi)}{t - \xi} \, dt = \frac{\pi}{2} [x(\xi +) + x(\xi -)] \quad .$$

Let $\varepsilon > 0$ be assigned. Choose an a and a $b > a$ such that

$$\frac{\|x\|}{|a - \xi|} < \frac{\varepsilon}{3} \quad , \quad \frac{\|x\|}{|b - \xi|} < \frac{\varepsilon}{3} \quad ,$$

and $\xi \, \varepsilon \, (a, b)$. With this a and b choose an A such that for $\alpha > A$,

$$\left| \int_a^b x(t) \frac{\sin \alpha(t - \xi)}{t - \xi} \, dt - \frac{\pi}{2} \left[x(\xi +) + x(\xi -) \right] \right| < \frac{\varepsilon}{3} \quad .$$

Now

$$\int_{-\infty}^{\infty} x(t) \frac{\sin \alpha(t - \xi)}{t - \xi} \, dt = \int_{-\infty}^a + \int_a^b + \int_b^{\infty} \quad ,$$

and

$$\left| \int_{-\infty}^a x(t) \frac{\sin \alpha(t - \xi)}{t - \xi} \, dt \right| \leqq \int_{-\infty}^a \frac{|x(t)|}{|t - \xi|} \, dt \leqq \frac{\|x\|}{|a - \xi|} < \frac{\varepsilon}{3} \quad ,$$

and

$$\left| \int_b^{\infty} x(t) \frac{\sin \alpha(t - \xi)}{t - \xi} \, dt \right| \leqq \int_b^{\infty} \frac{|x(t)|}{|t - \xi|} \, dt \leqq \frac{\|x\|}{|b - \xi|} < \frac{\varepsilon}{3} \quad .$$

Hence, for $\alpha > A$,

$$\left| \int_{-\infty}^{\infty} x(t) \frac{\sin \alpha(t - \xi)}{t - \xi} \, dt - \frac{\pi}{2} \left[x(\xi +) + x(\xi -) \right] \right| < \frac{\varepsilon}{3} + \frac{\varepsilon}{3} + \frac{\varepsilon}{3} = \varepsilon \quad .$$

We may write this as

$$\tfrac{1}{2} [x(\xi +) + x(\xi -)] = \lim_{\alpha \to \infty} \frac{1}{\pi} \int_{-\infty}^{\infty} x(t) dt \int_0^{\alpha} \cos \beta(t - \xi) d\beta \quad .$$

Since the infinite integral

$$\int_{-\infty}^{\infty} x(t) \cos \beta(t - \xi) dt$$

converges uniformly in β,

$$\int_{-\infty}^{\infty} x(t) dt \int_0^{\alpha} \cos \beta(t - \xi) d\beta = \int_0^{\alpha} d\beta \int_{-\infty}^{\infty} x(t) \cos \beta(t - \xi) dt \quad ,$$

and

$$\tfrac{1}{2} [x(\xi +) + x(\xi -)] = \lim_{\alpha \to \infty} \frac{1}{\pi} \int_0^{\alpha} d\beta \int_{-\infty}^{\infty} x(t) \cos \beta(t - \xi) dt$$

$$= \frac{1}{\pi} \int_0^{\infty} d\beta \int_{-\infty}^{\infty} x(t) \cos \beta(t - \xi) dt \quad .$$

Now replace $\cos \beta(t - \xi)$ by

$$\tfrac{1}{2}[e^{j\beta(t-\xi)} + e^{-j\beta(t-\xi)}] \quad ,$$

and we have

$$\tfrac{1}{2}[x(\xi +) + x(\xi -)]$$

$$= \frac{1}{2\pi} \int_{-\infty}^{0} d\beta \int_{-\infty}^{\infty} x(t)e^{-j\beta(t-\xi)}dt + \frac{1}{2\pi} \int_{0}^{\infty} d\beta \int_{-\infty}^{\infty} x(t)e^{-j\beta(t-\xi)}dt$$

$$= \frac{1}{2\pi} \int_{-\infty}^{\infty} e^{j\beta\xi} d\beta \int_{-\infty}^{\infty} x(t)e^{-j\beta t}dt \quad .$$

Letting

$$X(\beta) = \int_{-\infty}^{\infty} x(t)e^{-j\beta t}dt \quad ,$$

we obtain the inversion formula

$$\tfrac{1}{2}[x(\xi +) + x(\xi -)] = \frac{1}{2\pi} \int_{-\infty}^{\infty} X(\beta)e^{j\beta\xi} d\beta \quad .$$

ANSWERS

Chapter 1

Section 1

2. (i) 25.3   (ii) 152.64 .

Section 8

1. $x = \dfrac{7\alpha - 2}{19}$

   $y = \dfrac{11\alpha + 5}{19}$

   $z = \alpha$,

      where α is an arbitrary real number.

3. $x = -1 - 2\alpha$

   $y = 2 + \alpha$

   $z = \alpha$

   where α is an arbitrary real number.

Chapter 2

Section 2

3. $\Gamma(4.70) = 15.431$,

   $\Gamma(-1.30) = 3.328$

Section 5

1. $\displaystyle\int_0^1 \frac{x^n}{\sqrt{1 - x^2}}\, dx = \frac{\pi n!}{2^{n+1}\left[\left(\dfrac{n}{2}\right)!\right]^2}$ n even

2. $\displaystyle\int_0^1 \frac{x^2}{\sqrt{1 - x^4}}\, dx = \frac{4{,}194{,}304}{2{,}028{,}117}$.

Section 6

  $10! = 3.6288 \times 10^6$.

  Stirling's formula yields 3.5987×10^6 .

Section 10

1. $\displaystyle\int_0^4 e^{-x^2}dx = 0.88620$, $|E| \leq \frac{1}{60}$.

2. $\displaystyle\int_0^1 \frac{\sin x}{x}\,dx = 0.94609$ Exact value $= 0.94608$.

Chapter 3

Section 3

1. $y(x) = \dfrac{x^2 e^x}{2}$.

2. $y(x) = 7e^{2x}(1 + \cos x)$.

3. $y(x) = x + e^{-(x-1)}$.

4. $y(x) = -4x\sin x$.

Section 10

2. $u(z) = \sqrt{z}[AJ_{\frac{1}{3}}(\frac{2}{3}kz\sqrt{z}) + BJ_{-\frac{1}{3}}(\frac{2}{3}kz\sqrt{z})]$.

7. $y_1(x) = A\displaystyle\sum_{n=0}^{\infty} \frac{(-1)^n(n+1)}{(n+3)!}x^{n+2}$,

   $y_2(x) = B\displaystyle\sum_{n=0}^{\infty} \frac{(-1)^n(n-2)}{n!}x^{n-1}$.

One can also write the solution in closed form as

$$Y_1(x) = A\left(\frac{1}{x} - \frac{1}{2}\right) ,$$

$$Y_2(x) = B\,e^{-x/2}\left[\cosh\frac{x}{2} - \frac{\sinh\frac{x}{2}}{\frac{x}{2}}\right] .$$

8. $y_1(x) = A\left[\dfrac{1}{12} + x^2 + \displaystyle\sum_{n=2}^{\infty} \frac{(-1)^n(2n-4)!2^n}{(n-2)![5\cdot 9\cdot 13\cdot\,\cdots\,(4n-3)]}x^{2n}\right]$

   $y_2(x) = Bx^{\frac{3}{2}}\left[\dfrac{1}{3} + \dfrac{x^2}{2} - \displaystyle\sum_{n=2}^{\infty} \frac{(-1)^n[1\cdot 5\cdot 9\cdot 13\cdot\,\cdots\,(4n-7)]}{2^n n!}x^{2n}\right]$

9. $y_1(x) = Axe^{-x/2}$,

   $y_2(x) = B[xe^{-x/2}\log\dfrac{x}{2} - \dfrac{4}{x} - 2 + x - \dfrac{1}{2^2}\dfrac{1}{(2!)^2}x^3$

   $+ \dfrac{1}{2^3}\dfrac{(2+3)}{(3!)^2}x^4 - \dfrac{1}{2^4}\dfrac{(2\cdot 3 + 2\cdot 4 + 3\cdot 4)}{(4!)^2}x^5$

   $+ \dfrac{1}{2^5}\dfrac{(2\cdot 3\cdot 4 + 2\cdot 3\cdot 5 + 2\cdot 4\cdot 5 + 3\cdot 4\cdot 5)}{(5!)^2}x^6 - \cdots]$.

10. $y_1(x) = Ax^{-3}J_3(x)$,
    $y_2(x) = Bx^{-3}Y_3(x)$.

11. $y(x, 1) = A\left[x + \dfrac{1}{2}x^3 - \dfrac{3}{5!}x^5 - \dfrac{209}{7!}x^7 - \dfrac{2503}{9!}x^9 + \cdots\right]$

12. If

$$F(\alpha, \beta, \gamma, x) = 1 + \frac{\alpha \cdot \beta}{1 \cdot \gamma} x + \frac{\alpha(\alpha + 1)\beta(\beta + 1)}{1 \cdot 2 \cdot \gamma(\gamma + 1)} x^2$$
$$+ \frac{\alpha(\alpha + 1)(\alpha + 2)\beta(\beta + 1)(\beta + 2)}{1 \cdot 2 \cdot 3 \cdot \gamma(\gamma + 1)(\gamma + 2)} x^3 + \cdots$$

then

$$y_1(x) = AF(\alpha, \beta, \gamma, x) \quad,$$

and

$$y_2(x) = Bx^{1-\gamma}F(\alpha - \gamma + 1, \beta - \gamma + 1, 2 - \gamma, x) \quad.$$

The function $F(\alpha, \beta, \gamma, x)$ is called the *hypergeometric series*.

13. Under the transformation $x = z/2$, this equation becomes Bessel's equation of order $\frac{2}{3}$.

14. Under the transformation $y = x^2 u$, this equation becomes Bessel's equation of order zero.

15. Under the transformations $x = z^2$ and $y = u/z$, this equation becomes Bessel's equation of order one.

16. Under the transformations $x = (\frac{5}{6}z)^{\frac{6}{5}}$ and $y = z^{-\frac{3}{5}}u$, this equation becomes Bessel's equation of order $\frac{3}{5}$.

17. The current equation is

$$i'' + (10 + t)i' + 2i = 0 \quad,$$

which under the transformation $x = 10 + t$ with $i(t) \equiv y(x)$ becomes

$$y'' + xy' + 2y = 0$$

whose solutions are

$$y_1(x) = A \sum_{n=0}^{\infty} \frac{(-1)^n x^{2n+1}}{2^n n!} \quad,$$

$$y_2(x) = B \sum_{n=0}^{\infty} \frac{(-1)^n 2^n n!}{(2n)!} x^{2n} \quad.$$

18. Making the substitution $y = u - T$, the steady-state equation for the temperature becomes

$$y'' + \frac{1}{2 + x} y' - 2y = 0 \quad,$$

and one solution is

$$y_1(x) = A \left[x - \frac{x^2}{4} + \frac{5}{12} x^3 - \frac{11}{96} x^4 + \frac{3}{40} x^5 - \cdots \right] \quad.$$

Chapter 4

Section 2

1. $f(x) = \dfrac{3}{4} - \dfrac{2}{\pi^2} \displaystyle\sum_{n=1,\,3,5,\,\cdots}^{\infty} \dfrac{1}{n^2} \cos n\pi x - \dfrac{1}{\pi} \displaystyle\sum_{n=1}^{\infty} \dfrac{1}{n} \sin n\pi x \quad.$

2. $f(x) = \dfrac{16}{\pi^3} \displaystyle\sum_{n=1}^{\infty} \dfrac{(-1)^n}{n^3} (6 - n^2\pi^2) \sin \dfrac{n\pi x}{2} \quad.$

3. $e(t) = \dfrac{2E}{\pi} + \dfrac{4E}{\pi} \displaystyle\sum_{n=2,4,6,\,\cdots}^{\infty} \dfrac{1}{1 - n^2} \cos n\omega t \quad.$

Section 3

2. $f(x) = \dfrac{2}{3}\pi^2 - 4\displaystyle\sum_{n=1}^{\infty}\dfrac{(-1)^n}{n^2}\cos nx$.

3. $f(t) = \dfrac{ha}{T} + \dfrac{2ha}{T}\displaystyle\sum_{n=1}^{\infty}\left(\dfrac{\sin n\pi a/T}{n\pi a/T}\right)^2\cos\dfrac{2n\pi}{T}t$.

4. $f(x) = \dfrac{3}{4} - \dfrac{4}{\pi^2}\displaystyle\sum_{n=1,3,5,\ \ldots}\dfrac{1}{n^2}\cos\dfrac{n\pi x}{2} - \dfrac{8}{\pi^2}\displaystyle\sum_{n=2,\,6,\,10,\ \ldots}\dfrac{1}{n^2}\cos\dfrac{n\pi x}{2}$,

$\quad f(x) = \dfrac{4}{\pi^2}\displaystyle\sum_{n=1,3,5,\ \ldots}\dfrac{1}{n^2}(-1)^{\frac{n-1}{2}}\sin\dfrac{n\pi x}{2} - \dfrac{2}{\pi}\displaystyle\sum_{n=1}^{\infty}\dfrac{(-1)^n}{n}\sin\dfrac{n\pi x}{2}$.

Section 4 (First selection)

1. $y(x) = \dfrac{P_0 L^4}{EI}\dfrac{4}{\pi^5}\displaystyle\sum_{n=1,3,5,\ \ldots}\dfrac{1}{n^5}\sin\dfrac{n\pi x}{L}$.

2. $u(x, t) = \dfrac{4T}{\pi}\displaystyle\sum_{n=1,3,5,\ \ldots}\dfrac{1}{n}\sin\dfrac{n\pi x}{L}e^{-\left(\frac{n\pi c}{L}\right)^2 t}$.

Section 4 (Second selection)

1. $u(x, y) = \dfrac{4T}{\pi}\displaystyle\sum_{n=1,\,3,\,5,\ \ldots}\dfrac{1}{n}\sin\dfrac{n\pi}{2a}x\,e^{-\frac{n\pi}{2a}y}$

$\quad = \dfrac{2T}{\pi}\arctan\left(\dfrac{\sin\pi x/2a}{\sinh\pi y/2a}\right)$.

2. $u(x, y) = -\dfrac{4T}{\pi}\displaystyle\sum_{n=1,3,5,\ \ldots}\dfrac{\sin\dfrac{n\pi x}{a}\sinh\left(\dfrac{n\pi y}{a}-n\pi\right)}{n\sinh n\pi}$.

3. $u(x, t) = \dfrac{2}{L}\displaystyle\sum_{n=1}^{\infty}\left[\displaystyle\int_0^L f(z)\sin\dfrac{n\pi z}{L}\,dz\right]\sin\dfrac{n\pi x}{L}\cos\dfrac{n\pi a}{L}t$.

4. $e(x, t) = \dfrac{2E}{\pi}\displaystyle\sum_{n=1,3,5,\ \ldots}\dfrac{1}{n}\sin\dfrac{n\pi x}{L}e^{-\left(\frac{n\pi}{L}\right)^2\frac{t}{RC}}$

$\quad - \dfrac{4E}{\pi}\displaystyle\sum_{n=2,6,10,\ \ldots}\dfrac{1}{n}\sin\dfrac{n\pi x}{L}e^{-\left(\frac{n\pi}{L}\right)^2\frac{t}{RC}}$.

Section 5

3. $u(x, t) = U_0\,\mathrm{erf}\,\dfrac{x}{2c\sqrt{t}}$.

4. $u(x, t) = \dfrac{2}{\pi a}\displaystyle\int_0^{\infty}g(\xi)d\xi\displaystyle\int_0^{\infty}\dfrac{1}{\beta}\sin\beta x\sin\beta\xi\sin a\beta t\,d\beta$

$\quad = \dfrac{1}{2a}\displaystyle\int_{x-at}^{x+at}u_t(\xi, 0)d\xi$,

where $u_t(x, 0) = g(x)$ for $x > 0$ and $u_t(x, 0) = -g(-x)$ for $x < 0$.

5. $u(x, y, t) = \dfrac{1}{4c^2\pi t} \displaystyle\int_{-\infty}^{\infty} \int_{-\infty}^{\infty} F(\xi, \eta) e^{-[(\xi-x)^2 + (\eta-y)^2]/4c^2 t} d\xi\, d\eta$.

Section 9

1. (i) $w(f) = 2\alpha \left[\dfrac{1}{\alpha^2 + (\beta + \omega)^2} + \dfrac{1}{\alpha^2 + (\beta - \omega)^2} \right]$, $\omega \geqq 0$,

$$S(\omega) = S(-\omega) = \frac{w(f)}{2} \quad , \quad f \geqq 0 \quad .$$

(ii) $\omega = \sqrt{\gamma(2\beta - \gamma)}$ where $\gamma^2 = \alpha^2 + \beta^2$.

(iv) $w_{\max}(f) = \dfrac{\alpha}{\beta(\gamma - \beta)}$.

(v) $\rho(\Omega) = \dfrac{\phi}{\pi}$, where $\phi = \arctan \dfrac{2\alpha\Omega}{\gamma^2 - \Omega^2}$ is an angle which ranges between 0 and π.

2. (i) $S(\omega) = S(-\omega) = \dfrac{w(f)}{2}$, $f \geqq 0$.

(ii) $\psi(\tau) = KW \left(\dfrac{\sin 2\pi W\tau}{2\pi W\tau} \right)$.

(iii) $\rho = KW$.

4. $\psi(\tau) = \dfrac{1}{\pi\tau^3} \left[(\tau^2 - 1) \sin \tau + \tau \cos \tau \right]$.

$\rho = 2/3\pi$.

$S(\omega) = \dfrac{1 + \omega^2}{2}$, $|\omega| < 1$

$\quad\quad = 0$, $|\omega| > 1$.

Section 10

1. $u(r, \theta) = \dfrac{T}{2r} + T \displaystyle\sum_{n=0}^{\infty} \dfrac{(-1)^{n+1}(2n)!(4n + 3)}{2^{2n+2}(n!)^2(n + 1)} P_{2n+1}(\cos \theta) r^{-(2n+2)}$.

2. $u(r, t) = \dfrac{2}{a^2} \displaystyle\sum_{n=1}^{\infty} \dfrac{1}{J_1^2(\lambda_n)} \left[\int_0^a sf(s) J_0\left(\lambda_n \dfrac{s}{a}\right) ds \right] J_0\left(\lambda_n \dfrac{r}{a}\right) e^{-k\lambda_n^2 t/a^2}$

3. $u(r, \theta, t) = \dfrac{1}{\pi a^2} \displaystyle\sum_{m=1}^{\infty} \dfrac{1}{J_1^2(\lambda_m)} \int_0^{2\pi} d\phi \int_0^a sf(s, \phi) J_0\left(\lambda_m \dfrac{s}{a}\right) ds J_0\left(\lambda_m \dfrac{r}{a}\right) e^{-k\lambda_m^2 t/a^2}$

$\quad\quad + \dfrac{2}{\pi a^2} \displaystyle\sum_{n=1}^{\infty} \sum_{m=1}^{\infty} \dfrac{1}{J_{n+1}^2(\lambda_{mn})} \int_0^{2\pi} d\phi \int_0^a sf(s, \phi) \cos n\phi \, J_n\left(\lambda_{mn} \dfrac{s}{a}\right) ds$

$\quad\quad\quad\quad\quad\quad\quad\quad \cos n\theta \, J_n\left(\lambda_{mn} \dfrac{r}{a}\right) e^{-k\lambda_{mn}^2 t/a^2}$

$\quad\quad + \dfrac{2}{\pi a^2} \displaystyle\sum_{n=1}^{\infty} \sum_{m=1}^{\infty} \dfrac{1}{J_{n+1}^2(\lambda_{mn})} \int_0^{2\pi} d\phi \int_0^a sf(s, \phi) \sin n\phi \, J_n\left(\lambda_{mn} \dfrac{s}{a}\right) ds$

$\quad\quad\quad\quad\quad\quad\quad\quad \sin n\theta \, J_n\left(\lambda_{mn} \dfrac{r}{a}\right) e^{-k\lambda_{mn}^2 t/a^2}$.

4. $u(r, t) = \dfrac{2}{a^2} \displaystyle\sum_{n=1}^{\infty} \dfrac{1}{J_1^2(\lambda_n)} \int_0^a sf(s)J_0\left(\lambda_n \dfrac{s}{a}\right) ds J_0\left(\lambda_n \dfrac{r}{a}\right) \cos \lambda_n \dfrac{k}{a} t$.

5. $u(r, t) = \dfrac{2}{a^2} \displaystyle\sum_{n=1}^{\infty} \dfrac{1}{J_0^2(\omega_n)} \int_0^a sf(s)J_0\left(\omega_n \dfrac{s}{a}\right) ds J_0\left(\omega_n \dfrac{r}{a}\right) e^{-k(\omega_n/a)^2 t}$.

6. $u(r, \theta, t) = \displaystyle\sum_{n=0}^{\infty}\sum_{m=1}^{\infty} [a_{nm} \cos n\theta + b_{nm} \sin n\theta] J_n\left(\omega_{mn}\dfrac{r}{a}\right) e^{-k(\omega_{mn}/a)^2 t}$,

where

$$a_{nm} = \frac{2}{\pi a^2} \frac{\omega_{mn}^2}{\omega_{mn}^2 - n^2} \frac{1}{J_n^2(\omega_{mn})} \int_0^{2\pi} d\phi \int_0^a sf(s, \phi) \cos n\phi \, J_n\left(\omega_{mn}\frac{s}{a}\right) ds \quad,$$

$$b_{nm} = \frac{2}{\pi a^2} \frac{\omega_{mn}^2}{\omega_{mn}^2 - n^2} \frac{1}{J_n^2(\omega_{mn})} \int_0^{2\pi} d\phi \int_0^a sf(s, \phi) \sin n\phi \, J_n\left(\omega_{mn}\frac{s}{a}\right) ds \quad,$$

$$a_{om} = \frac{1}{\pi a^2} \frac{1}{J_0^2(\omega_{mo})} \int_0^{2\pi} d\phi \int_0^a sf(s, \phi)J_0\left(\omega_{mo}\frac{s}{a}\right) ds \quad.$$

8. $u(x, t) = \dfrac{\alpha Tx}{1 + \alpha L} + 2\alpha T \displaystyle\sum_{n=1}^{\infty} \dfrac{\cos \beta_n L}{\beta_n(L\alpha + \cos^2 \beta_n L)} \sin \beta_n x \, e^{-k\beta_n^2 t}$,

where the β_n are the positive roots of $\alpha \tan \beta L + \beta = 0$.

Chapter 5

Section 3

1. $\dfrac{a}{s^2 - a^2}$.

2. $\arctan \dfrac{a}{s}$.

3. $\dfrac{s^2 + 2s}{(s^2 + 2s + 2)^2}$.

4. $\dfrac{\sqrt{\pi}}{2} e^{(s/2)^2} \operatorname{cerf}\left(\dfrac{s}{2}\right)$.

5. $te^{-at} \sin bt$.

6. $J_0(t)$.

7. $t^{-1}(2 - e^t - e^{-t})$.

8. $y(t) = e^t - 3e^{-t} + 2e^{-2t}$.

9. $y(t) = -2 - t - t^2 + \frac{3}{2}e^t + \frac{1}{2}e^{-t}$.

10. $y(t) = \frac{3}{4}(\cos t - \sin t) + \dfrac{5 - \sqrt{2}}{8} e^{(1+\sqrt{2})t} + \dfrac{5 + \sqrt{2}}{8} e^{(1-\sqrt{2})t}$.

11. $y(t) = \dfrac{1}{3}\left[1 + 2e^{t/2}\cos\dfrac{\sqrt{11}}{2}t - \dfrac{2}{\sqrt{11}}e^{t/2}\sin\dfrac{\sqrt{11}}{2}t\right]$.

12. $y(t) = e^t(t^3 + t - \frac{2}{3}) + e^{-2t}(t + \frac{2}{3})$.

13. $x(t) = \frac{1}{5}e^{-t} - \frac{6}{5}e^{-2t}\cos 3t + \frac{3}{5}e^{-2t}\sin 3t$.

14. $x(t) = -0.744 \cos 3t + 0.904 \sin 3t + e^{-t/2}[0.744 \cos 0.866t - 2.702 \sin 0.866t]$.

Section 4

1. $\dfrac{0.3107}{s - 0.7549} - \dfrac{0.3107s + 0.7798}{s^2 + 1.7549s + 1.3247}$.

2. $\dfrac{-2}{s + 2} + \dfrac{2}{s + 3} + \dfrac{3}{(s + 3)^2}$.

3. $\dfrac{1}{s^2} - \dfrac{3}{2s} + \dfrac{3}{s + 1} - \dfrac{3}{2(s + 2)}$.

4. $\dfrac{1}{s^2 + 4} - \dfrac{2}{s + 1} + \dfrac{3s}{(s + 2)^2 + 1}$.

Section 5

1. $\dfrac{2\pi T}{s^2T^2 + 4\pi^2} \coth \dfrac{sT}{4}$.

2. $\dfrac{2h}{Ts^2} \tanh \dfrac{sT}{4}$.

3. $\dfrac{h}{s} [e^{-as} - e^{-bs}]$.

4. $K_0(s)$.

Section 6

1. $v(x, t) = \frac{1}{2} [f(x + at) + f(x - at)]$, $x > at$
$\qquad = \frac{1}{2} [f(x + at) - f(- x + at)]$, $x < at$.

2. $v(x, t) = \dfrac{x}{2a\sqrt{\pi}} \displaystyle\int_0^t f(t - \lambda)\lambda^{-\frac{3}{2}} e^{-x^2/4a^2\lambda} \, d\lambda$.

3. If $\sigma(t)$ is the stress at $x = L$, then $\sigma(t)$ is periodic of period $4L/a$, where

$$\sigma(t) = - \frac{EV_0}{a} \quad , \quad 0 < t < \frac{2L}{a} \quad ,$$

$$\sigma(t) = + \frac{EV_0}{a} \quad , \quad \frac{2L}{a} < t < \frac{4L}{a} \quad .$$

Section 7

2. $x(t) = e^{-t} \cos \sqrt{2}t + \dfrac{3}{\sqrt{2}} e^{-t} \sin \sqrt{2}t + \dfrac{1}{\sqrt{2}} \displaystyle\int_0^t g(\lambda)e^{-(t-\lambda)} \sin \sqrt{2}(t - \lambda)d\lambda$.

3. $f(t) = \dfrac{t}{2} - \dfrac{1}{4} + \dfrac{5}{4} e^{-2t}$.

4. $f(t) = - \sin t - \cos t - \dfrac{t}{2} \sin t$.

Chapter 6

Section 6

1.

$$\| \theta \| = \begin{Vmatrix} p & p & 0 & p & 0 & 0 \\ p & 3p & p & p & 0 & 0 \\ 0 & p & 2p & 0 & 0 & 0 \\ p & p & 0 & p & 0 & 0 \\ 0 & 0 & 0 & 0 & 2 & 0 \\ 0 & 0 & 0 & 0 & 0 & 4p^{-1} \end{Vmatrix} ,$$

$$\| \beta \| = \begin{Vmatrix} 1 & 1 & 1 & 0 & 0 & 0 \\ 0 & 1 & 0 & -1 & 0 & -1 \\ 0 & 0 & -1 & 0 & -1 & 0 \end{Vmatrix} ,$$

$$\| Z \| = \begin{Vmatrix} 10p & 3p & -3p \\ 3p & 2p + 4p^{-1} & -p \\ -3p & -p & 2p + 2 \end{Vmatrix} .$$

$$E_1 = 10pi_1 + \qquad\qquad 3pi_2 - \qquad\qquad 3pi_3$$
$$- E_2 = \quad 3pi_1 + (2p + 4p^{-1})i_2 - \qquad\qquad pi_3$$
$$- E_2 = - 3pi_1 - \qquad\qquad pi_2 + (2p + 2)i_3 \quad.$$

2.

$$\| \theta \| = \left\| \begin{matrix} p & -p & p & 0 \\ -p & 2p & -p & 0 \\ p & -p & 2p & 0 \\ 0 & 0 & 0 & 2p^{-1} \end{matrix} \right\|,$$

$$\| \alpha \| = \left\| \begin{matrix} 1 & 0 & 0 & 1 \\ -1 & 1 & 1 & 0 \\ 0 & 0 & -1 & -1 \end{matrix} \right\|,$$

$$\| \gamma \| = \left\| \begin{matrix} 1 & -1 & 0 \\ 0 & 1 & 0 \\ 0 & 1 & -1 \\ 1 & 0 & -1 \end{matrix} \right\|,$$

$$\| Y \| = \left\| \begin{matrix} 3p^{-1} + \tfrac{1}{2}p & - 3p^{-1} & p^{-1} - \tfrac{1}{2}p \\ - 3p^{-1} & 5p^{-1} & - 2p^{-1} \\ p^{-1} - \tfrac{1}{2}p & - 2p^{-1} & p^{-1} + \tfrac{1}{2}p \end{matrix} \right\| \quad.$$

3. $\dfrac{E_2}{E_1} = \dfrac{2}{4p^2 + 1}$.

Section 10

2. (i) $w_1(f) = \pi[\delta(\omega - 1) + \delta(\omega - 2)]$; $\psi_1(\tau) = \tfrac{1}{2}[\cos \tau + \cos 2\tau]$.
(ii) $w_2(f) = 0$; $\psi_2(\tau) = 0$.

Section 11

$$w(f) = 1 \quad, \quad 0 \leqq \omega \leqq 1$$
$$= 0 \quad, \qquad \omega > 1 \quad.$$
$$\psi(\tau) = \frac{1}{2\pi} \frac{\sin \tau}{\tau} \quad.$$

Chapter 7

Section 5

1. Eight possibilities arise:

CASE 1. *A* occurs.	*B* occurs.	*C* occurs.
2. *A* occurs.	*B* occurs.	*C* does not occur.
3. *A* occurs.	*B* does not occur.	*C* occurs.
4. *A* occurs.	*B* does not occur.	*C* does not occur.
5. *A* does not occur.	*B* occurs.	*C* occurs.
6. *A* does not occur.	*B* occurs.	*C* does not occur.
7. *A* does not occur.	*B* does not occur.	*C* occurs.
8. *A* does not occur.	*B* does not occur.	*C* does not occur.

If Case k occurs N_k times, $k = 1, 2, 3, 4, 5, 6, 7, 8$; then, if

$$N = N_1 + N_2 + \cdots + N_8 \quad,$$

where N is large ,

$$p(A) = \frac{N_1 + N_2 + N_3 + N_4}{N} \quad, \quad p(B) = \frac{N_1 + N_2 + N_5 + N_6}{N} \quad,$$

$$p(C) = \frac{N_1 + N_3 + N_5 + N_7}{N} \quad, \quad p(A, B) = \frac{N_1 + N_2}{N} \quad,$$

$$p(A, C) = \frac{N_1 + N_3}{N} \quad, \quad p(B, C) = \frac{N_1 + N_5}{N} \quad, \quad p(A, B, C) = \frac{N_1}{N} \quad,$$

$$p(A + B) = \frac{N_1 + N_2 + N_3 + N_4 + N_5 + N_6}{N} \quad,$$

$$p(A + C) = \frac{N_1 + N_2 + N_3 + N_4 + N_5 + N_7}{N} \quad,$$

$$p(B + C) = \frac{N_1 + N_2 + N_3 + N_5 + N_6 + N_7}{N} \quad,$$

$$p(A + B + C) = \frac{N_1 + N_2 + N_3 + N_4 + N_5 + N_6 + N_7}{N} \quad,$$

$$p_A(B, C) = \frac{N_1}{N_1 + N_2 + N_3 + N_4} \quad, \quad p_B(A, C) = \frac{N_1}{N_1 + N_2 + N_5 + N_6} \quad,$$

$$p_C(A, B) = \frac{N_1}{N_1 + N_3 + N_5 + N_7} \quad, \quad p_{AB}(C) = \frac{N_1}{N_1 + N_2} \quad,$$

$$p_{AC}(B) = \frac{N_1}{N_1 + N_3} \quad, \quad p_{BC}(A) = \frac{N_1}{N_1 + N_5} \quad,$$

$$p(A + B + C) = p(A) + p(B) + p(C) - p(A, B) - p(A, C) - p(B, C) + p(A, B, C) \quad.$$

5. (i) $p(0) = \dfrac{1}{a}$.

(ii) $E[X] = 0$.

(iii) $\sigma^2 = \dfrac{a^2}{6}$.

6. (i) $p(0) = \dfrac{2}{3a}$.

(ii) $E[X] = -\dfrac{2a}{9}$.

(iii) $\sigma^2 = \dfrac{37}{162} a^2$.

11. $Q(y) = 1 - P\left(\dfrac{y - \beta}{-\alpha^2}\right)$.

12. $E[X] = 0$, $\sigma^2 = \infty$.

Section 9

4. $p(Y) = \dfrac{1}{\sigma^n 2^{\frac{n}{2}} \Gamma\left(\dfrac{n}{2}\right)} Y^{\frac{n}{2} - 1} e^{-Y/2\sigma^2}$

5. (i) $t(T) = \dfrac{1}{4\sigma^3} e^{-T^2/4\sigma^2} \left[2\sigma T e^{-T^2/4\sigma^2} + \sqrt{\pi}(T^2 - 2\sigma^2) \operatorname{erf} \dfrac{T}{2\sigma} \right]$, $T > 0$

$t(T) = 0$, $T < 0$.

(ii) $r(\Psi') = 0$, $\Psi' < 0$,

$$r(\Psi') = \frac{\Psi'}{4\pi^2} \quad , \quad 0 < \Psi' < 2\pi \quad ,$$

$$r(\Psi') = \frac{4\pi - \Psi'}{4\pi^2} \quad , \quad 2\pi < \Psi' < 4\pi \quad ,$$

$$r(\Psi') = 0 \quad , \quad 4\pi < \Psi' < \infty \quad .$$

6. $s(U) = \dfrac{1}{4a^2}(2a + U)$, $-2a < U < 0$,

$$s(U) = \frac{1}{4a^2}(2a - U) \quad , \quad 0 < U < 2a \quad ,$$

$$s(U) = 0 \quad , \quad \text{otherwise} \quad ,$$

$$t(V) = 0 \quad , \quad V < -3a \quad ,$$

$$t(V) = \frac{(V + 3a)^2}{16a^3} \quad , \quad -3a < V < -a \quad ,$$

$$t(V) = \frac{3a^2 - V^2}{8a^3} \quad , \quad -a < V < a \quad ,$$

$$t(V) = \frac{(V - 3a)^2}{16a^3} \quad , \quad a < V < 3a \quad ,$$

$$t(V) = 0 \quad , \quad 3a < V \quad .$$

Let $\psi(V) = a\, t(aV)$, where $E[V^2] = a^2$. Then $\psi(V)$ has mean zero and variance one.

$$\psi(V) = \frac{1}{\sqrt{2\pi}}\, e^{-V^2/2} \left[1 - \frac{1}{60} H_4(V) + \sqrt{2\pi} \sum_{n=6}^{\infty} a_n H_n(V) \right]$$

where

$$a_n = \frac{2}{n!\sqrt{2\pi}} \int_0^3 H_n(x)\psi(x)\,dx \quad , \quad n \text{ even} \quad ,$$

$$a_n = 0 \quad , \quad n \text{ odd} \quad .$$

10. X is normal $(0, \sigma)$.

Y is normal $(0, \omega\sigma)$.

Section 15

1. $r(X) = \dfrac{1}{2Aa}$, $|X| < Aa$

$\quad = 0$, $|X| > Aa$.

7. $r(X, Y) = \frac{1}{4}(1 - e^{-2m|\tau|})[\delta(X + a)\delta(Y - a) + \delta(X - a)\delta(Y + a)]$

$\qquad + \frac{1}{4}(1 + e^{-2m|\tau|})[\delta(X + a)\delta(Y + a) + \delta(X - a)\delta(Y - a)]$.

INDEX

INDEX

SOME DOVER SCIENCE BOOKS

SOME DOVER SCIENCE BOOKS

WHAT IS SCIENCE?,
Norman Campbell
This excellent introduction explains scientific method, role of mathematics, types of scientific laws. Contents: 2 aspects of science, science & nature, laws of science, discovery of laws, explanation of laws, measurement & numerical laws, applications of science. 192pp. 5⅜ x 8. 60043-2 Paperbound $1.25

FADS AND FALLACIES IN THE NAME OF SCIENCE,
Martin Gardner
Examines various cults, quack systems, frauds, delusions which at various times have masqueraded as science. Accounts of hollow-earth fanatics like Symmes; Velikovsky and. wandering planets; Hoerbiger; Bellamy and the theory of multiple moons; Charles Fort; dowsing, pseudoscientific methods for finding water, ores, oil. Sections on naturopathy, iridiagnosis, zone therapy, food fads, etc. Analytical accounts of Wilhelm Reich and orgone sex energy; L. Ron Hubbard and Dianetics; A. Korzybski and General Semantics; many others. Brought up to date to include Bridey Murphy, others. Not just a collection of anecdotes, but a fair, reasoned appraisal of eccentric theory. Formerly titled *In the Name of Science*. Preface. Index. x + 384pp. 5⅜ x 8.
20394-8 Paperbound $2.00

PHYSICS, THE PIONEER SCIENCE,
L. W. Taylor
First thorough text to place all important physical phenomena in cultural-historical framework; remains best work of its kind. Exposition of physical laws, theories developed chronologically, with great historical, illustrative experiments diagrammed, described, worked out mathematically. Excellent physics text for self-study as well as class work. Vol. 1: Heat, Sound: motion, acceleration, gravitation, conservation of energy, heat engines, rotation, heat, mechanical energy, etc. 211 illus. 407pp. 5⅜ x 8. Vol. 2: Light, Electricity: images, lenses, prisms, magnetism, Ohm's law, dynamos, telegraph, quantum theory, decline of mechanical view of nature, etc. Bibliography. 13 table appendix. Index. 551 illus. 2 color plates. 508pp. 5⅜ x 8.
60565-5, 60566-3 Two volume set, paperbound $5.50

THE EVOLUTION OF SCIENTIFIC THOUGHT FROM NEWTON TO EINSTEIN,
A. d'Abro
Einstein's special and general theories of relativity, with their historical implications, are analyzed in non-technical terms. Excellent accounts of the contributions of Newton, Riemann, Weyl, Planck, Eddington, Maxwell, Lorentz and others are treated in terms of space and time, equations of electromagnetics, finiteness of the universe, methodology of science. 21 diagrams. 482pp. 5⅜ x 8.
20002-7 Paperbound $2.50

THE PRINCIPLES OF ELECTROCHEMISTRY,
D. A. MacInnes

Basic equations for almost every subfield of electrochemistry from first principles, referring at all times to the soundest and most recent theories and results; unusually useful as text or as reference. Covers coulometers and Faraday's Law, electrolytic conductance, the Debye-Hueckel method for the theoretical calculation of activity coefficients, concentration cells, standard electrode potentials, thermodynamic ionization constants, pH, potentiometric titrations, irreversible phenomena. Planck's equation, and much more. 2 indices. Appendix. 585-item bibliography. 137 figures. 94 tables. ii + 478pp. 5⅝ x 8⅜.
60052-1 Paperbound $3.00

MATHEMATICS OF MODERN ENGINEERING,
E. G. Keller and R. E. Doherty

Written for the Advanced Course in Engineering of the General Electric Corporation, deals with the engineering use of determinants, tensors, the Heaviside operational calculus, dyadics, the calculus of variations, etc. Presents underlying principles fully, but emphasis is on the perennial engineering attack of set-up and solve. Indexes. Over 185 figures and tables. Hundreds of exercises, problems, and worked-out examples. References. Total of xxxiii + 623pp. 5⅝ x 8.   60734-8, 60735-6 Two volume set, paperbound $3.70

AERODYNAMIC THEORY: A GENERAL REVIEW OF PROGRESS,
William F. Durand, editor-in-chief

A monumental joint effort by the world's leading authorities prepared under a grant of the Guggenheim Fund for the Promotion of Aeronautics. Never equalled for breadth, depth, reliability. Contains discussions of special mathematical topics not usually taught in the engineering or technical courses. Also: an extended two-part treatise on Fluid Mechanics, discussions of aerodynamics of perfect fluids, analyses of experiments with wind tunnels, applied airfoil theory, the nonlifting system of the airplane, the air propeller, hydrodynamics of boats and floats, the aerodynamics of cooling, etc. Contributing experts include Munk, Giacomelli, Prandtl, Toussaint, Von Karman, Klemperer, among others. Unabridged republication. 6 volumes. Total of 1,012 figures, 12 plates, 2,186pp. Bibliographies. Notes. Indices. 5⅝ x 8½.   61709-2,
61710-6, 61711-4, 61712-2, 61713-0, 61715-9 Six volume set, paperbound $13.50

FUNDAMENTALS OF HYDRO- AND AEROMECHANICS,
L. Prandtl and O. G. Tietjens

The well-known standard work based upon Prandtl's lectures at Goettingen. Wherever possible hydrodynamics theory is referred to practical considerations in hydraulics, with the view of unifying theory and experience. Presentation is extremely clear and though primarily physical, mathematical proofs are rigorous and use vector analysis to a considerable extent. An Engineering Society Monograph, 1934. 186 figures. Index. xvi + 270pp. 5⅝ x 8.
60374-1 Paperbound $2.25

APPLIED HYDRO- AND AEROMECHANICS,
L. Prandtl and O. G. Tietjens

Presents for the most part methods which will be valuable to engineers. Covers flow in pipes, boundary layers, airfoil theory, entry conditions, turbulent flow in pipes, and the boundary layer, determining drag from measurements of pressure and velocity, etc. Unabridged, unaltered. An Engineering Society Monograph. 1934. Index. 226 figures. 28 photographic plates illustrating flow patterns. xvi + 311pp. 5⅝ x 8.   60375-X Paperbound $2.50

NUMERICAL SOLUTIONS OF DIFFERENTIAL EQUATIONS,
H. Levy & E. A. Baggott

Comprehensive collection of methods for solving ordinary differential equations of first and higher order. All must pass 2 requirements: easy to grasp and practical, more rapid than school methods. Partial contents: graphical integration of differential equations, graphical methods for detailed solution. Numerical solution. Simultaneous equations and equations of 2nd and higher orders. "Should be in the hands of all in research in applied mathematics, teaching," *Nature.* 21 figures. viii + 238pp. 5⅜ x 8. 60168-4 Paperbound $1.85

ELEMENTARY STATISTICS, WITH APPLICATIONS IN MEDICINE AND THE BIOLOGICAL SCIENCES, *F. E. Croxton*

A sound introduction to statistics for anyone in the physical sciences, assuming no prior acquaintance and requiring only a modest knowledge of math. All basic formulas carefully explained and illustrated; all necessary reference tables included. From basic terms and concepts, the study proceeds to frequency distribution, linear, non-linear, and multiple correlation, skewness, kurtosis, etc. A large section deals with reliability and significance of statistical methods. Containing concrete examples from medicine and biology, this book will prove unusually helpful to workers in those fields who increasingly must evaluate, check, and interpret statistics. Formerly titled "Elementary Statistics with Applications in Medicine." 101 charts. 57 tables. 14 appendices. Index. vi + 376pp. 5⅜ x 8. 60506-X Paperbound $2.25

INTRODUCTION TO SYMBOLIC LOGIC,
S. Langer

No special knowledge of math required — probably the clearest book ever written on symbolic logic, suitable for the layman, general scientist, and philosopher. You start with simple symbols and advance to a knowledge of the Boole-Schroeder and Russell-Whitehead systems. Forms, logical structure, classes, the calculus of propositions, logic of the syllogism, etc. are all covered. "One of the clearest and simplest introductions," *Mathematics Gazette.* Second enlarged, revised edition. 368pp. 5⅜ x 8. 60164-1 Paperbound $2.25

A SHORT ACCOUNT OF THE HISTORY OF MATHEMATICS,
W. W. R. Ball

Most readable non-technical history of mathematics treats lives, discoveries of every important figure from Egyptian, Phoenician, mathematicians to late 19th century. Discusses schools of Ionia, Pythagoras, Athens, Cyzicus, Alexandria, Byzantium, systems of numeration; primitive arithmetic; Middle Ages, Renaissance, including Arabs, Bacon, Regiomontanus, Tartaglia, Cardan, Stevinus, Galileo, Kepler; modern mathematics of Descartes, Pascal, Wallis, Huygens, Newton, Leibnitz, d'Alembert, Euler, Lambert, Laplace, Legendre, Gauss, Hermite, Weierstrass, scores more. Index. 25 figures. 546pp. 5⅜ x 8. 20630-0 Paperbound $2.75

INTRODUCTION TO NONLINEAR DIFFERENTIAL AND INTEGRAL EQUATIONS,
Harold T. Davis

Aspects of the problem of nonlinear equations, transformations that lead to equations solvable by classical means, results in special cases, and useful generalizations. Thorough, but easily followed by mathematically sophisticated reader who knows little about non-linear equations. 137 problems for student to solve. xv + 566pp. 5⅜ x 8½. 60971-5 Paperbound $2.75

FIVE VOLUME "THEORY OF FUNCTIONS" SET BY KONRAD KNOPP

This five-volume set, prepared by Konrad Knopp, provides a complete and readily followed account of theory of functions. Proofs are given concisely, yet without sacrifice of completeness or rigor. These volumes are used as texts by such universities as M.I.T., University of Chicago, N. Y. City College, and many others. "Excellent introduction . . . remarkably readable, concise, clear, rigorous," *Journal of the American Statistical Association.*

ELEMENTS OF THE THEORY OF FUNCTIONS,
Konrad Knopp
This book provides the student with background for further volumes in this set, or texts on a similar level. Partial contents: foundations, system of complex numbers and the Gaussian plane of numbers, Riemann sphere of numbers, mapping by linear functions, normal forms, the logarithm, the cyclometric functions and binomial series. "Not only for the young student, but also for the student who knows all about what is in it," *Mathematical Journal.* Bibliography. Index. 140pp. 5⅜ x 8. 60154-4 Paperbound $1.50

THEORY OF FUNCTIONS, PART I,
Konrad Knopp
With volume II, this book provides coverage of basic concepts and theorems. Partial contents: numbers and points, functions of a complex variable, integral of a continuous function, Cauchy's integral theorem, Cauchy's integral formulae, series with variable terms, expansion of analytic functions in power series, analytic continuation and complete definition of analytic functions, entire transcendental functions, Laurent expansion, types of singularities. Bibliography. Index. vii + 146pp. 5⅜ x 8. 60156-0 Paperbound $1.50

THEORY OF FUNCTIONS, PART II,
Konrad Knopp
Application and further development of general theory, special topics. Single valued functions. Entire, Weierstrass, Meromorphic functions. Riemann surfaces. Algebraic functions. Analytical configuration, Riemann surface. Bibliography. Index. x + 150pp. 5⅜ x 8. 60157-9 Paperbound $1.50

PROBLEM BOOK IN THE THEORY OF FUNCTIONS, VOLUME 1.
Konrad Knopp
Problems in elementary theory, for use with Knopp's *Theory of Functions,* or any other text, arranged according to increasing difficulty. Fundamental concepts, sequences of numbers and infinite series, complex variable, integral theorems, development in series, conformal mapping. 182 problems. Answers. viii + 126pp. 5⅜ x 8. 60158-7 Paperbound $1.50

PROBLEM BOOK IN THE THEORY OF FUNCTIONS, VOLUME 2,
Konrad Knopp
Advanced theory of functions, to be used either with Knopp's *Theory of Functions,* or any other comparable text. Singularities, entire & meromorphic functions, periodic, analytic, continuation, multiple-valued functions, Riemann surfaces, conformal mapping. Includes a section of additional elementary problems. "The difficult task of selecting from the immense material of the modern theory of functions the problems just within the reach of the beginner is here masterfully accomplished," *Am. Math. Soc.* Answers. 138pp. 5⅜ x 8. 60159-5 Paperbound $1.50

A COURSE IN MATHEMATICAL ANALYSIS,
Edouard Goursat

Trans. by E. R. Hedrick, O. Dunkel, H. G. Bergmann. Classic study of fundamental material thoroughly treated. Extremely lucid exposition of wide range
of subject matter for student with one year of calculus. Vol. 1: Derivatives and
differentials, definite integrals, expansions in series, applications to geometry.
52 figures, 556pp. 60554-X Paperbound $3.00. Vol. 2, Part I: Functions of a
complex variable, conformal representations, doubly periodic functions, natural boundaries, etc. 38 figures, 269pp. 60555-8 Paperbound $2.25. Vol. 2,
Part II: Differential equations, Cauchy-Lipschitz method, nonlinear differential
equations, simultaneous equations, etc. 308pp. 60556-6 Paperbound $2.50.
Vol. 3, Part I: Variation of solutions, partial differential equations of the
second order. 15 figures, 339pp. 61176-0 Paperbound $3.00. Vol. 3, Part II:
Integral equations, calculus of variations. 13 figures, 389pp. 61177-9 Paperbound
$3.00 60554-X, 60555-8, 60556-6 61176-0, 61177-9 Six volume set,
paperbound $13.75

PLANETS, STARS AND GALAXIES,
A. E. Fanning

Descriptive astronomy for beginners: the solar system; neighboring galaxies;
seasons; quasars; fly-by results from Mars, Venus, Moon; radio astronomy; etc.
all simply explained. Revised up to 1966 by author and Prof. D. H. Menzel,
former Director, Harvard College Observatory. 29 photos, 16 figures. 189pp.
5⅜ x 8½. 21680-2 Paperbound $1.50

GREAT IDEAS IN INFORMATION THEORY, LANGUAGE AND CYBERNETICS,
Jagjit Singh

Winner of Unesco's Kalinga Prize covers language, metalanguages, analog and
digital computers, neural systems, work of McCulloch, Pitts, von Neumann,
Turing, other important topics. No advanced mathematics needed, yet a full
discussion without compromise or distortion. 118 figures. ix + 338pp. 5⅜ x 8½.
21694-2 Paperbound $2.25

GEOMETRIC EXERCISES IN PAPER FOLDING,
T. Sundara Row

Regular polygons, circles and other curves can be folded or pricked on paper,
then used to demonstrate geometric propositions, work out proofs, set up well-
known problems. 89 illustrations, photographs of actually folded sheets. xii +
148pp. 5⅜ x 8½. 21594-6 Paperbound $1.00

VISUAL ILLUSIONS, THEIR CAUSES, CHARACTERISTICS AND APPLICATIONS,
M. Luckiesh

The visual process, the structure of the eye, geometric, perspective illusions,
influence of angles, illusions of depth and distance, color illusions, lighting
effects, illusions in nature, special uses in painting, decoration, architecture,
magic, camouflage. New introduction by W. H. Ittleson covers modern developments in this area. 100 illustrations. xxi + 252pp. 5⅜ x 8.
21530-X Paperbound $1.50

ATOMS AND MOLECULES SIMPLY EXPLAINED,
B. C. Saunders and R. E. D. Clark

Introduction to chemical phenomena and their applications: cohesion, particles,
crystals, tailoring big molecules, chemist as architect, with applications in
radioactivity, color photography, synthetics, biochemistry, polymers, and many
other important areas. Non technical. 95 figures. x + 299pp. 5⅜ x 8½.
21282-3 Paperbound $1.50

A SOURCE BOOK IN MATHEMATICS,
D. E. Smith
Great discoveries in math, from Renaissance to end of 19th century, in English translation. Read announcements by Dedekind, Gauss, Delamain, Pascal, Fermat, Newton, Abel, Lobachevsky, Bolyai, Riemann, De Moivre, Legendre, Laplace, others of discoveries about imaginary numbers, number congruence, slide rule, equations, symbolism, cubic algebraic equations, non-Euclidean forms of geometry, calculus, function theory, quaternions, etc. Succinct selections from 125 different treatises, articles, most unavailable elsewhere in English. Each article preceded by biographical introduction. Vol. I: Fields of Number, Algebra. Index. 32 illus. 338pp. 5⅜ x 8. Vol. II: Fields of Geometry, Probability, Calculus, Functions, Quaternions. 83 illus. 432pp. 5⅜ x 8.
60552-3, 60553-1 Two volume set, paperbound $5.00

FOUNDATIONS OF PHYSICS,
R. B. Lindsay & H. Margenau
Excellent bridge between semi-popular works & technical treatises. A discussion of methods of physical description, construction of theory; valuable for physicist with elementary calculus who is interested in ideas that give meaning to data, tools of modern physics. Contents include symbolism; mathematical equations; space & time foundations of mechanics; probability; physics & continua; electron theory; special & general relativity; quantum mechanics; causality. "Thorough and yet not overdetailed. Unreservedly recommended," *Nature* (London). Unabridged, corrected edition. List of recommended readings. 35 illustrations. xi + 537pp. 5⅜ x 8.
60377-6 Paperbound $3.50

FUNDAMENTAL FORMULAS OF PHYSICS,
ed. by D. H. Menzel
High useful, full, inexpensive reference and study text, ranging from simple to highly sophisticated operations. Mathematics integrated into text—each chapter stands as short textbook of field represented. Vol. 1: Statistics, Physical Constants, Special Theory of Relativity, Hydrodynamics, Aerodynamics, Boundary Value Problems in Math, Physics, Viscosity, Electromagnetic Theory, etc. Vol. 2: Sound, Acoustics, Geometrical Optics, Electron Optics, High-Energy Phenomena, Magnetism, Biophysics, much more. Index. Total of 800pp. 5⅜ x 8.
60595-7, 60596-5 Two volume set, paperbound $4.75

THEORETICAL PHYSICS,
A. S. Kompaneyets
One of the very few thorough studies of the subject in this price range. Provides advanced students with a comprehensive theoretical background. Especially strong on recent experimentation and developments in quantum theory. Contents: Mechanics (Generalized Coordinates, Lagrange's Equation, Collision of Particles, etc.), Electrodynamics (Vector Analysis, Maxwell's equations, Transmission of Signals, Theory of Relativity, etc.), Quantum Mechanics (the Inadequacy of Classical Mechanics, the Wave Equation, Motion in a Central Field, Quantum Theory of Radiation, Quantum Theories of Dispersion and Scattering, etc.), and Statistical Physics (Equilibrium Distribution of Molecules in an Ideal Gas, Boltzmann Statistics, Bose and Fermi Distribution. Thermodynamic Quantities, etc.). Revised to 1961. Translated by George Yankovsky, authorized by Kompaneyets. 137 exercises. 56 figures. 529pp. 5⅜ x 8½.
60972-3 Paperbound $3.50

CHANCE, LUCK AND STATISTICS: THE SCIENCE OF CHANCE,
Horace C. Levinson
Theory of probability and science of statistics in simple, non-technical language. Part I deals with theory of probability, covering odd superstitions in regard to "luck," the meaning of betting odds, the law of mathematical expectation, gambling, and applications in poker, roulette, lotteries, dice, bridge, and other games of chance. Part II discusses the misuse of statistics, the concept of statistical probabilities, normal and skew frequency distributions, and statistics applied to various fields—birth rates, stock speculation, insurance rates, advertising, etc. "Presented in an easy humorous style which I consider the best kind of expository writing," Prof. A. C. Cohen, Industry Quality Control. Enlarged revised edition. Formerly titled *The Science of Chance.* Preface and two new appendices by the author. xiv + 365pp. 5⅜ x 8.　21007-3 Paperbound $2.00

BASIC ELECTRONICS,
prepared by the U.S. Navy Training Publications Center
A thorough and comprehensive manual on the fundamentals of electronics. Written clearly, it is equally useful for self-study or course work for those with a knowledge of the principles of basic electricity. Partial contents: Operating Principles of the Electron Tube; Introduction to Transistors; Power Supplies for Electronic Equipment; Tuned Circuits; Electron-Tube Amplifiers; Audio Power Amplifiers; Oscillators; Transmitters; Transmission Lines; Antennas and Propagation; Introduction to Computers; and related topics. Appendix. Index. Hundreds of illustrations and diagrams. vi + 471pp. 6½ x 9¼.
61076-4 Paperbound $2.95

BASIC THEORY AND APPLICATION OF TRANSISTORS,
prepared by the U.S. Department of the Army
An introductory manual prepared for an army training program. One of the finest available surveys of theory and application of transistor design and operation. Minimal knowledge of physics and theory of electron tubes required. Suitable for textbook use, course supplement, or home study. Chapters: Introduction; fundamental theory of transistors; transistor amplifier fundamentals; parameters, equivalent circuits, and characteristic curves; bias stabilization; transistor analysis and comparison using characteristic curves and charts; audio amplifiers; tuned amplifiers; wide-band amplifiers; oscillators; pulse and switching circuits; modulation, mixing, and demodulation; and additional semiconductor devices. Unabridged, corrected edition. 240 schematic drawings, photographs, wiring diagrams, etc. 2 Appendices. Glossary. Index. 263pp. 6½ x 9¼.
60380-6 Paperbound $1.75

GUIDE TO THE LITERATURE OF MATHEMATICS AND PHYSICS,
N. G. Parke III
Over 5000 entries included under approximately 120 major subject headings of selected most important books, monographs, periodicals, articles in English, plus important works in German, French, Italian, Spanish, Russian (many recently available works). Covers every branch of physics, math, related engineering. Includes author, title, edition, publisher, place, date, number of volumes, number of pages. A 40-page introduction on the basic problems of research and study provides useful information on the organization and use of libraries, the psychology of learning, etc. This reference work will save you hours of time. 2nd revised edition. Indices of authors, subjects, 464pp. 5⅜ x 8.
60447-0 Paperbound $2.75

THE RISE OF THE NEW PHYSICS (formerly THE DECLINE OF MECHANISM),
A. d'Abro
This authoritative and comprehensive 2-volume exposition is unique in scientific publishing. Written for intelligent readers not familiar with higher mathematics, it is the only thorough explanation in non-technical language of modern mathematical-physical theory. Combining both history and exposition, it ranges from classical Newtonian concepts up through the electronic theories of Dirac and Heisenberg, the statistical mechanics of Fermi, and Einstein's relativity theories. "A must for anyone doing serious study in the physical sciences," *J. of Franklin Inst.* 97 illustrations. 991pp. 2 volumes.
20003-5, 20004-3 Two volume set, paperbound $5.50

THE STRANGE STORY OF THE QUANTUM, AN ACCOUNT FOR THE GENERAL READER OF THE GROWTH OF IDEAS UNDERLYING OUR PRESENT ATOMIC KNOWLEDGE, *B. Hoffmann*
Presents lucidly and expertly, with barest amount of mathematics, the problems and theories which led to modern quantum physics. Dr. Hoffmann begins with the closing years of the 19th century, when certain trifling discrepancies were noticed, and with illuminating analogies and examples takes you through the brilliant concepts of Planck, Einstein, Pauli, de Broglie, Bohr, Schroedinger, Heisenberg, Dirac, Sommerfeld, Feynman, etc. This edition includes a new, long postscript carrying the story through 1958. "Of the books attempting an account of the history and contents of our modern atomic physics which have come to my attention, this is the best," H. Margenau, Yale University, in *American Journal of Physics*. 32 tables and line illustrations. Index. 275pp. 5⅜ x 8.
20518-5 Paperbound $2.00

GREAT IDEAS AND THEORIES OF MODERN COSMOLOGY,
Jagjit Singh
The theories of Jeans, Eddington, Milne, Kant, Bondi, Gold, Newton, Einstein, Gamow, Hoyle, Dirac, Kuiper, Hubble, Weizsäcker and many others on such cosmological questions as the origin of the universe, space and time, planet formation, "continuous creation," the birth, life, and death of the stars, the origin of the galaxies, etc. By the author of the popular *Great Ideas of Modern Mathematics*. A gifted popularizer of science, he makes the most difficult abstractions crystal-clear even to the most non-mathematical reader. Index. xii + 276pp. 5⅜ x 8½.
20925-3 Paperbound $2.50

GREAT IDEAS OF MODERN MATHEMATICS: THEIR NATURE AND USE,
Jagjit Singh
Reader with only high school math will understand main mathematical ideas of modern physics, astronomy, genetics, psychology, evolution, etc., better than many who use them as tools, but comprehend little of their basic structure. Author uses his wide knowledge of non-mathematical fields in brilliant exposition of differential equations, matrices, group theory, logic, statistics, problems of mathematical foundations, imaginary numbers, vectors, etc. Original publications, appendices. indexes. 65 illustr. 322pp. 5⅜ x 8. 20587-8 Paperbound $2.25

THE MATHEMATICS OF GREAT AMATEURS, *Julian L. Coolidge*
Great discoveries made by poets, theologians, philosophers, artists and other non-mathematicians: Omar Khayyam, Leonardo da Vinci, Albrecht Dürer, John Napier, Pascal, Diderot, Bolzano, etc. Surprising accounts of what can result from a non-professional preoccupation with the oldest of sciences. 56 figures. viii + 211pp. 5⅜ x 8½.
61009-8 Paperbound $2.00

MATHEMATICAL PHYSICS, *D. H. Menzel*
Thorough one-volume treatment of the mathematical techniques vital for classical mechanics, electromagnetic theory, quantum theory, and relativity. Written by the Harvard Professor of Astrophysics for junior, senior, and graduate courses, it gives clear explanations of all those aspects of function theory, vectors, matrices, dyadics, tensors, partial differential equations, etc., necessary for the understanding of the various physical theories. Electron theory, relativity, and other topics seldom presented appear here in considerable detail. Scores of definition, conversion factors, dimensional constants, etc. "More detailed than normal for an advanced text . . . excellent set of sections on Dyadics, Matrices, and Tensors," *Journal of the Franklin Institute.* Index. 193 problems, with answers. x + 412pp. 5⅜ x 8. 60056-4 Paperbound $2.50

THE THEORY OF SOUND, *Lord Rayleigh*
Most vibrating systems likely to be encountered in practice can be tackled successfully by the methods set forth by the great Nobel laureate, Lord Rayleigh. Complete coverage of experimental, mathematical aspects of sound theory. Partial contents: Harmonic motions, vibrating systems in general, lateral vibrations of bars, curved plates or shells, applications of Laplace's functions to acoustical problems, fluid friction, plane vortex-sheet, vibrations of solid bodies, etc. This is the first inexpensive edition of this great reference and study work. Bibliography, Historical introduction by R. B. Lindsay. Total of 1040pp. 97 figures. 5⅜ x 8. 60292-3, 60293-1 Two volume set, paperbound $6.00

HYDRODYNAMICS, *Horace Lamb*
Internationally famous complete coverage of standard reference work on dynamics of liquids & gases. Fundamental theorems, equations, methods, solutions, background, for classical hydrodynamics. Chapters include Equations of Motion, Integration of Equations in Special Gases, Irrotational Motion, Motion of Liquid in 2 Dimensions, Motion of Solids through Liquid-Dynamical Theory, Vortex Motion, Tidal Waves, Surface Waves, Waves of Expansion, Viscosity, Rotating Masses of Liquids. Excellently planned, arranged; clear, lucid presentation. 6th enlarged, revised edition. Index. Over 900 footnotes, mostly bibliographical. 119 figures. xv + 738pp. 6⅛ x 9¼. 60256-7 Paperbound $4.00

DYNAMICAL THEORY OF GASES, *James Jeans*
Divided into mathematical and physical chapters for the convenience of those not expert in mathematics, this volume discusses the mathematical theory of gas in a steady state, thermodynamics, Boltzmann and Maxwell, kinetic theory, quantum theory, exponentials, etc. 4th enlarged edition, with new material on quantum theory, quantum dynamics, etc. Indexes. 28 figures. 444pp. 6⅛ x 9¼. 60136-6 Paperbound $2.75

THERMODYNAMICS, *Enrico Fermi*
Unabridged reproduction of 1937 edition. Elementary in treatment; remarkable for clarity, organization. Requires no knowledge of advanced math beyond calculus, only familiarity with fundamentals of thermometry, calorimetry. Partial Contents: Thermodynamic systems; First & Second laws of thermodynamics; Entropy; Thermodynamic potentials: phase rule, reversible electric cell; Gaseous reactions: van't Hoff reaction box, principle of LeChatelier; Thermodynamics of dilute solutions: osmotic & vapor pressures, boiling & freezing points; Entropy constant. Index. 25 problems. 24 illustrations. x + 160pp. 5⅜ x 8. 60361-X Paperbound $2.00

PRINCIPLES OF STRATIGRAPHY,
A. W. Grabau

Classic of 20th century geology, unmatched in scope and comprehensiveness. Nearly 600 pages cover the structure and origins of every kind of sedimentary, hydrogenic, oceanic, pyroclastic, atmoclastic, hydroclastic, marine hydroclastic, and bioclastic rock; metamorphism; erosion; etc. Includes also the constitution of the atmosphere; morphology of oceans, rivers, glaciers; volcanic activities; faults and earthquakes; and fundamental principles of paleontology (nearly 200 pages). New introduction by Prof. M. Kay, Columbia U. 1277 bibliographical entries. 264 diagrams. Tables, maps, etc. Two volume set. Total of xxxii + 1185pp. 5⅜ x 8.　　　　60686-4, 60687-2 Two volume set, paperbound $6.25

SNOW CRYSTALS, *W. A. Bentley and W. J. Humphreys*

Over 200 pages of Bentley's famous microphotographs of snow flakes—the product of painstaking, methodical work at his Jericho, Vermont studio. The pictures, which also include plates of frost, glaze and dew on vegetation, spider webs, windowpanes; sleet; graupel or soft hail, were chosen both for their scientific interest and their aesthetic qualities. The wonder of nature's diversity is exhibited in the intricate, beautiful patterns of the snow flakes. Introductory text by W. J. Humphreys. Selected bibliography. 2,453 illustrations. 224pp. 8 x 10¼.　　　　20287-9 Paperbound $3.25

THE BIRTH AND DEVELOPMENT OF THE GEOLOGICAL SCIENCES,
F. D. Adams

Most thorough history of the earth sciences ever written. Geological thought from earliest times to the end of the 19th century, covering over 300 early thinkers & systems: fossils & their explanation, vulcanists vs. neptunists, figured stones & paleontology, generation of stones, dozens of similar topics. 91 illustrations, including medieval, renaissance woodcuts, etc. Index. 632 footnotes, mostly bibliographical. 511pp. 5⅜ x 8.　　　　20005-1 Paperbound $2.75

ORGANIC CHEMISTRY, *F. C. Whitmore*

The entire subject of organic chemistry for the practicing chemist and the advanced student. Storehouse of facts, theories, processes found elsewhere only in specialized journals. Covers aliphatic compounds (500 pages on the properties and synthetic preparation of hydrocarbons, halides, proteins, ketones, etc.), alicyclic compounds, aromatic compounds, heterocyclic compounds, organophosphorus and organometallic compounds. Methods of synthetic preparation analyzed critically throughout. Includes much of biochemical interest. "The scope of this volume is astonishing," *Industrial and Engineering Chemistry.* 12,000-reference index. 2387-item bibliography. Total of x + 1005pp. 5⅜ x 8.　　　　60700-3, 60701-1 Two volume set, paperbound $4.50

THE PHASE RULE AND ITS APPLICATION,
Alexander Findlay

Covering chemical phenomena of 1, 2, 3, 4, and multiple component systems, this "standard work on the subject" (*Nature*, London), has been completely revised and brought up to date by A. N. Campbell and N. O. Smith. Brand new material has been added on such matters as binary, tertiary liquid equilibria, solid solutions in ternary systems, quinary systems of salts and water. Completely revised to triangular coordinates in ternary systems, clarified graphic representation, solid models, etc. 9th revised edition. Author, subject indexes. 236 figures. 505 footnotes, mostly bibliographic. xii + 494pp. 5⅜ x 8.
60091-2 Paperbound $2.75

COLLEGE ALGEBRA, *H. B. Fine*

Standard college text that gives a systematic and deductive structure to algebra; comprehensive, connected, with emphasis on theory. Discusses the commutative, associative, and distributive laws of number in unusual detail, and goes on with undetermined coefficients, quadratic equations, progressions, logarithms, permutations, probability, power series, and much more. Still most valuable elementary-intermediate text on the science and structure of algebra. Index. 1560 problems, all with answers. x + 631pp. 5⅜ x 8. 60211-7 Paperbound $2.75

HIGHER MATHEMATICS FOR STUDENTS OF CHEMISTRY AND PHYSICS, *J. W. Mellor*

Not abstract, but practical, building its problems out of familiar laboratory material, this covers differential calculus, coordinate, analytical geometry, functions, integral calculus, infinite series, numerical equations, differential equations, Fourier's theorem, probability, theory of errors, calculus of variations, determinants. "If the reader is not familiar with this book, it will repay him to examine it," *Chem. & Engineering News*. 800 problems. 189 figures. Bibliography. xxi + 641pp. 5⅜ x 8. 60193-5 Paperbound $3.50

TRIGONOMETRY REFRESHER FOR TECHNICAL MEN, *A. A. Klaf*

A modern question and answer text on plane and spherical trigonometry. Part I covers plane trigonometry: angles, quadrants, trigonometrical functions, graphical representation, interpolation, equations, logarithms, solution of triangles, slide rules, etc. Part II discusses applications to navigation, surveying, elasticity, architecture, and engineering. Small angles, periodic functions, vectors, polar coordinates, De Moivre's theorem, fully covered. Part III is devoted to spherical trigonometry and the solution of spherical triangles, with applications to terrestrial and astronomical problems. Special time-savers for numerical calculation. 913 questions answered for you! 1738 problems; answers to odd numbers. 494 figures. 14 pages of functions, formulae. Index. x + 629pp. 5⅜ x 8. 20371-9 Paperbound $3.00

CALCULUS REFRESHER FOR TECHNICAL MEN, *A. A. Klaf*

Not an ordinary textbook but a unique refresher for engineers, technicians, and students. An examination of the most important aspects of differential and integral calculus by means of 756 key questions. Part I covers simple differential calculus: constants, variables, functions, increments, derivatives, logarithms, curvature, etc. Part II treats fundamental concepts of integration: inspection, substitution, transformation, reduction, areas and volumes, mean value, successive and partial integration, double and triple integration. Stresses practical aspects! A 50 page section gives applications to civil and nautical engineering, electricity, stress and strain, elasticity, industrial engineering, and similar fields. 756 questions answered. 556 problems; solutions to odd numbers. 36 pages of constants, formulae. Index. v + 431pp. 5⅜ x 8. 20370-0 Paperbound $2.25

INTRODUCTION TO THE THEORY OF GROUPS OF FINITE ORDER, *R. Carmichael*

Examines fundamental theorems and their application. Beginning with sets, systems, permutations, etc., it progresses in easy stages through important types of groups: Abelian, prime power, permutation, etc. Except 1 chapter where matrices are desirable, no higher math needed. 783 exercises, problems. Index. xvi + 447pp. 5⅜ x 8. 60300-8 Paperbound $3.00

AN INTRODUCTION TO THE GEOMETRY OF N DIMENSIONS,
D. H. Y. Sommerville
An introduction presupposing no prior knowledge of the field, the only book in English devoted exclusively to higher dimensional geometry. Discusses fundamental ideas of incidence, parallelism, perpendicularity, angles between linear space; enumerative geometry; analytical geometry from projective and metric points of view; polytopes; elementary ideas in analysis situs; content of hyper-spacial figures. Bibliography. Index. 60 diagrams. 196pp. 5⅜ x 8.

60494-2 Paperbound $1.50

ELEMENTARY CONCEPTS OF TOPOLOGY, *P. Alexandroff*
First English translation of the famous brief introduction to topology for the beginner or for the mathematician not undertaking extensive study. This unusually useful intuitive approach deals primarily with the concepts of complex, cycle, and homology, and is wholly consistent with current investigations. Ranges from basic concepts of set-theoretic topology to the concept of Betti groups. "Glowing example of harmony between intuition and thought," David Hilbert. Translated by A. E. Farley. Introduction by D. Hilbert. Index. 25 figures. 73pp. 5⅜ x 8.

60747-X Paperbound $1.25

ELEMENTS OF NON-EUCLIDEAN GEOMETRY,
D. M. Y. Sommerville
Unique in proceeding step-by-step, in the manner of traditional geometry. Enables the student with only a good knowledge of high school algebra and geometry to grasp elementary hyperbolic, elliptic, analytic non-Euclidean geometries; space curvature and its philosophical implications; theory of radical axes; homothetic centres and systems of circles; parataxy and parallelism; absolute measure; Gauss' proof of the defect area theorem; geodesic representation; much more, all with exceptional clarity. 126 problems at chapter endings provide progressive practice and familiarity. 133 figures. Index. xvi + 274pp. 5⅜ x 8.

60460-8 Paperbound $2.00

INTRODUCTION TO THE THEORY OF NUMBERS, *L. E. Dickson*
Thorough, comprehensive approach with adequate coverage of classical literature, an introductory volume beginners can follow. Chapters on divisibility, congruences, quadratic residues & reciprocity. Diophantine equations, etc. Full treatment of binary quadratic forms without usual restriction to integral coefficients. Covers infinitude of primes, least residues. Fermat's theorem. Euler's phi function, Legendre's symbol, Gauss's lemma, automorphs, reduced forms, recent theorems of Thue & Siegel, many more. Much material not readily available elsewhere. 239 problems. Index. I figure. viii + 183pp. 5⅜ x 8.

60342-3 Paperbound $1.75

MATHEMATICAL TABLES AND FORMULAS,
compiled by Robert D. Carmichael and Edwin R. Smith
Valuable collection for students, etc. Contains all tables necessary in college algebra and trigonometry, such as five-place common logarithms, logarithmic sines and tangents of small angles, logarithmic trigonometric functions, natural trigonometric functions, four-place antilogarithms, tables for changing from sexagesimal to circular and from circular to sexagesimal measure of angles, etc. Also many tables and formulas not ordinarily accessible, including powers, roots, and reciprocals, exponential and hyperbolic functions, ten-place logarithms of prime numbers, and formulas and theorems from analytical and elementary geometry and from calculus. Explanatory introduction. viii + 269pp. 5⅜ x 8½.

60111-0 Paperbound $1.50

CELESTIAL OBJECTS FOR COMMON TELESCOPES,
Rev. T. W. Webb
Classic handbook for the use and pleasure of the amateur astronomer. Of inestimable aid in locating and identifying thousands of celestial objects. Vol I, The Solar System: discussions of the principle and operation of the telescope, procedures of observations and telescope-photography, spectroscopy, etc., precise location information of sun, moon, planets, meteors. Vol. II, The Stars: alphabetical listing of constellations, information on double stars, clusters, stars with unusual spectra, variables, and nebulae, etc. Nearly 4,000 objects noted. Edited and extensively revised by Margaret W. Mayall, director of the American Assn. of Variable Star Observers. New Index by Mrs. Mayall giving the location of all objects mentioned in the text for Epoch 2000. New Precession Table added. New appendices on the planetary satellites, constellation names and abbreviations, and solar system data. Total of 46 illustrations. Total of xxxix + 606pp. 5⅜ x 8.   20917-2, 20918-0 Two volume set, paperbound $5.00

PLANETARY THEORY,
E. W. Brown and C. A. Shook
Provides a clear presentation of basic methods for calculating planetary orbits for today's astronomer. Begins with a careful exposition of specialized mathematical topics essential for handling perturbation theory and then goes on to indicate how most of the previous methods reduce ultimately to two general calculation methods: obtaining expressions either for the coordinates of planetary positions or for the elements which determine the perturbed paths. An example of each is given and worked in detail. Corrected edition. Preface. Appendix. Index. xii + 302pp. 5⅜ x 8½.   61133-7 Paperbound $2.25

STAR NAMES AND THEIR MEANINGS,
Richard Hinckley Allen
An unusual book documenting the various attributions of names to the individual stars over the centuries. Here is a treasure-house of information on a topic not normally delved into even by professional astronomers; provides a fascinating background to the stars in folk-lore, literary references, ancient writings, star catalogs and maps over the centuries. Constellation-by-constellation analysis covers hundreds of stars and other asterisms, including the Pleiades, Hyades, Andromedan Nebula, etc. Introduction. Indices. List of authors and authorities. xx + 563pp. 5⅜ x 8½.   21079-0 Paperbound $3.00

A SHORT HISTORY OF ASTRONOMY, *A. Berry*
Popular standard work for over 50 years, this thorough and accurate volume covers the science from primitive times to the end of the 19th century. After the Greeks and the Middle Ages, individual chapters analyze Copernicus, Brahe, Galileo, Kepler, and Newton, and the mixed reception of their discoveries. Post-Newtonian achievements are then discussed in unusual detail: Halley, Bradley, Lagrange, Laplace, Herschel, Bessel, etc. 2 Indexes. 104 illustrations, 9 portraits. xxxi + 440pp. 5⅜ x 8.   20210-0 Paperbound $2.75

SOME THEORY OF SAMPLING, *W. E. Deming*
The purpose of this book is to make sampling techniques understandable to and useable by social scientists, industrial managers, and natural scientists who are finding statistics increasingly part of their work. Over 200 exercises, plus dozens of actual applications. 61 tables. 90 figs. xix + 602pp. 5⅜ x 8½.
61755-6 Paperbound $3.50

APPLIED OPTICS AND OPTICAL DESIGN,
A. E. Conrady
With publication of vol. 2, standard work for designers in optics is now complete for first time. Only work of its kind in English; only detailed work for practical designer and self-taught. Requires, for bulk of work, no math above trig. Step-by-step exposition, from fundamental concepts of geometrical, physical optics, to systematic study, design, of almost all types of optical systems. Vol. 1: all ordinary ray-tracing methods; primary aberrations; necessary higher aberration for design of telescopes, low-power microscopes, photographic equipment. Vol. 2: (Completed from author's notes by R. Kingslake, Dir. Optical Design, Eastman Kodak.) Special attention to high-power microscope, anastigmatic photographic objectives. "An indispensable work," *J., Optical Soc. of Amer.* Index. Bibliography. 193 diagrams. 852pp. 6⅛ x 9¼.

60611-2, 60612-0 Two volume set, paperbound $8.00

MECHANICS OF THE GYROSCOPE, THE DYNAMICS OF ROTATION,
R. F. Deimel, Professor of Mechanical Engineering at Stevens Institute of Technology
Elementary general treatment of dynamics of rotation, with special application of gyroscopic phenomena. No knowledge of vectors needed. Velocity of a moving curve, acceleration to a point, general equations of motion, gyroscopic horizon, free gyro, motion of discs, the damped gyro, 103 similar topics. Exercises. 75 figures. 208pp. 5⅜ x 8.

60066-1 Paperbound $1.75

STRENGTH OF MATERIALS,
J. P. Den Hartog
Full, clear treatment of elementary material (tension, torsion, bending, compound stresses, deflection of beams, etc.), plus much advanced material on engineering methods of great practical value: full treatment of the Mohr circle, lucid elementary discussions of the theory of the center of shear and the "Myosotis" method of calculating beam deflections, reinforced concrete, plastic deformations, photoelasticity, etc. In all sections, both general principles and concrete applications are given. Index. 186 figures (160 others in problem section). 350 problems, all with answers. List of formulas. viii + 323pp. 5⅜ x 8.

60755-0 Paperbound $2.50

HYDRAULIC TRANSIENTS,
G. R. Rich
The best text in hydraulics ever printed in English . . . by former Chief Design Engineer for T.V.A. Provides a transition from the basic differential equations of hydraulic transient theory to the arithmetic integration computation required by practicing engineers. Sections cover Water Hammer, Turbine Speed Regulation, Stability of Governing, Water-Hammer Pressures in Pump Discharge Lines, The Differential and Restricted Orifice Surge Tanks, The Normalized Surge Tank Charts of Calame and Gaden, Navigation Locks, Surges in Power Canals—Tidal Harmonics, etc. Revised and enlarged. Author's prefaces. Index. xiv + 409pp. 5⅜ x 8½.

60116-1 Paperbound $2.50

Prices subject to change without notice.

Available at your book dealer or write for free catalogue to Dept. Adsci, Dover Publications, Inc., 180 Varick St., N.Y., N.Y. 10014. Dover publishes more than 150 books each year on science, elementary and advanced mathematics, biology, music, art, literary history, social sciences and other areas.